R. S. Harwood

The Changing Climate

Submerged forest, seen at low tide, at Borth, Cardiganshire
(*Photograph Copyright H. H. Lamb*)

Tests carried out in the Cambridge University Radiocarbon Dating Laboratory, under the direction of Professor H. Godwin F.R.S. *and Dr E. H. Willis, have indicated that the trees grew about* 4000 B.C., *in the warmest climatic period since the ice age. After the forest died the stumps were apparently first buried by the peat of a growing bog, and the continuation of this forest layer can be found inland at depths of* 2 *to* 3 *metres in the peat of Borth bog.*

Because they have been held fixed in the peat, there might be some interest in a statistic of the directions in which the trunks of the fallen trees lie. Of 17 *trunks seen on the foreshore most appeared to have fallen from about WSW, all from directions between SW and NW.*

Changes of local sea level, associated with isostatic warping of the British Isles region of the Earth's crust as northern Britain continues to recover from its former load of ice and southern Britain sinks, are probably responsible for the subsequent erosion of part of this coastal bog by the sea. This has laid bare the tree stumps seen in the picture, at a level where they are exposed near low water spring tides. Also exposed is part of the peaty soil of the former forest floor (the dark areas of the picture).

Seen in the picture, to give an idea of scale, is Mr J. A. Taylor, Lecturer in Geography at the Department of Geography and Anthropology, University College of Wales, Aberyswyth, whose own work includes attention to weather patterns and climatic changes particularly as they have affected man's environment in Wales and as regards their continuing effects upon agriculture.

The Changing Climate

SELECTED PAPERS *by* H. H. LAMB

LONDON · 1966
METHUEN & CO LTD
11 NEW FETTER LANE EC4

First published 1966

Printed in Great Britain
by Fletcher & Son Ltd, Norwich

Contents

Preface

Recent years have seen a growing realization that climate is never quite constant. Indeed, the topic of climatic variation has been extraordinarily much debated and written about in scientific circles during the last twenty-five to thirty years. The earlier assumption, amounting to a general belief around the beginning of the century, that climatic changes were a thing of the geological past, or at least, that significant changes were encountered only over a geological time scale, has been shattered by changes during the present century that are certainly too great to be overlooked. There was first a sustained rise of average temperatures accompanied by systematic rainfall changes in many parts of the world – tendencies which turned out on investigation to have had their beginnings many decades ago – and then, since about 1940, an opposite trend seems to have set in. These changes have been enough to make many published tables of climatic statistics obsolete and to raise new questions about the proper use – and construction – of climatic tables. The twentieth-century shifts of the climatic zones, small as they are from one point of view, have affected the distributions of the natural fauna and flora and the human economy in a variety of ways – optimum practices and crops in farming, choice of fishing-grounds, open seasons for ports liable to ice, and so on.

The events referred to have posed a pressing demand for the improvement of knowledge: for establishment of the facts of climatic variation in all its aspects, over the whole world, and over the longest period of time for which the details can be re-captured, for interpretation of the changes observed and, if it should ever prove possible, for reliable forecasting of the climatic pattern over several decades ahead.

Forecasts, however great their potential economic value, must wait until an adequate scientific basis exists. For this, identification of all the relevant processes in the atmosphere and oceans, of all external influences which affect these processes and of the magnitudes of their several effects, will be necessary. Already, however, it begins to appear possible that Man might himself be able to modify world climates either by deliberate contrivance or as an accidental by-product of his other activities. There are clearly great hazards involved in any grandiose scheme to change the world distribution of climate significantly – for instance, by such costly and technically difficult operations as removal of the Arctic sea-ice – unless and until all the consequences can be predicted with reasonable accuracy and confidence. These aspects of our present situation, and the new knowledge gained in recent years (since the invention of the radio-sonde) of the large scale circulation of the atmosphere in depth, have revolutionized the study of climatology and made the subject of climatic variation one of the most active fields of meteorological research.

The results to date of this research have widened our understanding of the behaviour of the atmosphere and oceans. It is clear that they are relevant to the long history of our terrestrial environment, climate, fauna and flora and even to the past evolution of diseases. They also constitute an important part of the foundations of long range weather forecasting in individual seasons.

The author of the papers which make up the present book has been able to play some part in marshalling our knowledge of the climates of the past and our observations of the large-scale circulation of the winds over the globe in recent, and not so recent, years. This contributes to the proper assessment of our present situation and has already found some application in monthly and seasonal weather forecasting. It now appears that publication of this collection of papers in a handy form is desirable to make more readily available for reference some of the accumulating knowledge about the slow, long-term processes in the atmosphere and oceans that have to do with changes of climate in the past, present and future.

A fuller presentation has been asked for, but attention to this continues to be delayed by concentration on further research. It will only become possible, therefore, after a lapse of some years.

The facts of the past, including the direct meteorological observations made in recent centuries, have hitherto been hidden away in literature, log-books and diaries of the greatest diversity, and in many different places, or have come to light in compilations in diverse languages and in published research papers representing many fields of learning. Archaeology, history, botany, zoology, geology and glaciology, as well as meteorology and oceanography, are prominently represented. In bringing this material into some sort of order and submitting it to meteorological analysis, the author has depended greatly upon the labours of several generations of compilers in every branch of natural history. He has been given every opportunity for the work in the research division of the U.K. Meteorological Office and was fortunate in having at hand the surely unrivalled archives of weather reports from all over the world possessed by the Meteorological Office Library. He has also had access to the wealth of earlier material in the British Museum and the Public Records Office, London. And he has profited by friendly personal contacts with, and advice from, workers in many disciplines and many countries. His thanks are due particularly to the Director-General of the Meteorological Office for the generous facilities, and confidence in providing them, that made the work possible. He also thanks Professor Gordon Manley, Department of Environmental Studies, University of Lancaster (formerly of London) for the supply of basic data and numerous consultations about it. He gratefully acknowledges his especial debt to Professor H. Godwin, F.R.S., Department of Botany, Cambridge University for introductions to research workers in a wide range of disciplines, and from many parts of the world, and the opportunity to discuss their work. The author's thanks are due also to Professor H. Flohn, Meteorologisches Institut der Universität, Bonn; to Professor R. W. Fairbridge, Department of Geology, Columbia University, New York; and to Dr H. E. Wright, jr. for introduction to much significant work. And he is indebted to Dr E. H. Willis of the Cambridge University Radiocarbon Dating Laboratory for guidance in that field, the results of which are essential to establishing the evolution of the world distribution of climates during and since the last ice age and have a bearing besides upon the condition of the atmosphere itself.

The author and publishers express their gratitude to the original publishers of the papers here reprinted for their readiness to make this book possible. Papers 1 and 8 originally appeared in *Weather*, the monthly magazine published by the Royal

Meteorological Society, London; and Paper 6 appeared in the *Quarterly Journal of the Royal Meteorological Society* so recently that work on this book had already begun. Paper 2 first appeared as a chapter in the book *Descriptive Palaeoclimatology*, editor A. E. M. Nairn, published in 1961 by Interscience Publishers Inc. (John Wiley and Sons, Ltd., of New York); Paper 5 constituted a chapter in the book *Problems of Palaeoclimatology* produced by John Wiley and Sons, Ltd., London, New York and Sydney in 1964 – both these other books contain items by other authors likely to be of value to students of climatic changes over geological time. Paper 3 was first published in the book *Changes of Climate*, reporting the proceedings of a joint symposium organized by WMO and UNESCO in Rome in 1961, published by UNESCO as Vol. XX in the Arid Zone Research series 1963, containing a great diversity of research papers on the facts and theoretical interpretation of the climatic changes since the ice age. Paper 4 was a lecture delivered at Oxford, in October 1963, and already published in abbreviated form in *Experimental Cartography – Report on the Oxford Symposium*, Oxford University Press 1964 and reprinted in full here by permission. Paper 7 was a lecture given before Section X of the British Association for the Advancement of Science at its Southampton Meeting, on 2 September 1964, printed here by permission and not previously published.

H. H. LAMB

Guildford, November 1964

ONE

Our changing climate, past and present

NOT so very long ago—between the wars in fact—climate was widely considered as something static, except on the geological time scale, and authoritative works on the climates of various regions were written without allusion to the possibility of change, sometimes without mention of the period to which the quoted observations referred. This attitude seems to have been a by-product of the idea that if only a long enough series of observations could be amassed, this would produce an average—described as the '*normal*'—value of each element to which, in the climate of any given place, the element would always tend to return. Climate was described as 'average weather' and climatology was looked upon merely as the dry-as-dust book-keeping branch of meteorology. That sort of climatology has little appeal. Moreover it ignores the more interesting facts of the case, as may been seen for instance from a glance at the various possible climatic tables for London or tables of ice at the coast of Iceland which could be compiled by using different 'normal' periods (see Tables 1 and 2). In reality, of course, climate is always changing,

TABLE 1. Climatic figures for London

Temperatures °C (generally Kew; Greenwich values identified by brackets)

	JANUARY				JULY			
	1841–70	1871–1900	1901–30	1950s	1841–70	1871–1900	1901–30	1950s
Average daily maximum	(6·2)	6·0	7·4	6·5	(23·4)	21·7	22·4*	21·4
Average daily minimum	(1·5)	1·2	1·8	2·1†	(11·7)	12·3	12·5	13·3

* Average daily maximum 1921–50 in July was 22·7°

† The continued rise of the January minimum temperatures right up to the 1950s, when the maxima have fallen, may be tentatively attributed to 'city effect'—the increased size and warmth of the town area

Rainfall (Kew) mm

JULY (Averages by decades)

1860s	1870s	1880s	1890s	1900–09	1910–19	1920s	1930s	1940s	1950–58
44	61	62	60	49	67	72	49	54	64

Period	mm	Period	mm
1896–1905	38	1886–95	78
1861–70	39	1875–84	72
1953–58	76		

TABLE 2. Ice at the Coast of Iceland

Average number of weeks/year (By decades)

1780s	1790s	1800–09	1810–19	1820s	1830s
12·7	8·4	9·6	9·0	8·9	8·4
1840s	**1850s**	**1860s**	**1870s**	**1880s**	**1890s**
3·2	7·2	12·9	7·7	12·3	6·9
1900–09	**1910–19**	**1920s**	**1930s**	**1940s**	**1947–56**
5·1	5·5	1·5	1·4	(1·7)	(3·7)

Figures 1780s–1930s from Koch (1945).

1940s and since estimated from data published in Iceland Year Books

just as the controlling influences are never quite the same, and the word 'normal' is correspondingly misleading. '*Datum period*' would be a better term, and it does not very much matter what datum period is chosen to measure departures from, provided that all elements and aspects of the climate of a place under consideration at any time are habitually related to the same years. This is far from being general practice yet, though some events must be completely inexplicable in terms of the basic parameters of other years.

Interest in the subject of climatic change was aroused once the considerable warming of our climate in most seasons of the year from the 1890s to the 1930s and '40s became obvious to all. As a matter of fact, I find that this trend was quite clearly recognized in a discussion in the Society as early as 1911. It now seems as if widespread public discussion only got going when the trend had already ceased or been quite seriously interrupted in several sectors (see Figs. 1 and 2). Our forefathers in the 17th, 18th and early 19th centuries had been aware of an opposite tendency, and efforts were made to organize official observation networks partly with the object of increasing knowledge about it. Efforts of this kind were made by French Governments of the 1770s and in 1821 and by the Prussian Ministry of the Interior in 1817.

A few years ago there was some speculation about the possibility that by the end of this century there might be no pack ice left in the Arctic. The implications of a continuance of the warming trend of the early 20th century to such a point might well be serious, although recently certain Great Powers are reported to have been toying with the idea of attempts at artificially removing the ice with a view to warming the climates in the temperate zone. Weather control along these lines, even if it were possible, might have some undesirable results—not all of them predictable. It seems likely, for instance, that there would be some northward spread of the desert zone in the southern parts of Europe, in central Asia and north America: the intensity of desert

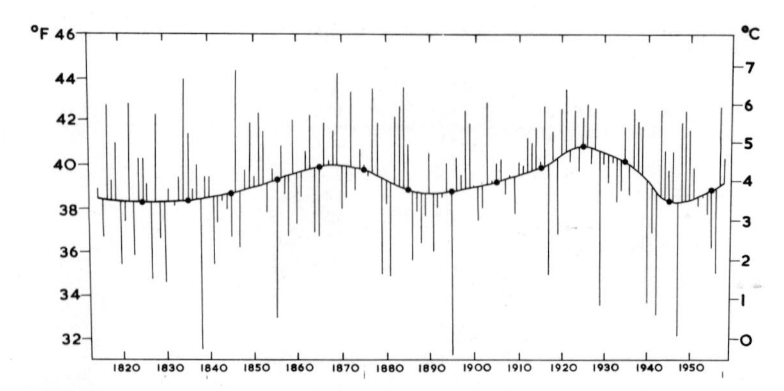

Fig. 1. Mean temperature (°F) of each winter 1815–1958 at Oxford. The curve is drawn to join the 10-year means, shown by round spots. The January-February temperatures for the individual winters are indicated by the extremities of the lines showing the departures from the mean curve. (Diagram by Mr. L. P. Smith, reproduced from *The Farmer's Almanac* by permission)

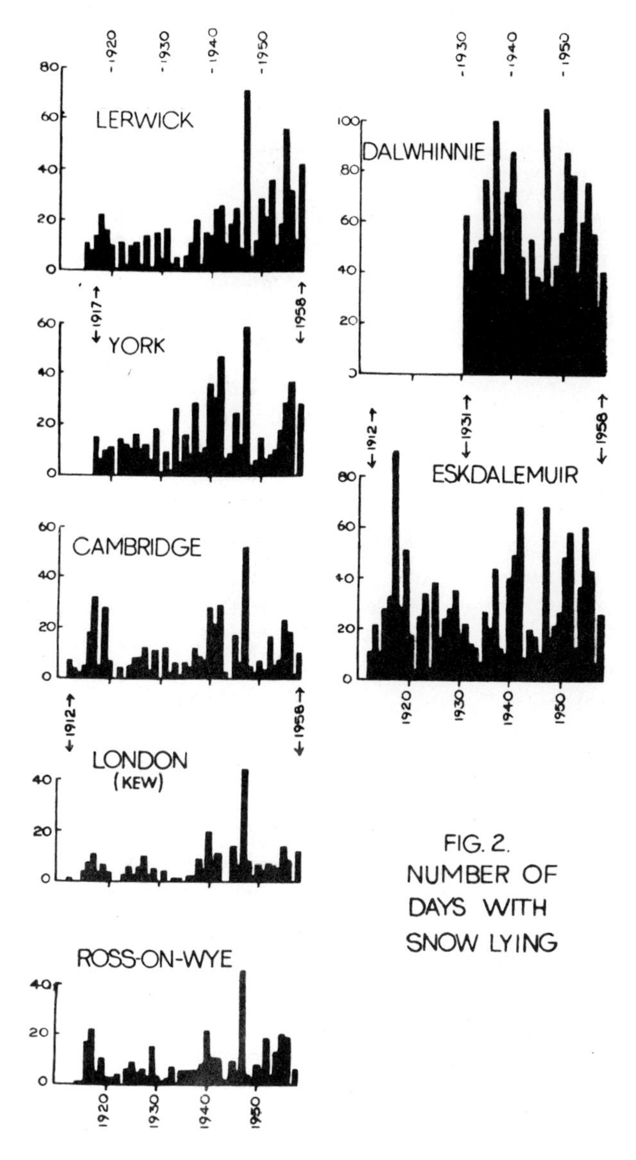

FIG. 2.
NUMBER OF DAYS WITH SNOW LYING

development in the heart of the zone over Africa and Asia might however be diminished.

A more immediate aim should be to seek physical understanding of the long-term changes of the atmospheric circulation and the climates with which it is associated. At present there is no lack of theories :

(i) Variations of *solar output*, especially in the ultra-violet where (alone) there appear to be associations with the 11-year sunspot period.
(ii) Variations of other astronomical factors affecting primarily *solar distance* (e.g. ellipticity of the Earth's orbit).
(iii) Variations of *atmospheric transmission and absorption* due to volcanic dust, also perhaps dust from nuclear explosions, carbon dioxide, water vapour, cloudiness.

(iv) Variations of surface or atmospheric *albedo*.

(v) Long-term changes in the *Earth's surface conditions*, affecting albedo, heat storage and friction upon the atmosphere : e.g. pole wandering, continental drift, mountain building.

(vi) Variations of *heat stored in the oceans*.

(vii) Variations of *extent of polar ice*—both (vi) and (vii) being principally responses to changes in the external conditions or in the atmosphere, with an important lag carried over into the next climatic period.

(viii) *Changes in the general circulation of the atmosphere*.

(ix) *Diversion of ocean currents* either as a response to changed atmospheric circulation or due to physical barriers (ice jams, earthquake and volcanic effects, and possibly due to silt movements)—both the atmospheric and ocean circulations ((viii) and (ix)) affecting the redistribution of heat over the earth's face.

Most of these theories are however unsupported by demonstration or by any precise knowledge of the magnitude of the effects produced.

Too often empirical studies of climatic change have concentrated on the variations of one element at one place and usually without the application of statistical tests. In this way a great diversity of fragmentary evidence has been amassed, until it is scarcely easier to see what has been going on during the period of instrument records than during the earlier periods for which we have only literary, geological or biological evidence. I, for one, must confess to having been bewildered and left quite pessimistic by some discussions of climatic variation : though I believe the position can be radically improved by methods which I shall suggest later.

The first need at the moment is to marshal our evidence into some sort of order. There must be stress upon the necessity of dating everything and specifying periods of validity. It will only be profitable to consider the evidence in assemblages each related to one period. Then the data can be explored for the workings of known perturbations and identifiable processes.

The motive is of course to enable planners to make intelligent provision for the future. The economic stake in providing wisely for the vagaries of climate has for generations needed no stressing. We should obviously be ready to exploit any lasting improvement in climate, although the recent past suggests that there is more danger of this being overdone. Most people are ready enough to abandon precautions and 'take things easy' after a few favourable years. (This has been quite serious in Caithness in the heavy snowfalls of recent years, since the old habit of laying in stocks of food and fuel in order to be able to hold out through some weeks of being snowed up had largely died out.) Modern agriculture is much better equipped than the husbandry of even a century ago (remember the Irish Potato Famine of the 1840s) to overcome the hazards of bad weather and, through international co-operation, even of runs of bad years. It may be however that our highly organized civilization is as vulnerable as any of its predecessors to lasting climatic changes, especially when nationalistic and racial fevers are allowed for.

THE CHRONICLE OF PAST EVENTS

Before coming to efforts at interpretation of climatic change I must give you the salient facts. In the process, you will see the impact of climatic variability on many aspects of human affairs and of animal and vegetable life. Hence this subject is a fertile field for collaboration between various branches of learning.

In considering the manifold allusions to biological and social phenomena which follow you should not imagine that their association with meteorology is a one-to-one relationship : nevertheless in all cases I believe that the weather played a part and that in some it was decisive. Some biological species may actually be usable as climatic indicators, in cases where it can be established that some particular threshold value (for instance, of summer or winter temperature) is decisive.

Climatic variation has been a much neglected topic in the world of affairs in this country and in English writing, although the influence of bad years in Scotland in the 1690s caught the attention of G. M. Trevelyan in connection with the Union of England and Scotland.

Trevelyan wrote (1942, p. 432) :

> The last half dozen years of William's reign [i.e. the 1690s] had been the ' dear years ' of Scottish memory, six consecutive seasons of disastrous weather when the harvest would not ripen. The country had not the means to buy food from abroad, so the people had laid themselves down and died. Many parishes had been reduced to a half or a third of their inhabitants. This sombre experience, from which the nation was slowly emerging during the years when the Treaty of Union was under debate, coloured the North Briton's outlook, deepened his superstitions and darkened his political passions, especially in relation to the hated English who had watched the kindly Scots die of hunger, and had moved no finger . . . Fortunately a cycle of fat years . . . followed.

We see from this the complex psychological factors of which the historian must take account. The Union was however the decision of those in power rather than of the grumbling rank and file, the majority of whom probably opposed it in both countries. It seems to have been a case of dire necessity since there were further harvest failures later—for instance, in 1709. This is also the background to the ' Dickens' Christmasses ', to some of Keats's poetry and possibly to some of the fearful descriptions of mountain landscapes at home and abroad in the 18th and early 19th centuries.

Climatic variation is a subject which cannot be neglected in the more northern lands. Indeed the history of Iceland consists of little else. It obviously should not be neglected by countries on the arid fringe either. And there are signs that our engineers concerned with hydro-electric and irrigation projects in Africa, as well as our planners (for instance of forest and crop development) at home, are finding it necessary to consider the implications.

At least six or eight distinct climatic stages can be recognized in Europe and the surrounding regions since the last major ice age. There may be something to be learnt both by meteorologists and by workers in pre-history by trying to establish the prevailing synoptic patterns of each phase. I hope you will be able to form some picture of these from what I propose to say now.

1. *The last major ice sheet* disappeared from Scandinavia, and glaciers from Britain, somewhere about 8000–7000 B.C. The Fennoscandian end moraine has been dated as 8300 B.C. The most advanced centres of early civilization (about 6000 B.C.) were in the Indus Valley and Mesopotamia. The last stages of the Ice Age were a period of lowered rainfall in the Mediter-

ranean and North Africa and possibly in most parts of the world ; according to one writer (Butzer 1958) the Mediterranean evidence of this is dated 15000–5000 B.C. I suppose the lowered temperature of the oceans—and consequently less moisture in the atmosphere—would account for much of this dryness.

2. *By 4000–2000 B.C. the post-glacial Climatic Optimum* had been reached with world temperature 2–3°C higher than now. It is doubtful whether the general sea level was much higher than now because there was probably still much water locked up in the ice sheets on land—e.g. the Brenner Pass may not have been open before 1800 B.C., that is to say not until after several thousand years of warm climate, and indeed not until the warmest phase was past. There must have been less Arctic pack ice than now ; Brooks's idea that there was none is a reasonable but possibly extreme view (*cf.* Flohn 1952*a* ; Crary, Kulp and Marshall 1955). The latitudinal range of temperature was presumably less than now.

Forest spread rapidly north over Europe after the retreat of the ice ; but about 5000 B.C. rainfall became too great for a while, killing much of the forest and replacing it by peat bogs and expanded lakes. Much later the climate became drier again and forest reconquered some of the bogs.

Contemporary with the Climatic Optimum, there was a 'sub-pluvial' period 5000–2400 B.C. in North Africa. This was the time of settlements in the Sahara from which the surviving cave drawings tell us about migration routes used by animals and men across what is now full desert. The rule of the Pharaohs in Egypt dates from about 3000 B.C. when the climate was already becoming drier. The elephant and giraffe became extinct in Egypt a little before this (3600 B.C. has been suggested), but elephants survived in isolation in Algeria until Roman times (Hannibal used Algerian elephants).

There seems to be something meteorologically curious about the conjunction of pluvial times and conditions for life in the Sahara with the warmest post-glacial epoch in the temperate zone. Explanation in simple terms of a poleward shift of all the climatic zones would hardly be adequate. One writer has suggested the prevalence of a 'southerly meridional type' in the European-African sector during this epoch. Perhaps, however, a good deal is explained by higher ocean surface temperatures than now and correspondingly increased moisture in the atmosphere. The Sahara seems to have been still relatively the driest zone.

3. *Decline from the Climatic Optimum* was at first gradual but became abrupt and accompanied by catastrophe to some of the human civilizations of the time about 500 B.C. The later stages of the Climatic Optimum had on the whole been drier and gradually cooler, with pines gaining ground at the expense of oak forests in Europe. There had, it is true, been some sort of flood disaster about 1300 B.C. which caused the eruption from the Hungarian plain of the tall, fair-haired, grey-eyed Achaeans, later known as Hellenes, who brought bronze and iron objects of the upper Austrian Hallstatt culture into Greece. This was however a passing phase and not the endpoint of the climatic deterioration in central and northern Europe. About 500 B.C. began

a rainy, cool period but (it has been suggested) with mild winters. The lakes in Europe rose and swamped the dwellings on the peat bogs (Hallstatt ' Lake Dwellings ') ; the Boden See rose about 10 m ; the Alpine glaciers re-advanced, closing the passes, which were not greatly used for traffic again until about 700 A.D.

Maximum rainfall has been ' placed ' at about 400 B.C. There was however no really dry season in the Mediterranean even in the 2nd Century A.D. (*Diary* of Claudius Ptolomaeus of Alexandria). In Classical Greece, from perhaps 800 B.C. onwards until Roman times, this was apparently a favourable period with plenty of forest and presumably more rainfall than now. The Mediterranean climates of today would be improved by some summer rain.

A period of uncomfortable climate with great storminess in the North Sea is believed to have set the early Celtic and Teutonic peoples on the move from the western part of the German plain about 120 B.C.

The climate gradually became drier (and probably rather warmer) during the Roman Era, the latter part of which was one of prosperous estates in southern Britain—some of the estates surviving in Somerset well after the Roman withdrawal (*c.* 400 A.D.). With the good climate of the late Roman era in Britain a good southern aspect was preferred for houses. The increasing drought in Asia has been suggested as having possibly triggered off the Barbarian invasions of Europe.

4. *There was a secondary optimum of climate between 400 and 1200 A.D.*, the peak probably being 800–1000 A.D. This was on the whole a dry, warm period and apparently remarkably stormfree in the Atlantic and in the North Sea. It was the time of lowland settlement in the Saxon lands and of considerable flowering of Celtic and Northumbrian cultures. Missions from the Celtic Church in Ireland were sent as far as Africa and Iceland. It was also the time of great Viking voyages and the settlement of Iceland and Greenland. The early Norse burials in Greenland were deep in ground which is now permanently frozen. There were several visits to America (probably many timber-getting voyages between Greenland and Labrador) and there is evidence which suggests that at least one Viking ship got through the North-West Passage and ultimately reached the Gulf of California (*cf.* Ives 1953).

In Domesday Book (1085) 38 vineyards were recorded in England besides those of the king. The wine was considered almost equal with the French wine both in quantity and quality as far north as Gloucestershire and the Ledbury area of Herefordshire where the soil is said to resemble that of the Rhine and Moselle wine districts. The London basin, the Medway valley and the Isle of Ely were also favoured districts. The northernmost vineyards were near York but the most favoured country was from Northants and the Fenland southwards. This implies summer temperatures perhaps 1 to 2°C higher than today, general freedom from May frosts (particularly suggested by the exposure to the north of several low-lying vineyard sites, e.g. at Tewkesbury, in the Fens and at Teynham, Kent) and mostly good Septembers.

There are some curious records of occasional severe frosts in the Mediterranean during this epoch, the Tiber at Rome and the Nile at Cairo being frozen over once or twice. Butzer (1958) mentions bearing ice on the Nile at Cairo in 829 and 1010/11 also the northern Adriatic frozen in 859/60 : in other words right at the peak of the storm-free, warm epoch in the north. Presumably this points to a northward shift of the anticyclone belt as characteristic of the epoch and much Siberian cold air occasionally reaching the Mediterranean.

There is evidence of greater rainfall than now in southern Europe. The mediaeval bridge at Palermo, Sicily (1113), was built to span a river much larger than that of today.

5. *Decline set in again.* The period 1200–1400 A.D. contained some remarkable climatic instability in western Europe with great floods and droughts, notably severe and notably mild winters. Polar ice was much more in evidence in Iceland and Greenland waters than formerly and there is much more mention of storminess. The links between Scandinavia and Iceland became tenuous and that with Greenland virtually ceased to exist. Iceland was engulfed in poverty, disasters befalling with volcanic eruptions as well as ice ; grain growing almost died out and the forest disappeared. In Greenland, after the links with the outside world had been severed, the stature of the people declined, until by 1400 the normal height of these people of Norse stock is believed to have been less than 5 ft (1 m 50 cm), and the colony ultimately died out. Some of these phenomena might be explained by the depression track moving south at a time when there was still much heat stored in the main part of the Atlantic Ocean. Colder conditions set in therewith in Iceland and Greenland, but cooling did not become important for some considerable time in Europe. Vine growing only gradually declined in England and on the Continent. At one time (1128–1437) wine had been produced in East Prussia. Grapes grew even at Tilsit (55°N) in Lithuania and in south Norway as well as in southern England and as high as 780 m above sea level in the Black Forest. The highest vineyards in Germany today are about 560 m near the Boden See in Baden. The mediaeval English vineyards were almost all less than 100 m above sea level, though one exceptionally favoured height at about 200 m is suggested in Herefordshire. It is not to be supposed that the northernmost wines were nice. The fact that the fruit ripened and that they could be produced at all is sufficiently remarkable if we think of comparisons with the modern climates of the regions mentioned. The wines were needed by the abbeys for the sustenance of travellers who had no other hospices to go to in those days. No doubt the standards of acceptability changed in northern lands once it became possible to transport the southern wines so far, though there is little doubt that in their heyday some of the English wines were good. The sourer northern wines were sweetened, or rendered more palatable, by the addition of red currant, rosemary, fennel, carnation or violet (latterly this was probably done in England too) and were not produced after 1500 at latest when English and Hanseatic shippers were making the better southern wines more widely and cheaply available.

Terraces of an English medieval vineyard near Ledbury, Herefordshire, as they appear today. Aspect south, photograph taken looking west *Photograph by H. H. Lamb*

General appearance in 1959 of the sloping ornamental meadow (park) with south aspect where the terraces in Plate I were photographed. The height is between 200 and 300 feet above sea level. From the age of the trees, including several yews, near the south-west corner (left-hand edge) it is evident that the ground has not been cultivated as a vineyard for a very long time, although portions of quite a number of grass-grown terraces remain. The terraces end abruptly where the south aspect ends

Photograph by H. H. Lamb

The decline of the wine harvests since the Middle Ages in the vine growing Land Baden is portrayed in Fig. 3, based on the data given by Müller (1953). The decline in England, perhaps mainly between 1250–1400, seems to fit better with the time of climatic deterioration than with the increase of competition with French wines : trade must have expanded considerably after the accession of the Garronne to the English crown in 1152, yet many English vineyards were established after that date. The accounts of the abbey at Ely are known to record sales from the abbey vineyards up to as late as 1469, though with much trouble with bad years when the juice was worthless and no wine could be made. Things had been better in the 1200s.*

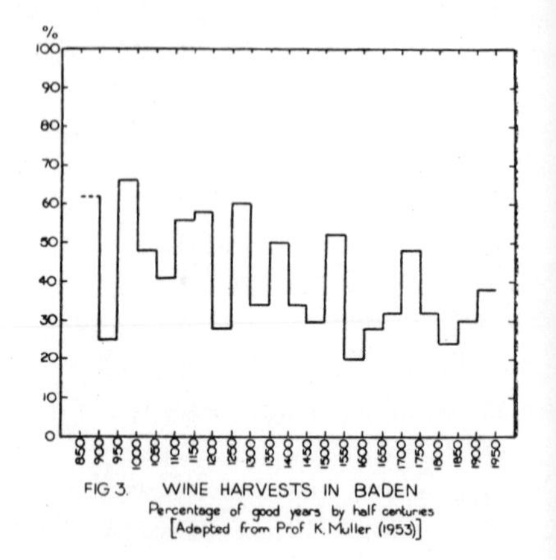

FIG 3. WINE HARVESTS IN BADEN
Percentage of good years by half centuries
[Adapted from Prof K. Muller (1953)]

The period 1350–1600 seems to have been a time when plagues and diseases were particularly rife in Europe, perhaps encouraged by poor summers and mild winters. After the Black Death the plague died out quickest in high latitudes.

6. *The period 1400–1550 was one of partial recovery ;* although there were a few harsher winters than before in Europe in the 1430s, and increasingly after 1500, and upland villages were abandoned perhaps partly for this reason in England and Germany. On the whole the times became more prosperous in Iceland and Scotland and notably so in England. Southern fruits were introduced into English gardens, e.g. apricot, figs, peach and quince. There was some renewed attention to the vine by the gentry who took over great gardens from the Abbeys, but apparently not much success in fruiting. Growing cherries in orchards is said to have started about 1460.

Houses in England tended to be built on the northern slopes and face north or east, shunning the ' unhealthy south wind and the violent west wind and to admit only the gentle east and the north wind which drives away pestiferous vapours ' (quoted by J. P. Williams Freeman 1928).

The great voyages of discovery from about the 1490s may have been encouraged by a period of somewhat reduced storminess over most of the oceans, though the Cape of Storms (now the Cape of Good Hope) and the Horn had a bad name.

7. *The period from 1550 to about 1850 has been called the Little Ice Age.* The glaciers of Europe reached their most advanced positions since the Ice Age and the polar pack ice on the North Atlantic probably also became more

* In most centuries since the decline of the English mediaeval vineyards there have been a few able enthusiasts who have produced wine from grapes grown in their own vineyards ; but, so far as the writer has been able to discover, this has only been done at a few specially favoured sites between the London area, Cardiff and the Hampshire coast. By contrast, some of the vineyards of former times seem to have been in places that are now notorious for late spring, and even summer, night frosts.

extensive than at any other time that we have been talking about. Although its limits on the ocean cannot be determined, I think the evidence suggests that by 1780–1800 the ice commonly extended more than half way from Greenland to Norway and affected the coasts of Iceland for much of the year. The first attempts on the North-East Passage 1553 (Chancellor) and the North-West Passage 1585 (Davis) were evidently undertaken at an unfortunate time.

Winters with east winds in western Europe were prominent in the early stages (1550–1600), though later on weak circulations seem to have been more characteristic. The siting of houses in England showed a desire for shelter from all directions and, since it was dry epoch, at least from 1600 to 1750, low-lying sites were not avoided.

In the days of the older London Bridges, which restricted the movement of water in and out of the upper river, the Thames used occasionally to freeze over in London. This does not seem to have happened more than once or twice a century until the 1500s. Its more frequent occurrence after that date is shown in Table 3. The frost fairs seem to have begun in late Tudor times. Henry VIII may have set the fashion for making sport of the freeze by driving down the Thames with his queen in 1536 to Greenwich. Queen Elizabeth was daily on the river ice in 1564–65 and sport began with the Court, which was then at Westminster. Iron skates were introduced from Holland in 1662.

TABLE 3. Thames Frozen over in London

Number of recorded occasions per century								
900s	1000–1099	1100s	1200s	1300s	1400s	1500s	1600s	1700s
1	1	2	2	0	1	4	8	6

Records cease to be comparable in the nineteenth century because the new London Bridge built 1831 allowed freer tidal movement of water in and out of the river. It seems possible that the introduction of locks and weirs on the river above Teddington has also reduced the liability to freezing-over in London by preventing ice coming down from the upper river. In the nineteenth century the only recorded freeze was in 1814: none has occurred since, although ice floes have been abundant in the severest winters.

There were years of distress in all northern countries; farms or farmland had to be abandoned to the ice in Iceland, Norway and the Alps. Growing of cereals completely ended in Iceland, only to be resumed in the 1920s and after. There were years of dearth in Scotland and Scandinavia, especially in the 1590s, 1690s and 1780s, occasioned by poor summers as well as harsh winters. The woods were dying near the north-west coast of Scotland (Earl of Cromertie 1710), perhaps owing to increased windiness and salt spray, and these shores remain treeless today. Plague and malaria however disappeared from Europe north of the Alps. Malaria died out in the continental regions concerned as early as the 1690s, but I am informed by Professor Manley that it still existed in the Cambridgeshire fens until the mid-nineteenth century. (Oliver Cromwell is believed to have died of English malaria.)

Jon Eythorsson (1952) quotes the following Icelandic parish record which gives a vivid impression of climatic disaster:

1709. *Breiðamörk* (farm). Half King's ownership, half owned by the farmer. Derelict . . . a little woodland, now surrounded by glacier . . .

Fjall (farm). Owned by the Church. Derelict. Lies north-east of Breiðamörk. Fourteen years ago had farmhouse and buildings, all now come under the glacier . . .

Similar entries in a book dated 1712, add that Fjall was abandoned in 1700 or earlier, Breiðamörk in 1698. 'There was some grass visible then, but since the glacier has covered all except the hillock on which the farmhouse at Breiðamörk stood and that is surrounded by ice so that it is no use even for sheep.' Later that hillock too was overrun by the ice.

Utterström (1955) gives details of the sufferings in Norway and Sweden in the 1590s and in the 1690s. Both were decades in which there was important volcanic activity in the world, and it may be that the reported climatic vicissitudes lend some credence to the theory that a veil of volcanic dust in the upper atmosphere was effectively reducing insolation. Utterström quotes from the parish records of Alem near Kalmar in Sweden :

> In that year (1601) the sun did not have its right natural shine or heat, but in a clear sky shone as though through smoke until 9 or 10 in the day and in mid-evening lost its shine again.

Utterström also mentions that in the diocese of Stavanger in Norway there were severe famines in 1596–98 so that the people ate bark and ground hay, straw and chaff into bread.

The change of climate was taken more lightly in England, but vine growing was abandoned and there was less success with other southern fruits. Upland estates and farms on the Pennines became poorer.

By the 1780s we can put together a picture of the actual temperature levels prevailing. In central England the average for January was some 2½°C lower than in the 1920s and '30s. In southern England at least the summers were not significantly different from now, though the sea temperatures off our western coasts appear to have been 1 to 2°C lower (perhaps even 3°C lower in the north) and in his tour of Scotland in 1769 Thos. Pennant, F.R.S., reported that the highest Cairngorm summits had perpetual snow and one of the highest lochans had ice on it ' the latter end July '.

CHANGES TO BE CONSIDERED IN THE PERIOD OF INSTRUMENT RECORDS

The last of these climatic phases brings us to the era for which a good deal of information may be gleaned from early instrument records and from diaries (some of them specifically weather diaries) from which frequencies of east and west winds, rain days, etc., may be counted up. The barometer was invented in 1643, the thermometer about the same time and the first, somewhat curious, raingauges were set up between 1676 and the 1690s. By a century later there seem to have been a good many reasonable barometers, thermometers and raingauges about whose readings we can use. Unfortunately there was considerable chaos in the matter of units—not even yet completely ironed out. Between this difficulty and the details of site and exposure there is a good deal of trouble in making use of old records for any period before about 1860. We must be very much indebted to people like Professor Manley and his opposite numbers in other countries who have devoted a lot of time to providing us with homogeneous records of temperature and other elements for a number of places in Europe and elsewhere over periods going well back into the eighteenth century.

I do not think we shall get much farther however until we consider the significant changes during the instrumental period by some synoptic method.

There have been changes during the past 100–200 years in many climatic elements in many parts of the world which reach statistically significant levels. These may be summed up by saying that the nearly world-wide climatic amelioration—seen at its most rapid in the warming of the Arctic and ice recession—from the 1830s to the 1930s has brought us into yet another climatic phase, partly resembling the warmer periods in the Middle Ages.

This is the first climatic change which can be measured and plotted out in terms of instrument readings. Nevertheless the data have not yet been much exploited by mapping methods. Several researches have shown that the atmospheric circulation over the North Atlantic intensified materially from 1880–1900 to 1920–40. This was probably the period of most rapid shrinkage of the Arctic ice. Work which we have been doing at Harrow suggests that one can reconstruct monthly mean pressure patterns over a much longer period (over a restricted region back to the 1760s) and that the intensification of the general circulation has been a continued trend from about 1800 to the 1920s (compare Figs. 4 and 5). A similar trend can be identified in the southern hemisphere from about 1850 to 1910–1920.

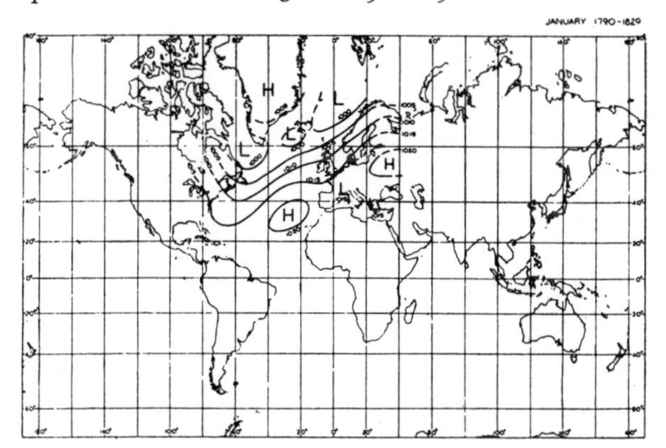

Fig. 4. Average pressure at mean sea level in January 1790–1829

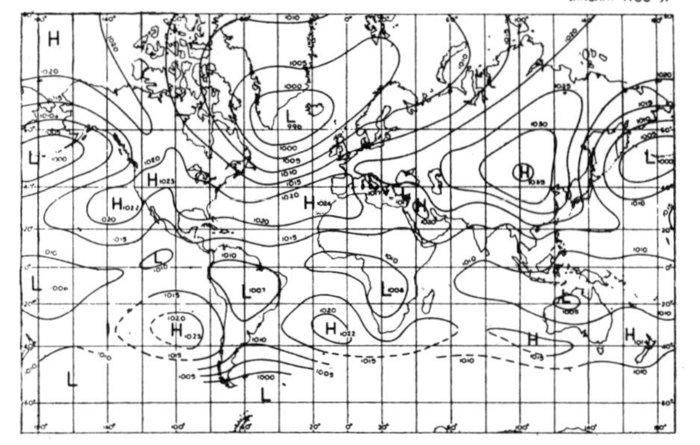

Fig. 5. Average pressure at mean sea level in January 1900–1939

This intensification of the general circulation over widely separated parts of the world—including the northern and southern westerlies and the trades—seems to be a most enlightening basis of reference in terms of which practically all the reported changes in other climatic elements or phenomena known to me promise to 'fall into place'. I think this permits some optimism about the prospect of simplifying the welter of heterogeneous data on climatic changes and gaining better understanding. The most obvious effect of intensified atmospheric circulation is increased extent of oceanic influence, especially in winter, when the very low surface temperatures associated with inversions over the continents and over the polar ice became rarer. In this way the gradients of surface temperature in winter decreased, although the upper air temperature and 'thickness' gradients may well have increased. The temperature gradient in summer between the heated continents and the ice-covered Arctic Ocean increased to the years of most intense circulation about the 1920s and '30s and has decreased a little since (*cf.* Figs. 6 and 7).

Although our records of upper air observations are pitifully short for climatic variation studies, it seems possible that some deductions may legitimately be made from the surface pressure patterns and also from the surface observations at mountain peaks (Flohn 1952*b*). There is evidence that the

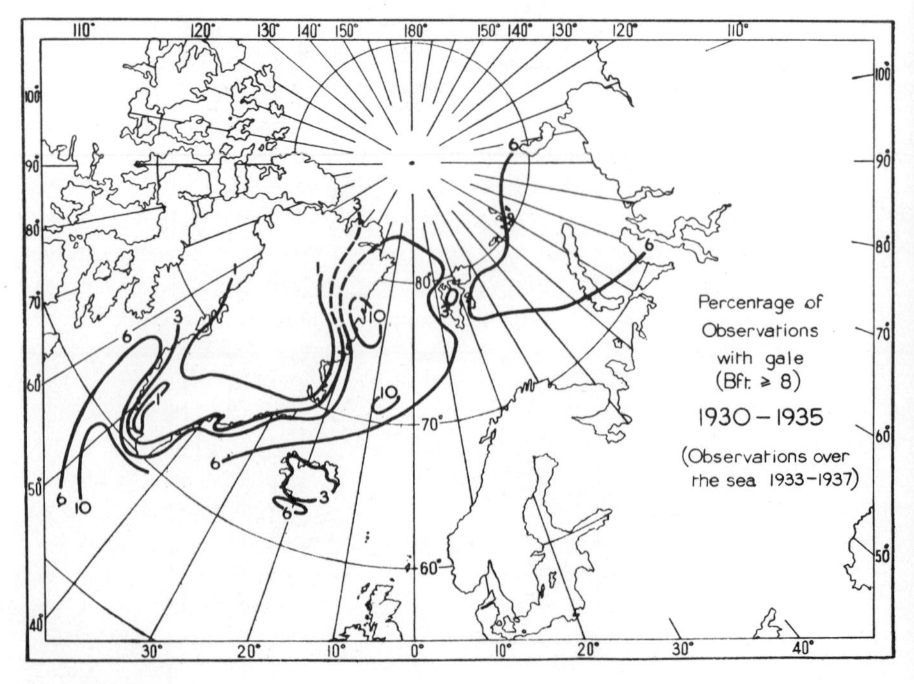

Fig. 6. Percentage of observations with gale (Bft.≥8) 1930–1935. (Observations over the sea 1933–1937)
Reproduced from the *Geographical Journal* by permission

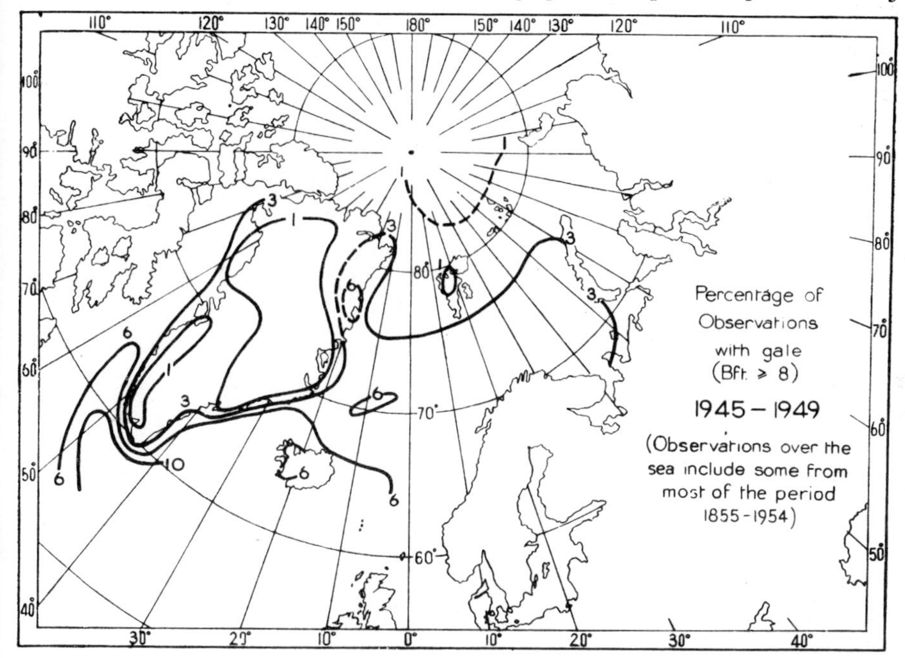

Fig. 7. Percentage of observations with gale (Bft.≥8) 1945–1949. (Observations over the sea 1855–1954, which compare well with those for land stations 1945–1949) Reproduced from the *Geographical Journal* by permission

troughs in the upper westerlies affecting both the western North Atlantic and the southern Indian Ocean were farther west 100 years ago than they are now (*cf.* Loewe, Radok and Grant 1952).

I have recently come across in the Meteorological Office Library what I believe is the earliest survey of water currents and ocean surface temperatures carried out on behalf of the Admiralty (Rennell 1832). The water current observations, having been made from sailing ships, appear unreliable, except where the currents are very strong or very persistent. But the temperature observations look good ; these make it possible to present a picture of the change of temperature of the surface of the North and South Atlantic Oceans between the epoch 1780–1820 and the present century (Figs. 8 and 9). The pattern shows that the Gulf Stream was farther south than now and tended to turn away south before reaching the coast of Europe ; the Polar stream and Labrador current on the western Atlantic were broader than now ; the equatorial current of warm water from the South Atlantic recurved south along the coast of Brazil more than now and supplied less warm water to the Caribbean and North Atlantic. These differences are in good agreement with other evidence that the northern Atlantic was colder, the ice more extensive and the depression track farther south than now whilst the south Atlantic was warmer and the Antarctic ice belt narrower (farther south).

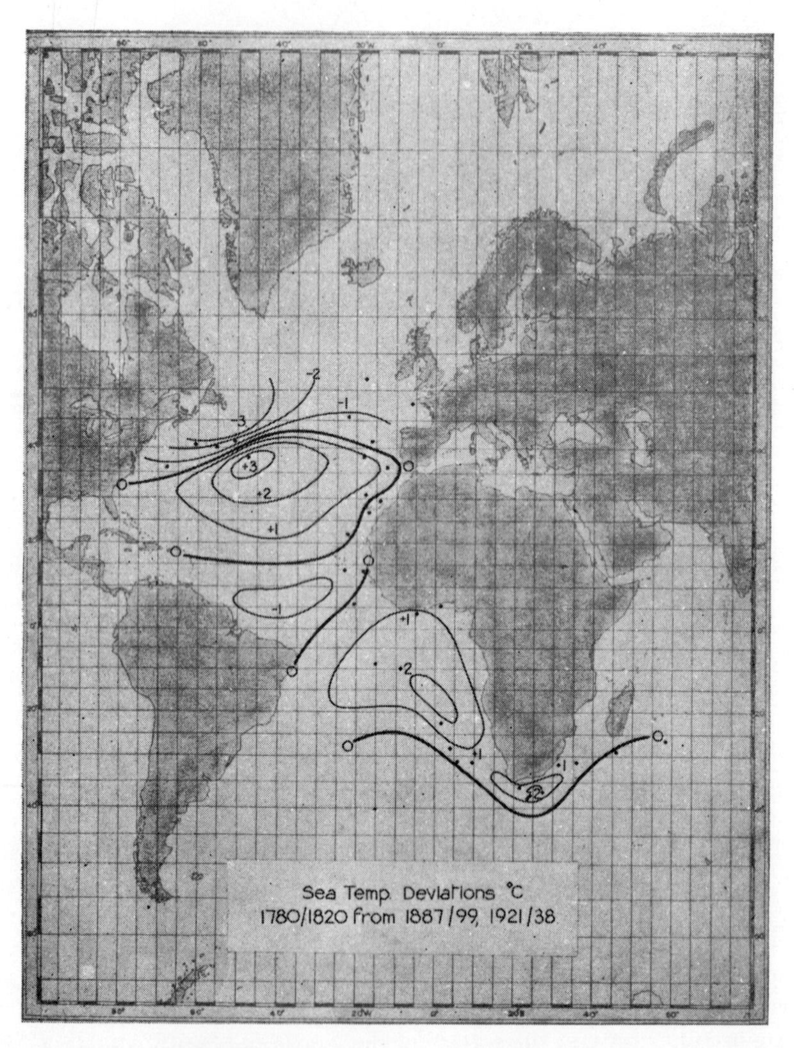

Fig. 8. Sea surface temperature deviations in °C in January: Rennell's 1780–1820 values compared with modern normals. Dots mark the points for which Rennell gave 'usual values' and from which the departure isopleths have been drawn

Superimposed upon the observed intensification and northward shift of the atmospheric circulation in the Atlantic sector from 1800 to the present century, there have been large oscillations of circulation intensity affecting ice extent and winter temperatures in Europe especially. These may be detected for instance in the figures of the incidence of ice on the coasts of Iceland (Table 2) and in the winter temperatures in our own country (Fig. 1). We do not

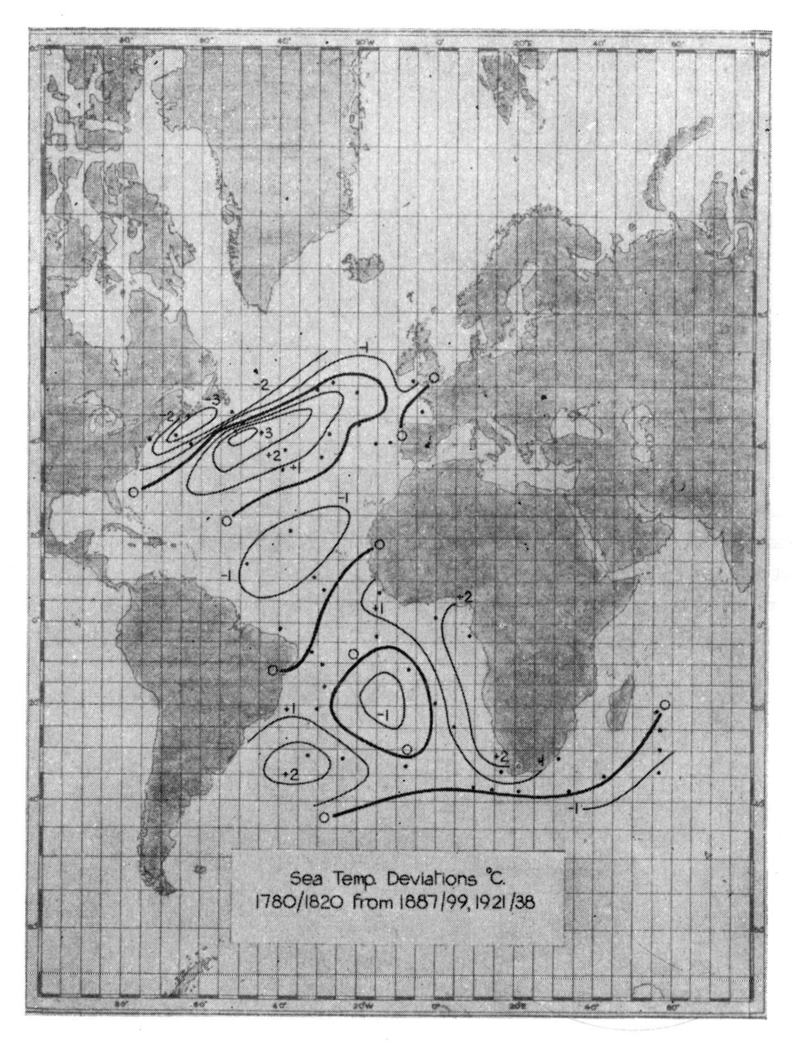

Fig. 9. Sea surface temperature deviations in °C in July: Rennell's 1780–1820 values compared with modern normals

yet know whether these oscillations are periodic: their times scales are of the order of 20 to 60 years. The 1880s and '90s were an epoch of cold winters and much ice, whereas there were hardly any cold winters between 1896 and 1939. Since the peak of mildness in the 1920s winters in this part of the world have again become colder and the atmospheric circulation has become weaker.

These changes may teach us more about the working of the atmospheric and ocean circulations which affect our climate. Related trends appear to be seen in many parts of the world, even perhaps in the rate of accumulation of snow on the Antarctic ice-cap at Southice (82°S) which showed a maximum about the 1920s and has since declined 30 per cent to the rate prevailing in the 1890s (Lister 1959). It is reasonable to suppose that at times of increased vigour of the general atmospheric circulation, more moisture and more precipitation would get carried into the interior of Antarctica than at other times. Over eastern North America, however, the average winter temperatures have been somewhat out of phase. There was a minor minimum in the 1920s and the peak was not until the early 1950s, if it has been reached yet.

Weakening of the atmospheric circulation in winter in the Atlantic and European sector including the Arctic became evident a little before 1940. Not until the 1950s was there evidence that this had resulted in an increased extent of the polar ice, but this is now increasingly apparent in Iceland and the European sector. Moreover this renewed, though so far not serious, increase of ice has occurred at a time when the greater part of the North Atlantic is still warmer than it has been since our temperature records began and when water of Gulf Stream origin under the polar ice in the central Arctic is reported to be, even in 1956, 0·8°C warmer than it was in 1938. It may be legitimate to see in this an indication that the quantity of pack ice formed on the surface of the Arctic Ocean responds more particularly to the quietness (or otherwise) of the atmospheric circulation—depending particularly on surface inversions of temperature being not too much disturbed.

CONCLUSIONS

What then of the future ?

Our attitude to climatic ' normals ' must clearly change. 1901–30 and still more 1921–50 were highly *abnormal* periods.

We in Britain do not (most of us) live near the climatic margins of our type of civilization. The changes of the figures in our climatic tables from one period to another do not look very impressive. Nevertheless, they are significant in various respects, affecting for instance the geographical limits of cod and herring and birds and the thriving of crop plants and trees. With some of these the response to climatic shifts is very quick. The winter climate of southern Finland in the 1930s was no severer than that of Denmark in the last century. The winter climate of London in 1780–1820 was about the same as that of the Rhineland in our times. The summer climate of southern England (as far north as a line from the Fens to Hereford) in the early Middle Ages was similar to that of the Paris-Touraine region of northern France nowadays : between 1930 and 1949 our summer climate again approached this level (and I believe peach trees and other southern varieties did well accordingly) but since 1950 the figures in summer, as in winter, are back to late nineteenth century standards.

We do not yet know whether the latest turn in our climatic fortunes, since the optimum years of the 1930s, marks the beginning of a serious downward trend or whether it is merely another wobble—one more of the semi-regular oscillations on a time scale of 20 to 60 years. There have been other striking 'ameliorations' before—even during the Little Ice Age: the mild periods around the 1630s, 1730s, 1770s and 1840s must all have been quite impressive. But we must not bank on such periods too heavily without more understanding. I have always thought it a misfortune that the general introduction of plumbing into British houses coincided with the quite unusual run of mild winters between 1896 and 1936. And possibly some of the modern glass architecture and the hill-top sites with an open south-west aspect which became so desirable a few years ago seem less to be recommended in the 1950s.

The solution of these problems, I feel sure, is to be sought in a better understanding of the general circulation of the atmosphere and oceans and of the changing influences upon them exerted by external agencies. We should, I think, reconstruct the synoptic patterns of the past 100-200 years—taking as a starting point the monthly means and their averages in different decades and longer periods. Pressure and wind, temperature, ocean currents, sea temperature and rainfall should all be studied in strictly corresponding periods. Then various shadowy ideas about possible associations and reported changes will certainly become clearer.

BIBLIOGRAPHY

The best book on this subject for the general reader is Brooks, C. E. P. *Climate through the ages*. London (Ernest Benn). 2nd ed. 1949.

Particular aspects of causation are well treated in the various chapters of Shapley, H., and others *Climatic change*. Harvard. 1953.

Those who read German will find the central importance of the general circulation of the atmosphere well developed in Wagner, A. *Klima-änderungen und Klimaschwankungen*. Braunschweig. 1940.

REFERENCES

BUTZER, K. W. 1958 Studien zum vor- und früh-geschichtlichen Landschaftswandel der Sahara. *Akad. der Wiss. und der Lit. in Mainz, Math-Naturwiss. Klasse* 1958 Nr. 1, Wiesbaden (Steiner).

CRARY, A. P., KULP, J. L., and MARSHALL, E. W. 1955 Evidences of climatic change from ice island studies, *Science*, **122,** pp, pp. 1171-1173, Washington

CROMERTIE, EARL of 1710 An account of the mosses in Scotland, *Phil. Trans. Roy. Soc.*, **27,** pp. 296-301

EYTHORSSON, J. 1952 History of Breiða (in Icelandic), *Jökull*, **2,** pp. 17-20, Reykjavik

FLOHN, H. 1952*a* Allegemeine atmosphärische Zirkulation und Paläoklimatologie, *Geol. Rundschau*, **40,** pp. 153-178, Stuttgart

FLOHN, H. 1952*b* Hochgebirge und allgemeine Zirkulation, *Berichte des dt. Wetterdienst* U.S. Zone, Nr. 31, pp. 17-23, Bad Kissingen

WILLIAMS FREEMAN, J. P. 1928 *Antiquity*, p. 208, Gloucester

IVES, R. L. 1953 Climatic studies in western North America, *Proc. Toronto Met. Conf.*, pp. 218-222.

KOCH, L. 1945 The East Greenland ice, *Medd. om Grönland*, **130,** Nr. 3, Copenhagen

LISTER, H. 1959 Glaciological research on the Transantarctic Expedition, lecture (unpublished) at the Royal Geographical Society, London

LOEWE, F., RADOK, U. and GRANT, A. 1952 Eine säkuläre Klimaänderung im südlichen Indischen Ozean? *Berichte des dt. Wetterdienst U.S. Zone*, **7,** Nr. 42, pp. 11-15, Bad Kissingen

Müller, K.	1953	Geschichte des badischen Weinbaus, Laar in Baden (von Moritz Schauenburg)
Rennell, J.	1832	*An investigation of the currents of the Atlantic Ocean and of those which prevail between the Indian and the Atlantic Ocean.* London (Rivington)
Trevelyan, G. M.	1942	*English Social History.* London (Longmans)
Utterström, G.	1955	Climatic fluctuations and population problems in early modern history, *Scandinavian Econ. Hist. Rev.*, **3**, pp. 1-47, Stockholm

TWO

Fundamentals of climate

I. Introductory Survey

I.1 *Prime Importance of Solar Radiation and its Distribution According to Latitude*

The general circulation of the atmosphere and oceans is the mechanism of climate. The heat and energy of the system is supplied by the sun in quantities graded according to latitude and season. It may be surmised that the sun is to some extent a variable star, though it has not been possible to establish any measurable variation of solar energy over the few decades since pyrheliometric measurements at mountain observatories began.[41,73] The rôle of geography is to modify—within limits—the distribution of heat input, through the different responses of land, sea and ice to incoming radiation and through the mobile reserves of heat stored in the oceans, as well as to channel and constrain the free flow of the winds. The actual braking effect upon the atmosphere is most important at great mountain barriers, especially those arrayed north and south across the mainstreams of the atmospheric circulation.

In considering the climatology of past geological epochs, major differences of geographical setting must be contemplated and certain astronomical 'constants' must be treated as variables.[11,44] Thus, the tilt of the earth's axis relative to its orbit round the sun (the obliquity of the ecliptic), which affects the range of the seasons, is believed to vary at least between 22° and 24½° with a periodicity of the order of 40 000 years—the last maximum having been about 10 000 years ago. The eccentricity of the earth's elliptical orbit also varies between about 0 and 0·07 with a period of some 92 000 years. When the eccentricity is greatest, the intensity of the solar beam reaching the earth must undergo a seasonal range of over 30 per cent. At the present epoch a range of about 7 per cent is experienced, the least solar distance (earth in perihelion) occurring about the December solstice—an arrangement which makes the seasonal range of incoming radiation intensity greater in the southern than in the northern hemisphere. The season in which perihelion falls undergoes a cyclic variation with period 21 000 years (due to precession of the equinoxes and rotation of the elliptical orbit), so that some 10 000 years ago the northern hemisphere had the greater seasonal range.

Variable transmissivity of the earth's atmosphere, due to changes of moisture content, cloudiness, the slight carbon dioxide concentration and volcanic dust, is also thought to affect the intensity of the radiation reaching the earth's surface by several per cent. None of these things, however, seriously affect the permanently greater heating of the earth's equatorial zone than the polar caps, owing to the obliquity of the incident beam in high latitudes: the equator at present receives about 2·5 times as much heat in the course of a year as the poles. This is a near-constant which must be presumed to give the stamp of permanency to a general arrangement of climatic zones more or less parallel with the latitude circles and it is not surprising to find that the most fundamental features of the atmospheric circulation bear an obvious correspondence to this latitudinal arrangement of the energy drive.

It will be seen later (Sections II.1 and 4) that the most prominent feature of the atmospheric circulation considered in depth is the great circumpolar whirl of upper westerly winds, strongest in middle latitudes in either hemisphere (see Figs. 4a and b). These westerlies dominate the scene over extra-tropical latitudes (and at times even nearer the equator also) from a height of little more than 1 km up to great altitudes in the stratosphere and carry most of the momentum in the atmosphere. They are the mainstream of the atmospheric circulation and play a more fundamental rôle than the depressions and anticyclones familiar on the surface weather map; indeed, the development and maintenance of these surface features largely depend upon the upper westerlies, whose circumpolar form is witness to the planetary basis of the system.

The southern hemisphere, over 80 per cent of whose surface is water, presents us with the nearest observable approach to the conditions of a uniform globe and it is there that the observed pattern of the upper westerlies approximates most closely to the ideal circumpolar ring, though centred rather about the middle of the Antarctic ice region near 82°S, 60°E than at the pole itself (Fig. 4b). In the northern hemisphere the circumpolar ring of planetary westerlies is deformed by strong geographical influences (Fig. 4a): the annual mean pattern is dominated by the winter situation, when gradients are strongest, and shows marked 'cold troughs' towards the downstream ends of the great continents, attributable to continental winter cooling. The relative warmth of the northern Atlantic and Pacific Oceans produces marked bulges of the isotherms over them and distinct warm ridges in the upper atmospheric circulation with their crests over Alaska and near Spitzbergen; but the ridges and troughs by no means destroy the general circumpolar form of the circulation.

I.2 *The Heat Budget*

The earth's surface receives virtually all its heat from the sun, either directly or after diffusion in the atmosphere. The flow of geothermal heat from the earth's interior is by comparison negligible, and is generally supposed to have been negligible for at least the last 500 million years.

At the present epoch it is estimated that on a world-wide average 43 per cent of the incoming solar radiation reaches the earth's surface—about half of this as a direct beam, the rest after reflections and scattering during passage through the atmosphere—and is absorbed at the surface or partly transmitted to appreciable depths in the oceans.[28, 75] Another 42 per cent is lost by reflection to outer space, especially from cloud-tops, from the ocean surface and from ice and snow: the proportion reflected is a characteristic, known as the albedo, of each type of surface. Only the remaining 15 per cent is directly absorbed in the atmosphere, nearly half of this by ozone in the upper stratosphere and the rest chiefly by the water vapour distributed throughout the lower atmosphere.

By far the greatest portion of the heat absorbed by the atmosphere comes from the earth's surface. Some of the terrestrial radiation is reflected and re-radiated back to the earth, particularly under cloudy skies, but on balance an amount equivalent to about 15 to 20 per cent of the intensity of the incoming solar radiation passes from the earth to the atmosphere. The balance is completed by radiation escaping to space from the earth's surface and from the atmosphere.

An amount of heat estimated at about 20 per cent of the total incident solar radiation is involved in exchanges between earth and atmosphere in the evaporation–condensation cycle. In this way latent heat is converted into sensible heat in the atmosphere sometimes at places far from where the evaporation occurred and even well outside the same latitude zone.[13, 67]

The proportion of the incident solar radiation which is actually used for heating the earth's surface and the atmosphere is greatly affected by events in the atmosphere and by the nature of the surface. The albedo of different kinds of surface varies from about 7 to 20 per cent in the case of black soil, yellow sand or dry bushes to 90 per cent or more in the case of hard frozen snow or ice.[29] Dry land surfaces also heat and cool much more readily than oceans because of the great specific heat of water and the transmission and conduction of heat below the ocean surface, especially in the layers stirred by surface waves.[10, 11]

Losses during transmission tend to be greatest in high latitudes, where the path of the oblique rays through the atmosphere is longest, and wherever

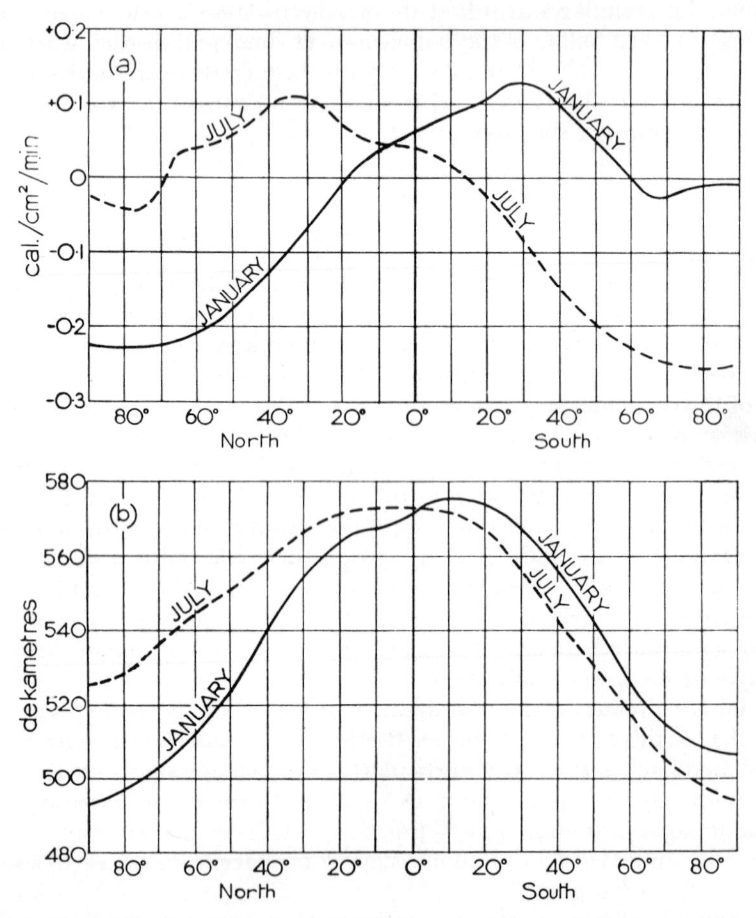

Fig. 1. Latitudinal distribution of: (a) intensity of net radiation receipt (after Simpson); (b) thickness of the layer between the 1000 and 500 mb pressure levels (brief name—1000–500 mb thickness or relative topography)

(Reproduced by courtesy of the Controller of Her Majesty's Stationery Office, London)

cloudiness is most extensive, as over the subpolar oceans and in the belt of equatorial rains. The albedo of completely overcast skies is 70 to 80 per cent.[3, 29]

These factors have a general tendency to increase thermal gradients over the earth in middle latitudes, and especially near the limits of the main snow and ice-fields and at the ocean margins, whereas the poleward gradient should be reduced or reversed near the equatorial belt on account of the great cloudiness there.

Curves (Fig. 1a) of the balance between incoming and outgoing radiation at each latitude, following computations by Simpson,[62] show the main gradient in middle latitudes and a particularly strong gradient in the northern summer over a narrow zone near 70°N, where the heated land masses of Asia and America abut upon the Arctic ice. The over-all gradients from equator to pole are, however, very much weaker in summer than in winter in both hemispheres.

In the 24-hour day about the solstice the poles may for a time, under suitably clear skies, receive more radiation *per diem* than anywhere else. The net radiation used for heating the surface is however reduced by the high reflectivity (albedo) of the ice and snow. The January radiation curve (Fig. 1a) should in fact dip rather lower than it does in the Antarctic, since Simpson underestimated the albedo of the ice-cap in summer.

Fig. 1b presents curves of the mean height difference ('thickness') between the 1 000 and 500 mb pressure levels for each latitude. This is a measure of the mean temperature of the lower half of the atmosphere. These curves are complicated by the effect of moisture content on atmospheric density, which is appreciable in the lower latitudes, but they display the expected correspondence with the cardinal features of the radiation heating curves in Fig. 1a. Some general smoothing of the thermal gradients in Fig. 1b as against 1a may probably be attributed to the effect of heat transport by the atmosphere.

The world maps of net radiation receipt (incoming *minus* outgoing) in January and July, reproduced in Figs. 2 and 3, are based on Simpson's calculations. They demonstrate a basically zonal distribution, especially in the southern hemisphere, and show that the strongest general gradient lies in middle latitudes, being especially strong in the winter hemisphere. Geography produces important gradients more locally near the coasts of north Africa and southern Australia and Chile in summer. There are local reversals of gradient in the equatorial rainbelt.

II. The Atmosphere in Motion: Surface and Upper Circulations and their Perturbations

II.1 *Establishment of the Basic Current: the Upper Westerlies*

The unequal heating of different portions of the earth's surface creates inequalities of density in the horizontal field in the atmosphere, thereby introducing a circulation tendency. The colder air sinks and spreads horizontally under the warmer air, which rises and spreads over the cold air. In this way the atmosphere may be regarded as a heat engine, which conveys heat from warm source to cold sink, performing work against ground friction in the process. The energy of the system is constantly fed by the heat sources, although friction would bring it to rest in a few days.

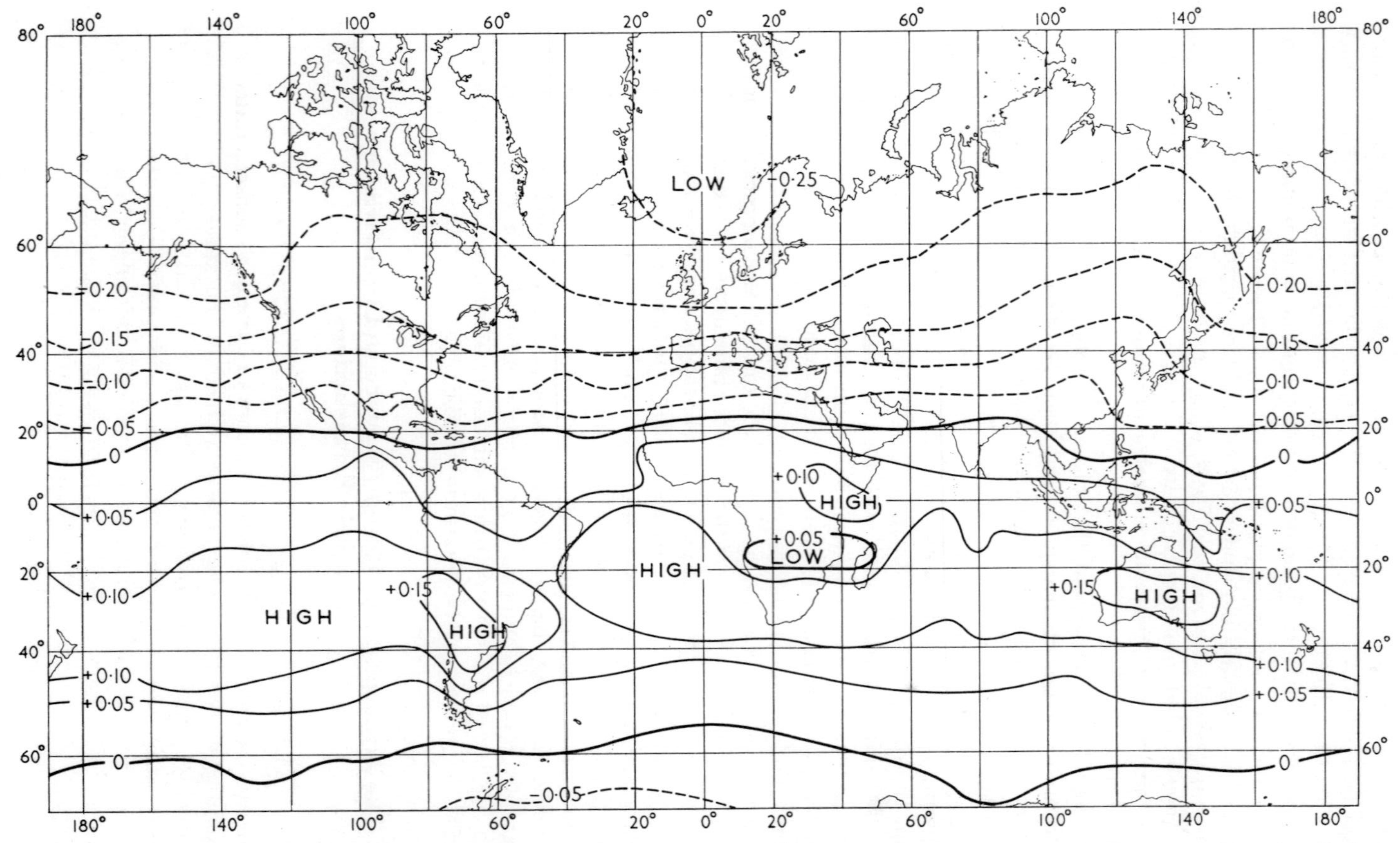

Fig. 2. Intensity of net radiation receipt in January, g cal cm^{-2} min^{-1} (after Simpson). Broken lines indicate net loss of radiation

(Reproduced by courtesy of the Royal Meteorological Society, London)

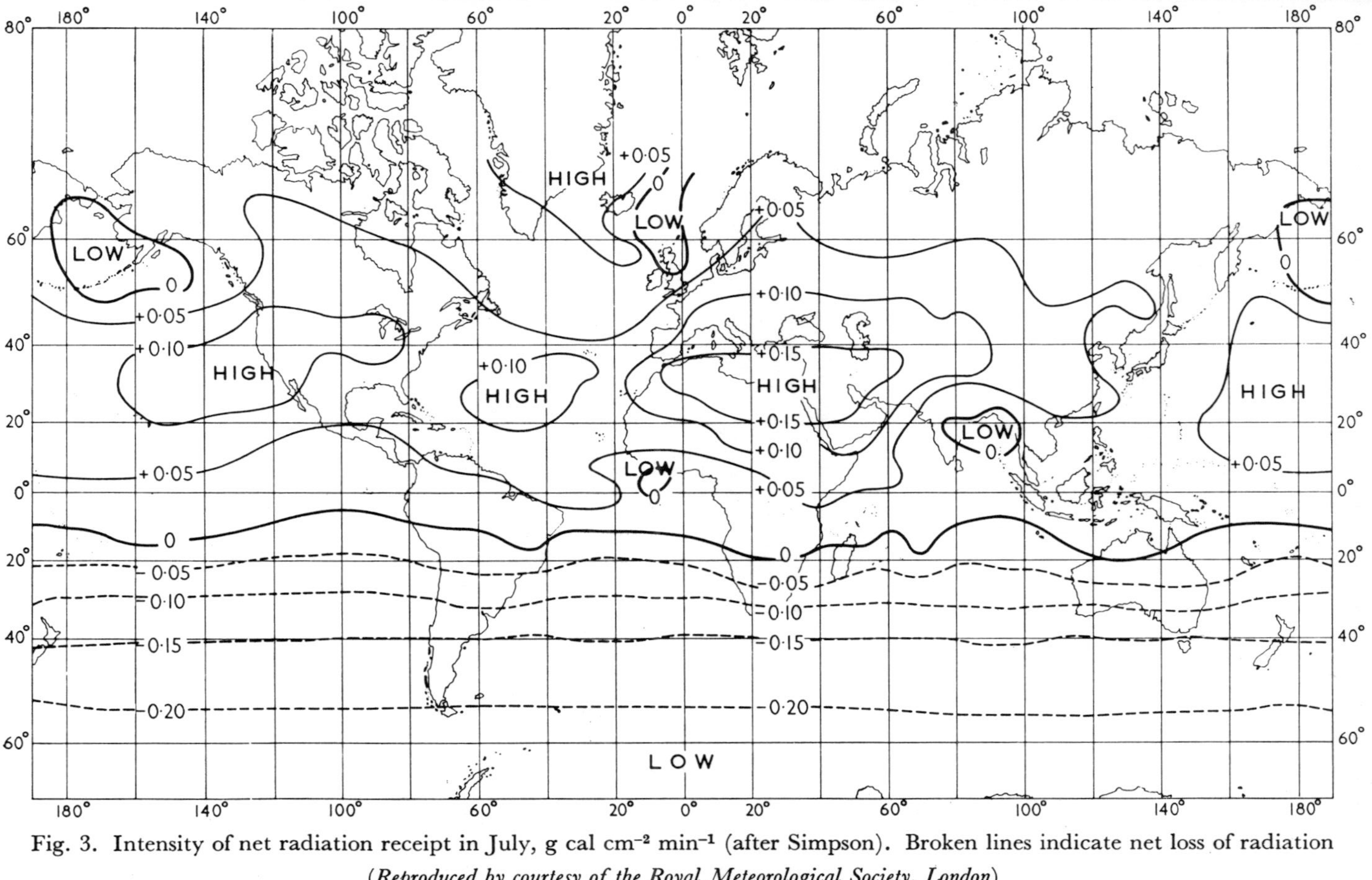

Fig. 3. Intensity of net radiation receipt in July, g cal cm^{-2} min^{-1} (after Simpson). Broken lines indicate net loss of radiation

(*Reproduced by courtesy of the Royal Meteorological Society, London*)

To understand how the observed circulation pattern arises, suppose the atmosphere momentarily at rest on the surface of the earth with no inequalities of pressure, no geographical complications and uniform heating in each latitude zone.

Owing to the relatively low density of the warmest air, there should be less of the atmosphere below any given altitude and more of the atmosphere at greater heights over the tropics than nearer the poles. This must result in a pressure gradient in the upper air from the warm zone to the cold zone, and this pressure gradient should increase up to the greatest height to which the density gradient continues in the same sense. Similarly, with regard to differences of temperature within any latitude zone, warm areas will appear in the upper atmosphere as ridges of high pressure extending polewards from the tropical zone and cold areas as troughs extending from the polar zone.

These pressure gradients do in fact hold sway above surface levels, as seen from Figs. 4a and b, which present the mean height (topography) of the 500 mb pressure level over the northern and southern hemispheres respectively.

The stronger the pressure gradient, the greater the accelerating force to which the air is subjected. The air does not, however, move directly from high to low pressures. As the earth rotates underneath it, moving air is deflected to the right in the northern and to the left in the southern hemisphere. This leads to an anticlockwise circulation around centres of low pressure in the northern, clockwise in the southern hemisphere. A centrifugal force arises and eventually an equilibrium is achieved with the air moving along the isobars (lines of equal pressure) with a balance between the pressure gradient and other forces acting in opposite directions. This equilibrium is expressed by the gradient wind equation:

$$\frac{1}{\rho}\frac{\partial p}{\partial s} = 2\omega \,.\, V \,.\, \sin \phi \pm \frac{V^2}{r} + A \qquad (1)$$

where ρ = air density, $\partial p/\partial s$ = the pressure gradient measured at right angles to the air's path, ω = angular velocity of the earth's rotation about its axis, ϕ = latitude, V = wind velocity, measured along its path, r = radius of curvature of the air's path, and A stands for other forces, represented chiefly by friction at the ground or due to turbulence.

The term $2\omega \,.\, V \,.\, \sin \phi$ represents the deflection due to earth rotation, the so-called geostrophic or Coriolis acceleration. The term V^2/r represents the centrifugal acceleration which operates against the pressure gradient (positive sign taken) when the air's path is cyclonically curved (about a low pressure region), but is in the same sense as the pressure gradient (negative sign taken) in the case of anticyclonic curvature.

The chief points to note at this stage are that under equilibrium conditions on a reasonably straight path, the V^2/r term being small, the wind moves (along the lines of equal pressure or contours of equal height of the given pressure level as in Figs. 4a and b) at a speed proportional to the pressure gradient; secondly, the equilibrium wind speed for a given pressure

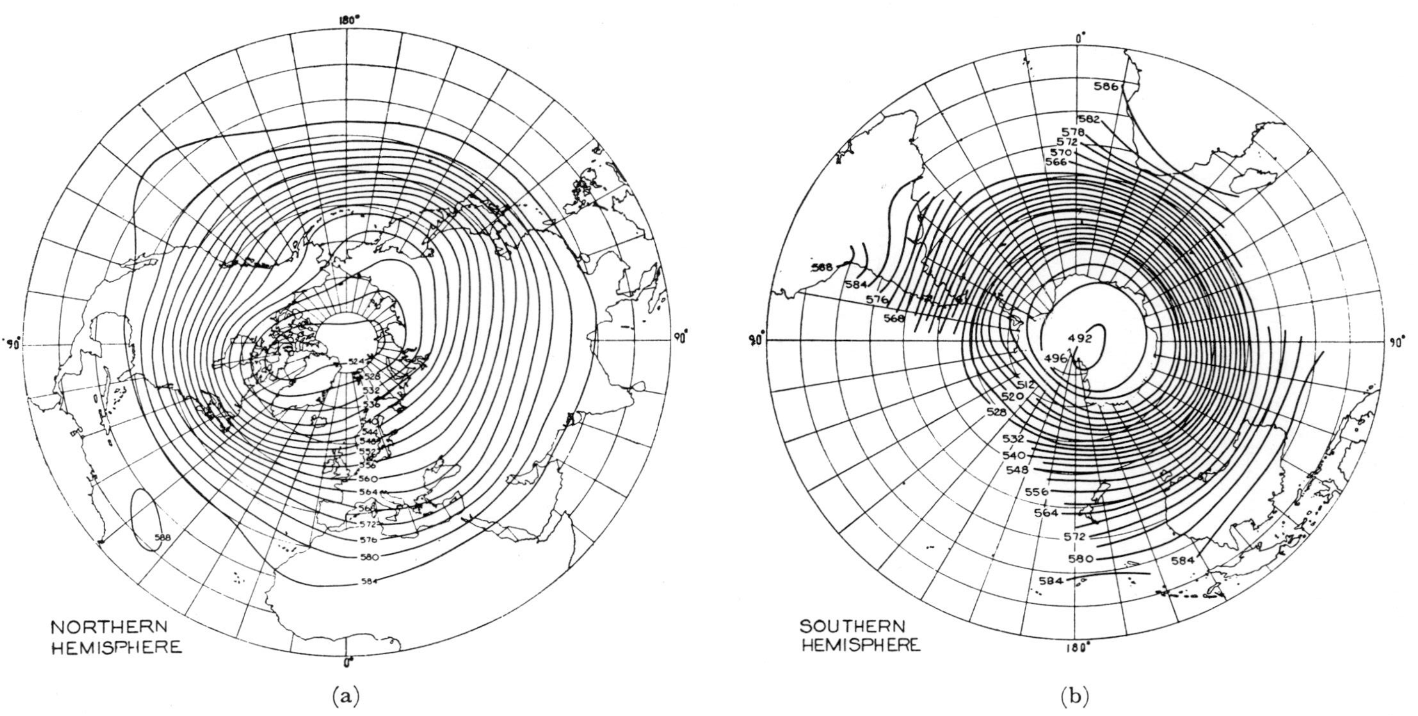

(a)

(b)

Fig. 4. Mean height of 500 mb surface in dekametres. (a) Northern hemisphere; (b) southern hemisphere. The contours and gradients of the 500 mb surface have nearly the same significance as isobars and pressure gradients at about the 5 to 6 km level. Under equilibrium conditions the wind blows along the contours anti-clockwise about the North Polar 'low' and clockwise about the South Polar 'low'.

(Reproduced by courtesy of the Controller of Her Majesty's Stationery Office, London)

gradient is greater the lower the latitude. Hence, if we suppose a uniform gradient from equator to poles the wind should be stronger in lower latitudes, increasing in proportion to cosec ϕ.

Thus the principal observed features of the upper wind circulation follow the pattern of the basic thermal distribution.

The observed form of the general circulation is very far from being the simple overturning of warm air rising in the tropics and spreading to the polar regions aloft, whilst its place is taken at the surface by airstreams spreading equatorwards all the way from the Pole. Nevertheless, the elements of this gravitational circulation (overturning) may be recognized in the broad-scale vertical circulation in the Trade Wind zone and the average circulation over the polar caps (see Fig. 5), as well as in the air motion on either side of strongly developed fronts between unlike airstreams, in coastal sea breezes and in the katabatic drainage of cold air off ice-caps and mountain regions exposed to radiation cooling.

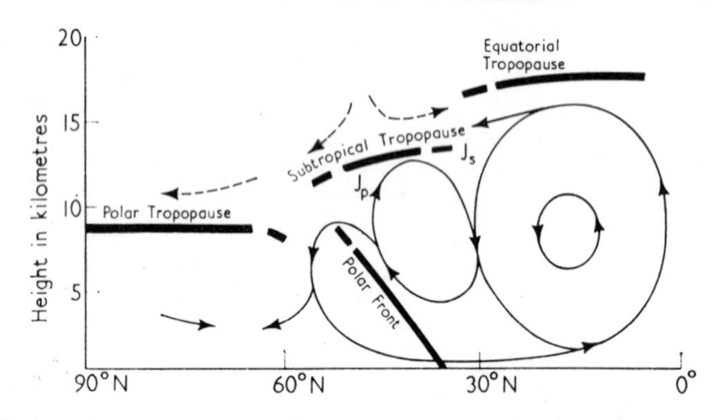

Fig. 5. Mean vertical, meridional circulation. J_p indicates position of the (westerly) polar front jet stream, and J_s indicates position of the (westerly) subtropical jet stream. Note: both jet streams blow approximately at right angles to the meridional plane represented by the paper.

(*Reproduced by courtesy of the Royal Meteorological Society, London*)

Fig. 5, adapted from Palmén,[49] presents the best picture at present available of the mean circulation in the vertical between the equator and the North Pole. Relative to the westerlies, this is a very slow circulation; it results from wind components occurring where the principal horizontal airstreams are out of equilibrium with the forces acting upon them (i.e. from 'ageostrophic' wind components). The simple 'direct' (or gravitational) circulation originally proposed by Hadley[27] takes place over the tropical zone and on a smaller scale over the polar regions; over middle latitudes the vertical circulation is rather in the 'indirect' (warm air sinking) sense. J_p and J_s mark the positions at which maxima of the west winds in the horizontal field are normally found; J_p (the 'polar front jet stream', normally at 9–10 km) is associated with confluence of rising air in the troposphere below and subsiding air in the stratosphere above, J_s (the 'subtropical jet stream', normally at about 12 km) is associated with confluence between air from north and south. The upper westerlies generally reach a maximum just below the tropopause (the discontinuity of vertical lapse rate of temperature which divides the lower atmosphere, or troposphere, from the stratosphere). Winds exceeding 100 kt are common in both polar front and subtropical jet streams; in the latter, extremes of 200–300 kt are occasionally observed. The stratosphere exists because of the entirely separate source of atmospheric heating (by direct absorption of solar radiation) in the ozone layer higher up. This gives rise to a very different horizontal temperature distribution and the westerlies are in most cases weakened in the stratosphere. Nevertheless, disequilibrium in the westerlies in the layer of maximum wind sets up vertical motion in which the lower stratosphere becomes involved. This vertical motion modifies the sharpness of the discontinuity at the tropopause.

II.2 *The Form and Intensity of the Upper Westerlies: Rossby Waves*

The winter cold troughs over north-east Asia and Quebec–Labrador, which are intense enough to impress themselves on the annual mean pressure distribution (Fig. 4a), are readily understood as a consequence of the maximum cooling of the air towards the downstream end of its passage over the continents.

Orographic disturbance of the flow of the upper west winds past the Rocky mountains and the mountains of Asia should also produce troughs in the regions downstream. The trough over north-eastern Canada is present to some extent throughout the year and the trough near north-east Siberia has its axis over the north-west Pacific in summer.[12] Maintenance of the troughs in the warm season may be largely due to the orographic braking of the circulation, although it happens that the cold waters of Hudsons Bay and the Canadian Arctic and of the Behring Sea and Okhotsk Sea should also tend to induce troughs in the observed regions. Furthermore, the extensive high plateaux of Tibet and Mongolia act as a specially effective heat source in summer, since the ground is strongly heated by solar radiation which has passed through materially less of the earth's atmosphere than elsewhere. These regions are covered by a high-level anticyclone in summer,[1] necessarily marked off by lower pressure over the sea to the east.

Rossby[56–59] assumed that the winds tend to maintain constant absolute vorticity as they move over the rotating earth. This appears to explain the long waves observed in the flow pattern of the upper westerlies. These waves move (generally eastwards) at a speed c which is less than that of the west winds themselves U, defined by the formula

$$c = U - \frac{\beta\lambda^2}{4\pi^2} \qquad (2)$$

where λ is the wavelength and β stands for d $(2\omega \,.\, \sin \phi)/\mathrm{d}\phi$. The wave pattern becomes stationary ($c = 0$) when $U = \beta\lambda^2/4\pi^2$. This expression defines a stationary wavelength which increases with the square root of the general speed of the westerlies: the wavelength is also greater in high latitudes.

Since orography and thermal inequalities in the zone of westerlies repeatedly generate ridges and troughs in certain longitudes, the atmospheric circulation has a tendency to settle down in a persistent pattern whenever the stationary wavelength harmonizes with these preferred wave positions. The régimes thus occurring always break down when the circulation intensity changes with the changing seasons; nevertheless the preferred wavelengths show up in the seasonal and yearly averages.

These Rossby waves are thought to account for the position of a secondary maximum of trough frequency seen on Fig. 4a as a minor trough with NE: SW axis from the Arctic coast of Siberia to the eastern Mediterranean; this is at about the appropriate wavelength downstream from the Canadian cold trough and itself induces a trough in the isotherms over eastern Europe and western Siberia.

Corresponding to circulation intensities prevailing at the present epoch, spacings of four or five troughs in the zone of westerlies around the hemisphere are commonest,[47,48] with often as few as three troughs in the stronger westerlies of the southern hemisphere; six or even seven troughs may appear at times of weak circulation in the northern hemisphere, especially in the lower latitudes and in summer.

The troughs observed in the mean circulation are therefore of mixed origin, partly thermal, partly orographic and partly produced by preferred wavelengths in the general upper westerly flow. The effect of the passing depressions and anticyclones of the surface weather map, advecting warm and cold air in turn, is to produce a moving train of warm ridges and cold troughs. More or less 'anchored' troughs are likely to appear downstream from the main mountain blocks, and the travelling depressions and anticyclones are steered around these bigger troughs by the mainstream of the upper westerlies. Investigations by Lamb[38] have shown that snow and ice surfaces introduce a stabilizing factor north of about 45°N in winter on account of radiation losses and the great quantities of latent heat required to thaw them. A snow or ice surface of more than about 1 500 miles west–east extent in winter apparently guarantees the existence of a more or less fixed cold trough in the higher latitudes.

The eccentric arrangement of the remarkably circular mean flow around the southern hemisphere, effectively a broad trough in the Indian Ocean sector, is also apparently related to the broadest part of the Antarctic cooling surface and the principal drainage of cold air off the ice-cap in this sector.[40]

Sverdrup[70] pointed out that the great ocean currents of the North Atlantic and North Pacific make an appreciable contribution to the poleward transport of heat in the northern hemisphere which exceeds anything in the southern hemisphere and is without parallel south of 40°S (see Lamb[39]). This weakens the thermal gradients (and hence the circulation intensity) in the atmosphere over the northern hemisphere. For this reason, and because surface friction is much less over water than land, the atmospheric circulation is much stronger over the southern than over the northern hemisphere in the present epoch (*cf.* Figs. 4a and b). The ratio of net westerly momentum (southern to northern hemisphere) averages 1·5. Whether as a consequence of the centrifugal forces associated with these respective circulations or because of the greater heating in the northern hemisphere, the meteorological equator does not precisely coincide with the geographical equator but has an over-all mean position about 4°N. The southern climatic zones are accordingly several degrees nearer the equator than their northern counterparts. This disparity may be subject to minor variations even from century to century.

Variations in the strong southern circulation must have important repercussions on the northern hemisphere.[9,39,40,46] Moreover, as long as the northernmost Atlantic offers the main outlet for Arctic ice drifting south, any general shift of the northern climatic zones towards or away from the equator is likely to be considerably amplified in the Atlantic sector and regions bordering upon it, including most of Europe and eastern North America.

II.3 *Perturbations of the Upper Westerlies and Development of Surface Pressure Systems*

A uniformly zonal circulation could not conceivably persist for any length of time without suffering perturbation, e.g. at mountain ranges, on passing coastlines (due to change of friction), or owing to the unequal heating and cooling of land and sea within each latitude zone.

A purely zonal circulation would be bound to break down at more or less frequent intervals even in the absence of these external disturbing factors, since it would transport no heat away from the tropics towards the polar

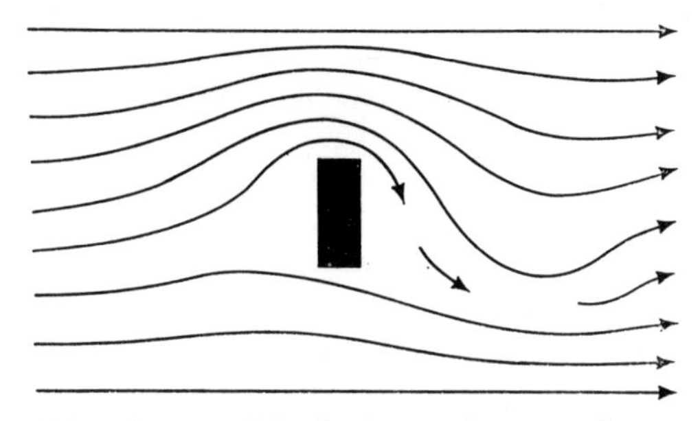

Fig. 6. Disturbance of the basic zonal current by a barrier (Northern hemisphere)

regions. The temperature difference would go on building up and the circumpolar westerlies would get ever stronger until dynamical effects of the enormous anticyclonic shear at the warm side of the jet stream brought about a breakdown.

Fig. 6 illustrates an idealized case of perturbation due to a physical barrier

B such as a mountain range. There is accelerated flow in the higher latitudes before the barrier and in the lower latitudes downstream. Examples on the grand scale occur at the Rocky Mountains, the Andes and the mountainous plateaux of Asia. The winter cold troughs over the northern continents and warm ridges over the oceans affect the flow similarly.

Each region of strengthened westerly flow means that the air entering this part of the pattern has to be accelerated and, for the time being, moves too slowly for equilibrium: here the pressure gradient force $\partial p/\partial s$ in equation (1) is able to produce a movement of the air across the isobars towards lower pressure, as at *P* in Fig. 7. Where the air emerges, as at *Q*, into regions of weaker pressure gradient it moves too fast for equilibrium with the pressure gradient and develops a component across the isobars towards the higher pressure side. Since the air farther out on either flank of the stream undergoes less acceleration and retardation, with smaller departures from equilibrium, convergence occurs to the left of the confluence and to the right of the exit (delta) from the strongest part of the stream. These effects could build up formidable differences of surface pressure, were it not that at the surface friction ensures that the lower air always moves too slowly for

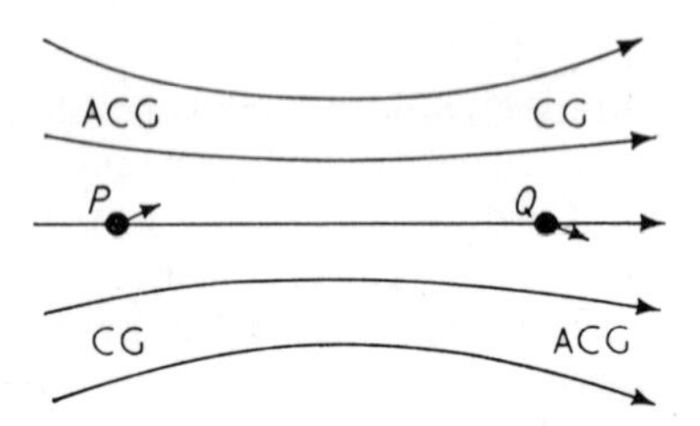

Fig. 7. Regions of convergence and divergence in the mainstream of the upper westerlies associated with surface pressure rise or anticyclogenesis (marked ACG) and surface pressure fall or cyclogenesis (marked CG). The main flow is represented by stream lines corresponding to air passing, under conditions of geostrophic balance, along the isobars. Small arrows at *P* and *Q* show the characteristic departures of flow direction observed in the confluences and diffluences of the mainstream.

equilibrium and has a component across the isobars from high to low pressure, tending to even out the pressure differences.

Attention has long been directed to a degree of unbalance between frictionally produced convergence at the surface and divergence at the level of strongest upper winds as the dynamic explanation of cyclonic development at the surface.[8, 20, 60, 66] More recent work has emphasized how much detail of surface pressure changes can be derived from the main atmospheric thermal pattern and the flow patterns of the upper troposphere;[50, 58, 68] indeed, this is the ultimate basis of most current approaches to numerical weather forecasting using electronic computers.[15, 31, 51]

Various causes combine to prolong the zone of strong winds downstream and give the greater weight to anticyclogenetic effects at the warm side of the stream and cyclogenetic effects at the cold side—i.e. to the developments expected at the exit from the strong stream. The warm side of the jet stream is marked by a belt of generally high pressure (subtropical anticyclones), interrupted more locally by low pressure (cell divisions) corresponding to the confluences in the upper circulation. At the cold side of the jet stream is the subpolar low pressure belt, interrupted at certain longtitudes by anticyclones or ridges associated with the confluences in the upper westerlies.

Factors which determine this preferred arrangement probably include:

(*a*) Frictional drag from the surrounding air, greatest where decreasing thermal gradients in the lower latitudes give rise to an important shear at the warm side of the jet stream.

(*b*) Radiation cooling at the cloud tops, which must be greatest at the warm side of the jet stream (emission being proportional to the fourth power of the temperature in °K and moisture content being generally greater the warmer the air). This produces a tendency for sinking and disturbs equilibrium in the horizontal field.

These, and probably other factors, combine to produce a net component of flow across the isobars towards the warm side of the jet stream at the level of maximum wind, compensated by a general poleward component at and near the surface in the same latitude zone. In middle latitudes, therefore, the upper westerlies correspond to prevailing SW or WSW winds at the surface in the northern hemisphere.

A good deal nearer the equator, the extreme fringe of the upper westerly winds is subjected to additional braking from vertical convection cells developing to great heights in the moister unstable air of the equatorial zone. At its maximum development, near the intertropical convergence, this vertical convection is forced up so high that adiabatic cooling of the rising (expanding) air and radiation cooling from the cloud masses formed in it introduce a cold equatorial zone in the high troposphere, with reversed thermal gradients and easterly wind components. Thus highest pressure occurs at some distance north and south of the meteorological equator at all levels up to nearly 20 km.

II.4 *Definition of the Main Zonal Arrangement of the Atmospheric Circulation*

The observed surface pressure and wind distributions are related to the thermally driven upper westerlies.

A. *Surface Pressure Systems and Average Pressure Distributions*

Surface pressure is illustrated by annual mean maps for the northern and southern hemispheres (Figs. 8a and b) and by profiles of mean pressure for January and July (Fig. 9). The latitude scale of the profiles is proportional to sin ϕ to indicate the lesser area of the high latitude zones and thereby the distribution of atmospheric mass. Notice the greater intensity of the southern circulation and the corresponding equatorward shift of the southern subtropical high-pressure belt.

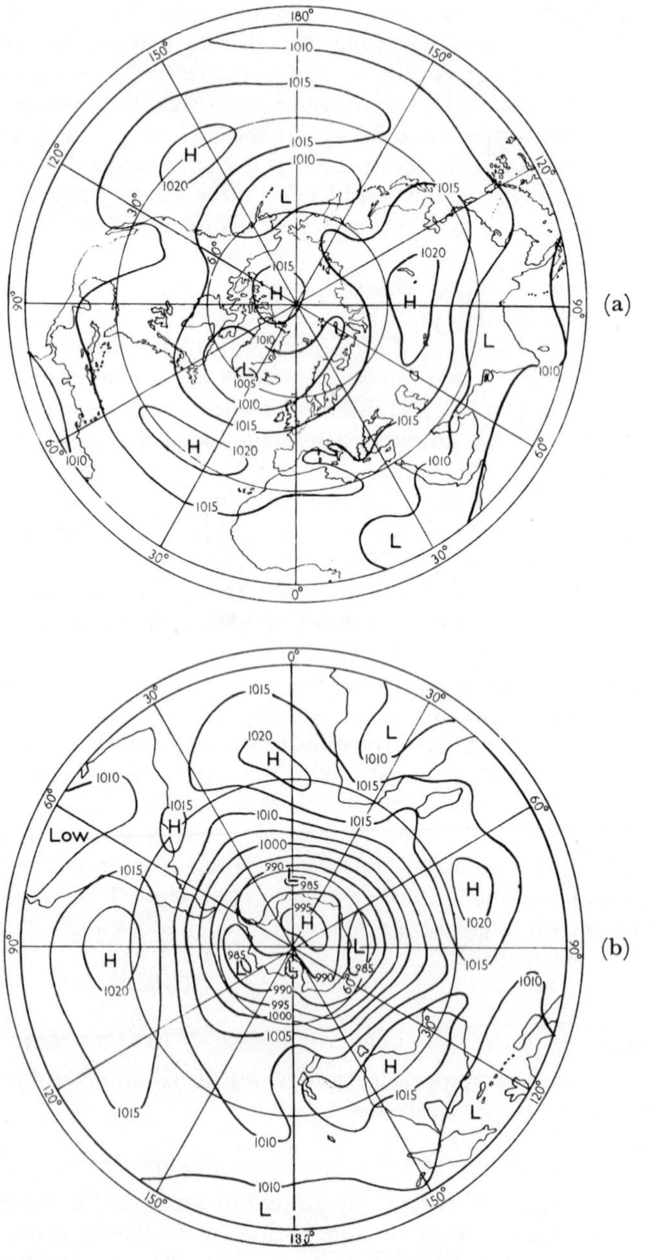

Fig. 8 (a). Annual mean pressure in millibars at sea level (northern hemisphere) for 1900–1940 approx.

(b) Annual mean pressure in millibars at sea level (southern hemisphere) for 1900–1950s approx.

(Reproduced by courtesy of the Controller of Her Majesty's Stationery Office, London)

The following zones may be distinguished:

(1) *Relatively High Pressure over the Polar Caps.* This is partly a consequence of the dynamic development of lowest pressure *close to* the cold side of the main upper westerlies. Also the ready accumulation of a dense mass of air in the lowest 1 to 2 km due to very low surface temperatures produces high pressure.

Occasionally, when dynamic anticyclogenesis takes place in association with the jet stream over the northern polar regions or over parts of the northern continents where intensely cold air can collect at the surface, extreme high pressures occur in the anticyclone centres. Computation readily shows that, at the winter temperatures (—25 to —30°C) commonly prevailing in the lowest 2 to 3 km over Siberia, this layer (capped by a temperature inversion which discourages penetration or disturbance by the

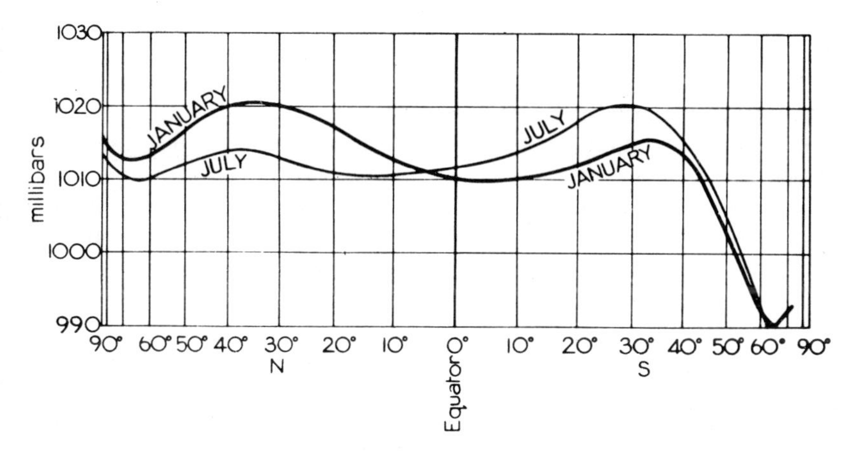

Fig. 9. Mean pressure of the atmosphere at M.S.L. in different latitudes; January and July.
(*Reproduced by courtesy of the Controller of Her Majesty's Stationery Office*)

dynamical processes of the middle and upper troposphere) may contribute by its density as much as 30 mb more to the surface pressure than at temperatures of 0 to +5°C. In these circumstances M.S.L. pressure may rise to over 1 070 mb in a high pressure system surrounded by extensive, and often strong, outblowing winds, capable of establishing a snow cover and persistent cold weather to quite low latitudes in winter.

Such high pressures are never reached over the Antarctic, there being a general deficit of mass south of the strong upper westerlies over the Southern Ocean (Fig. 9): this deficit exceeds 2 per cent (20 mb) when the zone 60–70°S is compared with 60–70°N.

Average pressure is not very high over either polar region, partly because of occasional invasions by travelling depressions developing their energy from the thermal contrast around the polar fringe.

(2) *The Subpolar Low Pressure Belts.* These belts are a feature of the cold side of the jet stream. At the surface they mark the meeting point of prevailing winds of polar origin with the Brave West Winds moving generally polewards in middle latitudes. The individual depressions may develop central pressures as much as 50 to 60 mb below the average for the region, which is characterized by frequent strong winds and gales from various directions. The convergence of airstreams of unlike density gives rise to extensive cloud sheets and frontal rains associated with overrunning by the uplifted warmer air.

The northern hemisphere circulation in this zone is liable to greater persistent anomalies from time to time than the southern, and anticyclones persisting for some weeks in parts of the zone 50–70°N are quite common. These are called *blocking anticyclones*, because they block or reverse for a time the prevailing west winds in middle latitudes; they are particularly common over north-east Siberia, Alaska, northern Greenland and Scandinavia, where their development may often be explained as a dynamical consequence of curvature of the thermal boundary between warm ocean water pushing far to the north and an established snow cover over the continent to the east and south-east.

The apparent weakness of the Iceland depression in Fig. 8a by comparison with the sub-Antarctic system is partly produced by this variability of pattern in the northern hemisphere. Moreover, the lowest pressure in the sub-Arctic zone tends to be transferred to positions over the continents in summer.

(3) *The Subtropical High Pressure Belts.* These are a feature of both hemispheres, principally related to the warm side of the broad belt of upper westerlies, though other factors (Section II.3) require a pressure maximum in subtropical or tropical latitudes at all heights up to nearly 20 km. In consequence, the belt of high pressure is quasi-permanent, producing the steadiness of the Trade Winds. Apart from regions of lower pressure in the cell divisions between the subtropical anticyclones, interruptions of the anticyclone belt do occur when the flow of the main upper westerlies is extremely contorted by large amplitude waves such as lead to blocking anticyclones in the higher latitudes. At such times, persistent low pressure systems (*cold lows*) occur in the subtropical zone south of the blocking anticyclones and the Trade Winds are liable to be disrupted in the sectors affected for periods lasting up to several weeks. Such cold lows are commonest in the Azores–Madeira region and near Hawaii; there is no obvious counterpart in the southern hemisphere, where persistent blocking anticyclones are almost unknown in the belt of westerlies over the ocean. Summer monsoon lows (see Section V) also intrude into the subtropical zone.

The geographical distribution of anticyclones, including the important erratic systems known as blocking anticyclones, is brought out by Figs. 10a, b, c, d, showing summer and winter frequencies for both hemispheres. Over the southern hemisphere there is a good approach to the ideal arrangement in polar and subtropical zones. The much more complicated pattern over the northern hemisphere leaves no doubt that the rather frequent occurrence of persistent blocking anticyclones is related to the geography of land and sea contrasts.

(4) *The Intertropical Zone or Meteorological Equator.* Between the subtropical anticyclone belts the Trade Winds, mainly from NE and SE in the northern and southern hemispheres respectively, meet in a zone of rather lower pressure. Convergence in this zone is associated with large scale ascent of air giving rise to great cloudiness (through adiabatic expansion leading to temperature fall and condensation) and equatorial rains. The rainfall is characteristically heavier than in the frontal rains of the subpolar depressions because of the greater water content of warm equatorial air and because of the strong vertical lapse rate of temperature which encourages vertical motion.

The intensity of the Trade Winds and of the equatorial rains seems to be related to the intensity of the subtropical anticyclones; hence they ultimately depend upon the prevailing strength of the circumpolar westerlies and the main poleward temperature gradient in either hemisphere.

Riehl[54] has pointed out that the intensity of the Trade Winds probably reacts upon the over-all intensity of the general circulation. The prevailing strength of the Trades is close to the critical speed for smooth or rough sea surface: so small changes in the average strength of the Trades might make a big difference to the amount of evaporation; and, since moisture in the atmosphere represents potential energy (through the latent heat of condensation), this might materially increase or decrease the vigour of the entire atmospheric circulation.

Tropical cyclones (hurricanes, typhoons) are a class of short-lived (3–10 days) disturbances of great violence which develop occasionally in the tropics when special conditions are satisfied.[7] They only form over the oceans and where the zone of intertropical convergence has become far enough displaced from the geographical equator for the Coriolis acceleration (the $2\,\omega\,.\,V \sin.\phi$ term in equation (1)) to be significant, so that horizontal air movements near the surface feeding the most violent and extensive vertical convection currents are sufficiently deflected over the spinning earth to acquire a cyclonic rotation in approaching the centre. Sea surface temperature must also be high enough (over 27°C) to promote high moisture content in the air. These storms have probably never been appreciably more frequent than now. The warm geological epochs may have had insufficient horizontal temperature contrasts to produce the required degree of vertical instability in the air masses moving equatorwards over the sea, and during the ice ages the zone of great convection (intertropical convergence) probably had too little freedom to wander far from the geographical equator except, perhaps, in the Pacific.

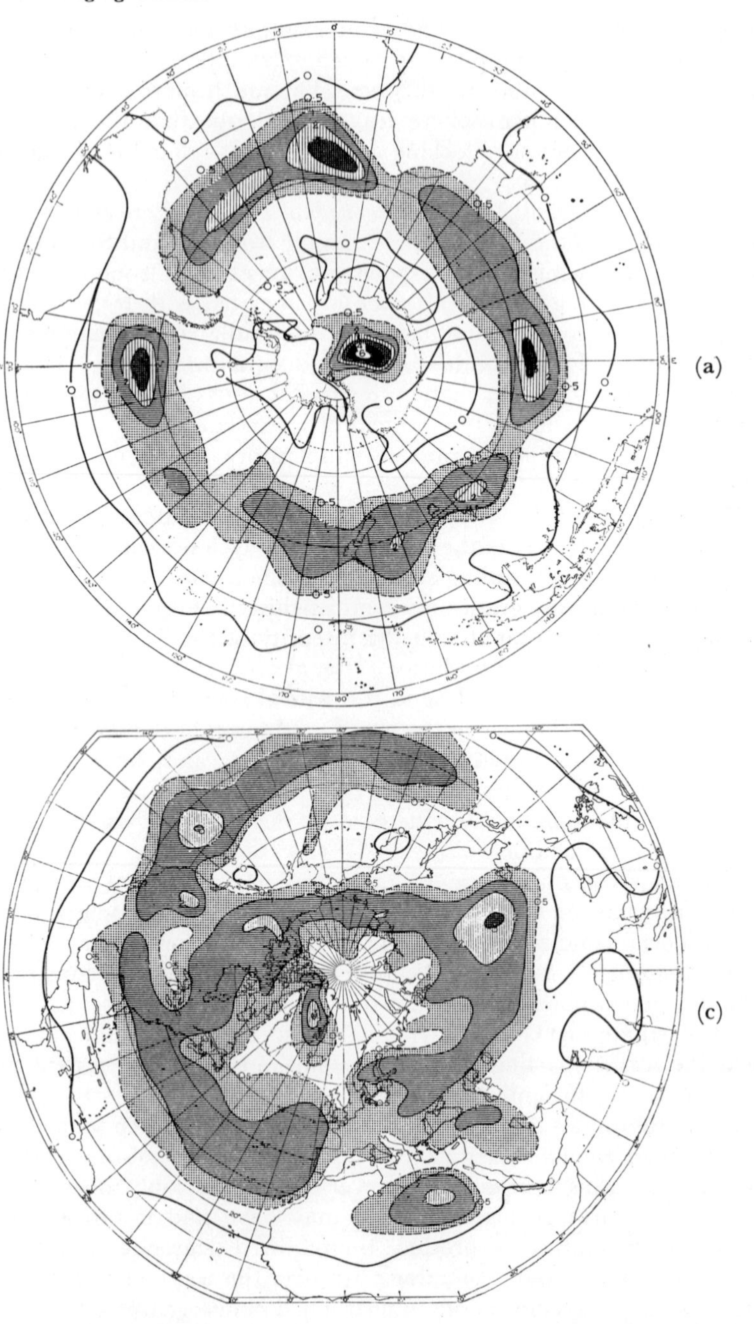

Fig. 10. Distribution of anticyclone centres: percentage frequency of (a) southern hemisphere, summer; (b) southern hemisphere, winter;
(Reproduced by courtesy of the Controller of

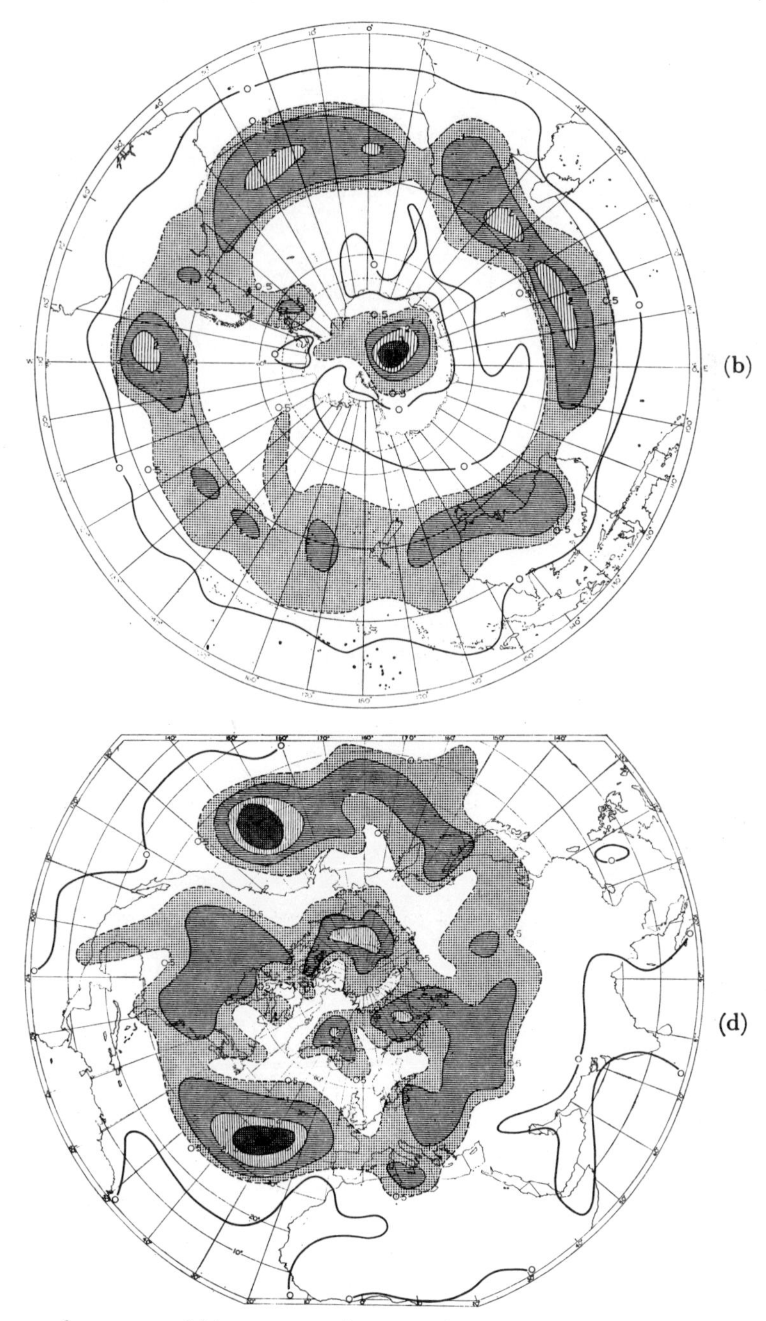

occurrence of a centre within an area of 100 000 km² about any point. (c) northern hemisphere, winter; (d) northern hemisphere, summer. *Her Majesty's Stationery Office, London*)

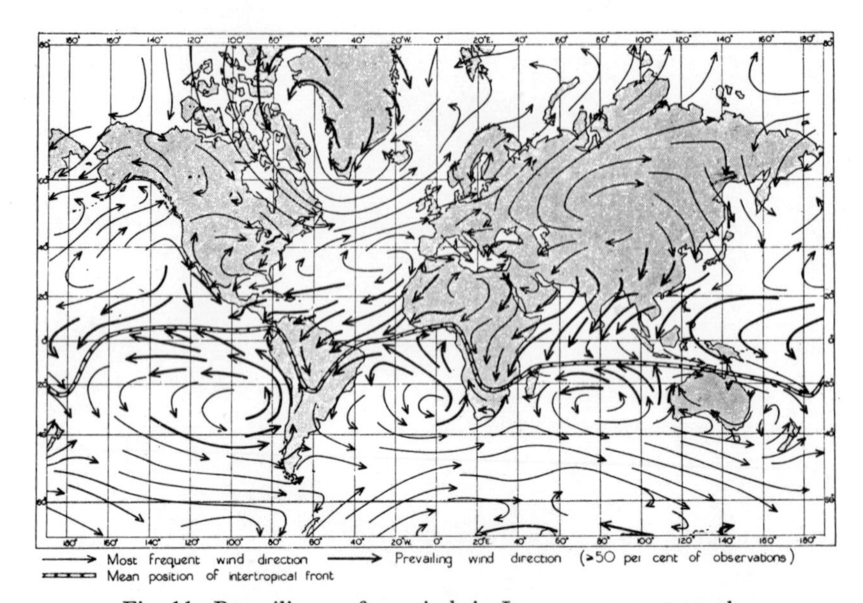

Fig. 11. Prevailing surface winds in January, present epoch.
(Reproduced by courtesy of the Controller of Her Majesty's Stationery Office, London)

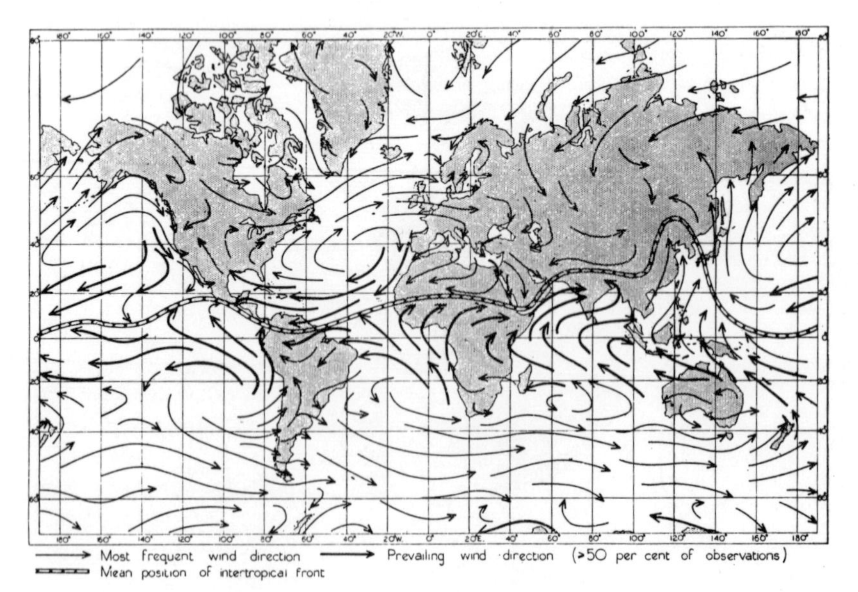

Fig. 12. Prevailing surface winds in July, present epoch.
(Reproduced by courtesy of the Controller of Her Majesty's Stationery Office, London)

B. *Surface Winds*

The prevailing surface winds shown in Figs. 11 and 12 result from the sea-level pressure distribution whose origins have been described; they are: (1) the rather variable *polar easterlies*, (2) the prevailing westerlies in middle latitudes (*Brave West Winds*), and (3) *the Trade Winds* (tropical easterlies).

Between (1) and (2) is a zone of variable winds affected by the centres of the subpolar depressions. Between (2) and (3) is the zone of light winds in the central regions of the subtropical anticyclones (Horse Latitudes). The Trade Winds meet in the Doldrums belt, where directions are again variable and the winds mainly light.

Conservation of total angular momentum in the earth and its atmosphere imposes certain restrictions upon the general atmospheric circulation.[65] As much angular momentum must be restored to the earth by friction in the zones of westerly surface winds as the atmosphere takes from the earth by friction upon the surface easterlies. This condition suggests that, assuming similar average speeds of the easterlies and westerlies, the total areas of surface east-wind and surface west-wind zones should be roughly equal (*cf.* reference 45). The condition is satisfied when the subtropical high pressure belt, dividing the Trade Winds from the westerlies of middle latitudes, has its axis on average just far enough on the equatorward side of latitude 30° to correspond to the additional area of prevailing east winds in the polar zones.

The persistence of the Trades and of the katabatic winds draining cold air off the ice-caps of Antarctica and Greenland is unmatched by other wind systems.

III. The Circulation of the Oceans

The ocean surface is set in motion by the wind stress upon it. To what extent accelerations due to horizontal density gradients in the water also play a part in the circulation is not sure; it appears to be a minor part, though there must be appreciable horizontal motion (lateral drift) of the surface water feeding the vertical overturning at boundaries of water currents of unlike temperature and salinity.[11,18,69] Horizontal eddies of appreciable size also occur along such boundaries.

Owing to the earth's rotation, water currents are deflected to the right in the northern hemisphere and to the left in the southern hemisphere. This causes a head of water to be built up in the central regions of the subtropical anticyclones, until an outward force due to this head of water balances the deflecting force due to the earth's rotation. In consequence, the mainstreams of the ocean surface circulation are in general alignment with the prevailing winds.

The principal features of the surface circulation in the Atlantic and Pacific Oceans are gyrals in which the water circulates anticyclonically around centres in the high pressure belts both north and south of the equator. The strongest flow is concentrated in relatively narrow streams moving polewards near the western margins of the oceans.[21,69]

The general shape of the coastline at the western limit of the Atlantic helps to guide the surface water towards higher latitudes. The nose of South America in 5°S is so shaped and placed as to guide into the northern hemisphere much of the water of the Equatorial Current which should otherwise recurve towards the south: this water helps to feed the Gulf Stream and maintain a general slow meridional overturning of the Atlantic Ocean—surface water moves north from the Sub-Antarctic and, after rounding the respective gyrals in the South and North Atlantic several times, reaches the Arctic by way of the Norwegian Sea and sinks beneath the ice-bearing currents of lesser salinity. There is a return current towards the south in the deeper layers of the ocean. It has been calculated that the water involved in this circulation has an average sojourn of 600 years in the deep Atlantic.

A different geography, particularly in the neighbourhood of the Brazilian coast, would make a great difference to the transport of heat from south to north by the Gulf Stream. The importance of the northernmost arm of this current entering the Norwegian Sea also evidently depends upon the depth of water over the submarine ridge between Iceland, the Faroes and Scotland.

A slight southward shift of the climatic zones in the North and South Atlantic or a weakening of the subtropical anticyclones, such as might occur if the southern circumpolar westerlies were to weaken temporarily, might well shift and weaken the ocean surface currents including the Equatorial Current, more of which would be deflected south along the Brazilian coast from 5°S. Both aspects should weaken the supply of equatorial warm water to the Gulf Stream. The net effects would appear to reinforce the postulated southward expansion of the polar zone in the North Atlantic and contraction of the Antarctic zone—an example of a self-maintaining mechanism of which there are many in the circulation of the atmosphere and oceans.

By contrast with the arrangement of the ocean surface circulation in gyrals favouring meridional transport of heat in the Atlantic and Pacific Oceans, the water currents in the Antarctic Ocean, which completely rings the earth in 60°S, are predominantly circumpolar. This again conforms with the prevailing winds.

IV. Oceanic and Continental Climates

The oceans exert less friction upon the wind than land surfaces and are the main source of the atmospheric water supply. Gales are most prevalent over and near the oceans, and rainfall is heaviest where moisture-bearing winds from the sea are forced up over the first mountain ranges or have vertical convection currents induced in them over the first strongly heated ground. Atmospheric moisture also energizes the circulation wherever horizontal convergence leads to ascent and condensation, liberating latent heat.

In important respects, however, the oceans exercise a moderating influence.

Poleward transport of heat in the ocean water reduces the over-all thermal gradients from which the energy supply of the atmospheric circulation is derived.

The diurnal and seasonal ranges of temperature of the ocean surfaces are also much less than those of dry land at the same latitude. Swampy ground has an intermediate behaviour. The great specific heat of water, partial penetration of solar radiation to some depth, and conduction and convection within the oceans all enter into this.[10] Consequently, the climates of islands are noted for their moderate ranges of temperature and the same applies in only gradually lessening degree as one goes inland from the windward coasts of the continents.

Mountain ranges barring the progress of oceanic winds have the effect of an abrupt wall between maritime and continental climates, the latter having greater extremes of temperature and low rainfall.

Table I. Extent of Snow and Ice Surface

	Area in km²	Equivalent[a] latitude of limit
Southern hemisphere		
Summer minimum	$19{\cdot}6 \times 10^6$	68°S
Winter maximum	35×10^6 approx.	60°S
Northern hemisphere		
Summer minimum	$12{\cdot}4 \times 10^6$	72°N
Winter maximum[b]	55 to 65 $\times 10^6$	50°N

[a] i.e. the latitude the limit would have if it were a circular area, centred at the pole.

[b] The winter maximum extent of snow and ice surface over the northern hemisphere is far from being a circular area but bulges far south over the continents occasionally beyond 30°N in Asia. The part south of 45°N is generally impermanent, much of it thin snow easily removed by sunshine or rain accompanying incursions of warm air. A better estimate for the winter maximum of *persistent* snow cover would be about 55°N—equivalent to an area of 46×10^6 km².

The greatest extremes of temperature and, on the whole, the slightest rainfalls in each latitude zone are encountered well towards the downstream end of the great land masses in the sense of the prevailing wind, often surprisingly near the leeward coast. The rainfall gradient is much sharpened across the mountain barriers.

Another aspect of the moderating influence of oceans is seen when we compare the (present) normal seasonal range of extent of snow and ice surface in the northern and southern hemispheres. The figures are given in Table I.

V. Seasonal Effects: Monsoons

The zones of the atmospheric circulation (see Section II.4) move north and south with the seasons. The movement is, however, much less than the seasonal shift of latitude of the zenith sun at noon. The seasonal shift of the sub-Antarctic low pressure belt, the southern subtropical high pressure belt and the southern upper westerlies is about the same as that of the ice limit: 8° of latitude (*cf.* Table I). In the northern hemisphere considerable differences between continental and oceanic sectors complicate the picture: the over-all seasonal range of the subtropical anticyclones is again about 8° of latitude; the prevailing depression tracks move north and south more or less with the general position of the ice limit in each sector. This association emphasizes how the latitudinal position of the strongest thermal gradient is largely controlled by the ice limit at the present epoch.

The intertropical convergence (meteorological equator) has a bigger seasonal movement, between about 5°S and 15°N, a range of 20°. Here the controlling factor is presumably the greater strength of the Trade Winds from the winter hemisphere, in which they also extend over the continental areas.[16,17]

In the summer hemisphere the subtropical high pressure belt and the Trade Wind zone are extensively disturbed by the monsoon depressions over land. '*Monsoon*' is in origin an Arabic word, meaning 'season' and in meteorology usually describes wind and pressure régimes which reverse with the seasons.

The common 'explanation' that continental summer heating produces low pressure by reducing the air density is inadequate, since it ignores dynamical processes; though it has been seen that, in winter, the extreme density of the very cold air in the bottom 1 to 3 km in moderate to high northern latitudes probably does explain the extremity of the highest pressures occurring. Over most of the southern hemisphere the present normal seasonal pressure changes are contrary to the conventional monsoon model: pressure is highest over most of the oceans in the southern hemisphere in winter and over the Antarctic ice it is highest in summer.

Monsoonal low pressure appears to develop over the heated continents in the early part of the warm season in association with waves in the planetary westerlies (*cf.* references 23, 26, 52). In spring the circulation in the upper troposphere over southern North America, over the Sahara and over south-west Asia is confluent in the western part owing to the heating (warm ridges) thrusting north over Mexico, Ethiopia and India respectively. Cyclogenesis (pressure fall) is thereby induced at the warm side of the confluence (*cf.* Fig. 7), i.e. *over the south-western sectors of each of the continents in 20 to 40°N.* The distribution of heated land tends to anchor the low pressure over these sectors of North America, Africa and Asia. A weaker but similar development pattern also becomes active over Indo-China later in the season.

Analogous patterns in the upper circulation at the equatorial fringe of the westerlies are found in the southern spring, and may be held responsible for the development of the lowest pressures near 20°S over South America, South Africa and western Australia.

The onset of the monsoons can be advanced or held back in a given year by favourable or unfavourable phase relationship with the Rossby waves in the westerlies of higher latitudes. The monsoon is therefore affected by deep persistent snow on the plateaux of Asia.[6,52,53]

It seems that the lowest pressure in summer monsoon circulations, initially associated with the equatorial fringe of the upper westerlies, should always be found rather towards the western side of any extensive land masses in the strongly heated zone. In accordance with Fig. 7, there should be another area of low average surface pressure in high latitudes in the eastern sector of great continents—as found over North America, Asia, and to some extent over and near the extreme south-east of Australia: the latter low pressure regions are produced by travelling depressions in the subpolar zone commonly deepening or becoming slow-moving in the given sector.

At the height of the northern summer in July and August the upper circulation over South Asia consists of a great easterly airstream from the China Sea to North Africa along the southern fringe of an elongated upper anticyclone, whose centre is associated with the intense heating of the high Tibetan plateau. At times the easterly jet stream over India reaches speeds of over 100 kt. A weaker, but generally easterly, airstream develops in the upper levels over other parts of the tropical zone (e.g. Caribbean and Gulf of Mexico). Waves travel forwards in the upper easterly stream similarly to the waves in the upper westerlies.[33,55] This arrangement favours cyclonic development according to the same principles operating in the case of the upper westerlies. In extreme cases tropical cyclones are induced over the seas, and in general a sequence of lesser disturbances travels westwards and ultimately feeds into the surface low pressure centres maintained towards the western limits of the principal land masses in the zone.

A special feature which changes the character of the Indian monsoon low is that, in spite of being centred near 30°N, it becomes intense enough to draw in the intertropical convergence and equatorial rains. The equatorial rain system at times also gets drawn into some of the smaller monsoon lows nearer the equator—e.g. over Africa, Australia and the Amazon basin, but not over Arizona and California which are too far north (the North American continent having too little longitudinal extent in the lower latitudes). The rainfall distribution is strongly influenced by orography.

Two factors which may influence the great northward bulge of the meteorological equator over Asia in the northern summer are:

(1) The great mountain land of Tibet and Mongolia which, partly mechanically and partly through its strong heating in summer, diverts the mainstream of the northern westerlies far to the north.

(2) The continual outflow of cold air off the Antarctic ice-cap which produces the main trough and most intense part of the southern hemisphere winter circulation in rather low latitudes in the Indian Ocean sector.

The amplitude of waves introduced into the circumpolar westerlies by direct heating and cooling of the land surfaces is greatest at times when the planetary westerlies are on the whole weak. It has been widely suggested that monsoonal circulations are most strongly developed at such times.

VI. Climatic Variations

VI.1 *Controlling Circumstances and the Lessons of Known Changes in Recent Times*

Changes in the *intensity of insolation*, whether due to possible changes of solar output or to variations in the transparency of the earth's atmosphere or interplanetary space, must alter the mean temperature of the atmosphere. The intensity of the thermal gradients between equator and pole and hence the over-all intensity of the atmospheric circulation would also be changed proportionately.

Increased insolation should, other things being equal, intensify the atmospheric circulation and decreased insolation should weaken it. Changes of this nature corresponding to variations in the prevailing amount of volcanic dust in the atmosphere during the last four or five centuries are strongly suggested by observation. Certainly the intensity of the atmospheric circulation seems to have undergone a general increase from 1800 to about 1930,[72] and there were more frequent great volcanic eruptions in the eighteenth and nineteenth centuries than since—though, of course, actual measurements of the dust in the atmosphere over the requisite period are lacking (see, however, references 19, 30, 72, 73).

Various hints have been found[61, 74, 76] of 11-year, 22-year, 80-year and 400-year cyclic variations of weather phenomena associated with variations of the general circulation of the atmosphere and presumably related to sunspot cycles. It has been suggested that variations in the ultra-violet intensity in the solar beam and in corpuscular radiation channelled to high latitudes by the earth's magnetic field may be responsible.

The intensity of the solar beam is, however, far from being the only thing controlling the amount of energy which drives the atmospheric circulation. Other factors affect the efficiency with which the incident radiation is used. The most important of these other factors are probably:

(1) *Ice and snow cover.* It has been seen that at the present time the mean seasonal *position of the ice and snow margin* appears to exercise the main control over the strongest thermal gradients (Section V). On account of the high albedo of snow and ice, the intensity as well as the position of the thermal gradient is affected. An increase of incoming solar heat sufficient to melt the polar ice-caps entirely would, therefore, reach a point where the thermal gradients abruptly decreased because of the more uniform albedo of the surface, and the atmospheric circulation should slacken. Brooks[11] has suggested that at the post-glacial climatic optimum about 2000–4000 B.C. there was no permanent ice on the northern polar seas and that an abrupt chilling of the climate and increase of storminess in Europe about 500 B.C. corresponded to the re-establishment of quasipermanent Arctic ice: it can be accepted as certain that there was a marked southward shift of the ice margin and of the depression tracks about the latter date, probably accompanied by general intensification.

(2) Possible *changes in the extent of land and water and in the relief of the land (and submarine ridges)* are chiefly important for their likely effects upon the existence, distribution and extent of ice and snow surfaces, secondly for their effect upon the pattern of maximum heating in the lower latitudes, and thirdly for their control of the preferred positions and intensities of waves in the upper westerlies.

(3) *Changes in the main ocean currents* must affect the extent to which oceanic heat transport can introduce thermal ridges and troughs which distort the planetary circulation of the atmosphere and strengthen or weaken it in certain sectors. It is doubtful, however, whether the influence of ocean currents can ever have been much greater than it is at present in the Atlantic sector. In warm epochs with no polar ice, the thermal gradients in the ocean surface would be much weakened, and on account of more uniform salinity a greater proportion of the transport of cold water equatorwards would take place at levels below the surface.

(4) *Changes in the moisture content of the atmosphere and of the prevailing cloudiness* affect the intensity of the atmospheric circulation in ways already referred to, but are hardly likely to affect the main zonal arrangement.

Changes in moisture content and cloudiness are themselves consequences of the general atmospheric circulation[4, 5] and of the available solar energy which drives it. This is one of many delicate internal mechanisms in the earth–atmosphere system, which induce persistence for a time of various atmospheric circulation patterns (self-maintaining mechanisms) or build up long-period oscillations in the atmospheric response to external controls.

Simpson[63, 64] has put forward the theory that a small increase in solar radiation at a time when there was no extensive polar ice might actually initiate an ice age by intensifying the atmospheric circulation and moisture transport and increasing the winter snowfall in high latitudes (especially on mountains and plateaux) more than could be melted in summer. Further increase of solar radiation might suffice to melt even the greatest ice-caps. In colder epochs on the other hand precipitation might be insufficient to sustain an ice-cap against the summer melting. Hence Simpson envisages a cycle in which we should distinguish not only ice ages but both warm and cold types of interglacial epoch, corresponding to the maxima and minima of the supposed solar variation.

VI.2 *Extreme Types of Atmospheric Circulation: Ice Age Type and Warm Epoch Type*

A. *General*

All the various atmospheric responses to changing circumstances discussed in the last section are but variations superimposed upon a single theme, the planetary circulation of the atmosphere and its wave patterns. Observational evidence of the circulation changes over the past 50 to 200 years has been published by Kraus[34–37] and Lamb.[39, 40, 77] Ahlmann[2] and Taulis[71] also provide useful data.

Fanciful constructions which purport to explain the ice age of the Carboniferous epoch as a result of extraordinary elevation of the present equatorial lands (where the evidence of glaciation is found) and extreme distortion of the climatic zones by special guidance of the main ocean currents cannot be accepted without much firmer evidence than has so far been put forward.

Expansion of the polar ice and of the ring of circumpolar westerlies may take place simultaneously in both hemispheres, leading to narrowing of the equatorial (Trade Wind) zone. At other times there may be an equatorward shift in one hemisphere and poleward in the other. Both cases are believed to cause greater changes in the Atlantic than in other sectors, as long as the northern Atlantic provides the sole effective outlet for the Arctic ice (see Figs. 13–16).

It seems likely that at the present epoch a small increase in the available solar radiation would increase the melting of the world's greatest ice-cap in the Antarctic, spreading cold melt-water of low salinity over a wider zone of the Southern Ocean and cooling the sub-Antarctic regions. This would tend to carry the belt of southern westerlies a degree or two nearer the equator and intensify the atmospheric circulation, pushing the meteorological equator a little farther north and increasing the supply of warm equatorial water to the Gulf Stream. In the northern hemisphere, and especially in the North Atlantic, this would reinforce the warming and northward shift of the climatic zones to be expected from milder winters and melting of the ice on the Arctic Ocean.[39] This is probably a fair description of the changes from the culmination of the 'Little Ice Age' around 1800 to 1940. In these 140 years world temperatures rose by between 1 and 2°C. A greater increase of the available solar radiation might ultimately redress the balance somewhat —by warming the sub-Antarctic zone also and allowing the meteorological equator to move nearer the geographical equator again.

The postulated secular shifts of the ice limit on the Southern Ocean and of the mean latitude of the southern westerlies are quite small. A change of one degree of latitude in the present average ice limit would mean a change of about 15 per cent in the total amount of ice on the Southern Ocean. The northward shift since 1800 may amount to rather over 1° in the Southern Ocean, but probably amounts to 2 or 3° in the North Atlantic.[32]

The present geography of the southern hemisphere, with a polar continent and surrounding ocean occupying most of the hemisphere apart from some strongly heated lands in the equatorial and desert zones, is about as favourable as it could be for developing a strong circulation. Hence if the existing displacement of the meteorological equator to 4°N is rightly attributed to the preponderant strength of the southern circulation, this displacement is unlikely to have been greatly exceeded in any other epoch.

Times of weak circulation are accompanied by increased wave number (shorter spacing between successive ridges and troughs) in the upper westerlies. The wave number decreases, however, the higher the latitude in which the westerlies are located. The amplitude of purely thermal ridges and

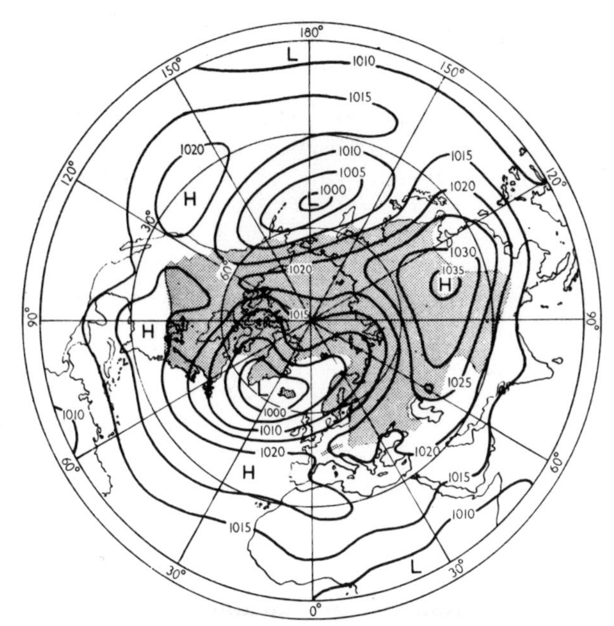

Fig. 13. Average barometric pressure in millibars at sea level in January, present epoch (1900–39). Ice and snow cover shaded.

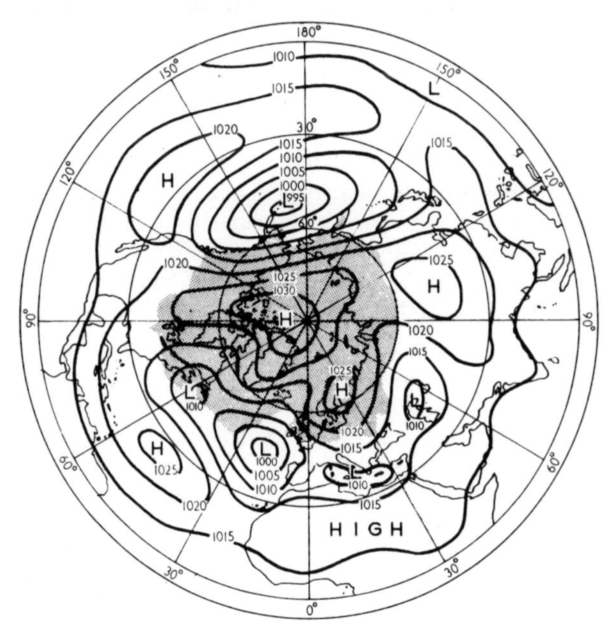

Fig. 14. Supposed average barometric pressure in millibars at sea level in January, maximum Quaternary glaciation. Ice sheet shaded; winter snow cover would extend beyond the ice over land especially when northerly wind components prevailed.

troughs associated with land–sea contrasts should also be increased when the general planetary circulation is weak.

Reconstruction of the atmospheric circulation patterns of the remote past is unavoidably speculative, but the maximum phases of the Quaternary ice age were in essence merely an extension of the circumstances of the present day. The pattern of events may with reasonable assurance be outlined as follows.

B. *Ice Age Circulation*

Figs. 13–16 give a tentative reconstruction of the mean surface pressure distribution over the northern hemisphere about the maximum of the Quaternary ice age and show the comparison with the present day.

The main features are the intensified circulation during the ice age, especially in summer, both in the belt of westerlies and in the Trades, and a general displacement of the zonal circulation towards lower latitudes. It is likely that in winter in the higher latitudes over the ice the circulation was weaker than now. The equatorward shift and the expansion of the ice sheet were greatest in the Atlantic sector, there being very little change from present positions in the Pacific.

Rainfall was presumably increased for some time in the lower middle latitudes and subtropics, which were affected by most travelling depressions associated with the upper westerlies. Intensified upper westerlies would cause greater mobility in the subtropical anticyclones, which presumably moved east in an endless sequence punctuated by 'intercellular' fronts and occasional frontal rains—as in the southern hemisphere today. There was less possibility than now of persistent anomalies in the subtropical zone associated with cold lows and less room for development of monsoon depressions, except over Asia. Probably the intense general circulation ensured that persistent anomalies were a rarity in all latitudes except over the ice. The northern part of the extensive summer low-pressure area over Asia (Fig 16) during glacial times would represent a sequence of low pressure systems travelling from west to east near the ice margin, as in winter. There was presumably less change of character of the general circulation from winter to summer than now: in this and other respects the situation probably bore more resemblance to that over the southern hemisphere today.

Flohn's estimates [24, 25] of surface temperatures about the maximum of the Quaternary ice age, partly based on geological and palaeobiological evidence, are more generally accepted than Simpson's suggestion [63, 64] of a general rise of temperature over the rest of the world. According to Flohn the air and ocean temperatures in the tropical zone were about 4°C lower than now, the upper westerlies were 10–15° nearer the equator, and there was an overall reduction of the amount of moisture in the atmosphere, and hence of precipitation, by about 20 per cent. The principal decrease of precipitation would be in the higher latitudes over the ice, where depression activity would be diminished. With more frequent calms and temperature inversions, the mean annual temperature over central Europe was probably 8–12°C lower

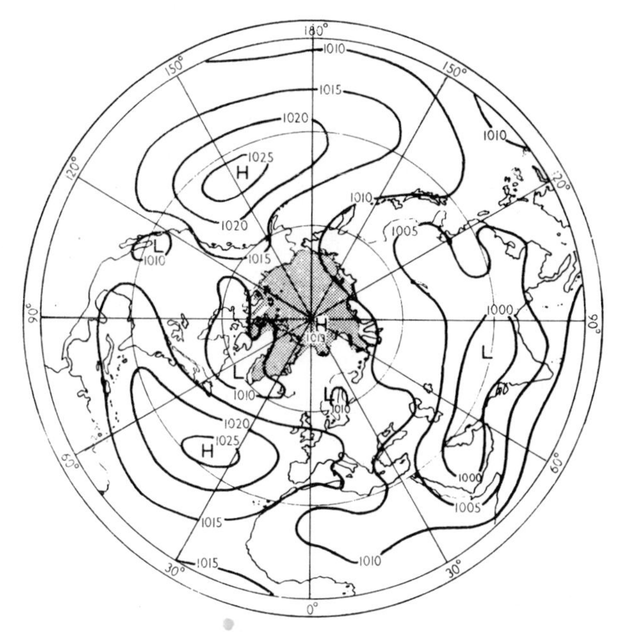

Fig. 15. Average barometric pressure in millibars at sea level in July, present epoch (1900–39). Ice and snow cover shaded.

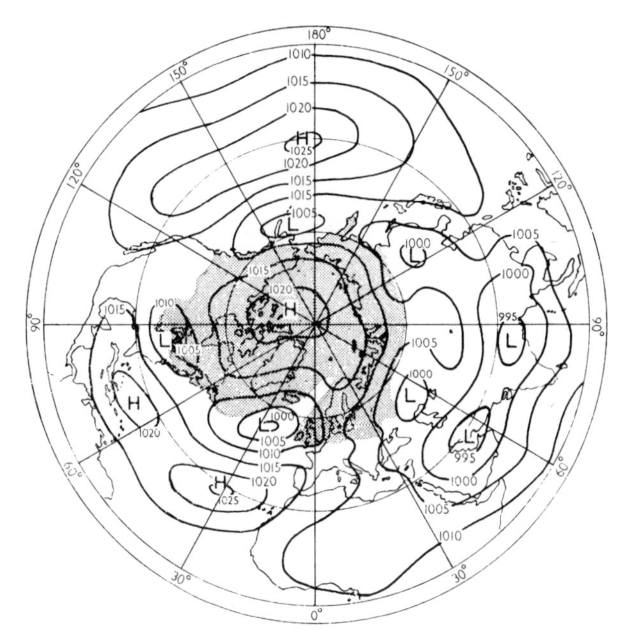

Fig. 16. Supposed average barometric pressure in millibars at sea level in July, maximum Quaternary glaciation. Ice and snow cover shaded.

than today. Over the Arctic Ocean the change would be much smaller than elsewhere. The snow line underwent an appropriate lowering on mountain ranges in the temperate and tropical zones.

The discrepancy between Flohn's evidence and Simpson's suggestions may perhaps be resolved if we accept Flohn's figures as applying to the Atlantic and adjacent sectors north of the equator, where the ice spread farthest. The southern hemisphere generally and most of the Pacific may well have been warmer than now, as required by Simpson, especially during the earlier phases of the ice age. This would increase the atmospheric moisture content and precipitation above present averages and would be consistent with greater snowfall over the ice-caps (*cf.* Meinardus[43]). It is uncertain how wide the ice-belt would be on the Southern Ocean, since greater outflow from Antarctica would be offset by greater melting especially in the sub-Antarctic zone.[42]

Butzer[14] adduces evidence that the climatic régime associated with the onset of each wave of the Quaternary ice age was chiefly characterized by world-wide increase of precipitation very much as required by Simpson's theory. At the maxima of the ice age the climate appears, however, to have been relatively dry even in the subtropical lands of the Mediterranean and Near East, perhaps because the spread of the ice ultimately lowered the temperature of the world's oceans and of the atmosphere in general.

The distribution of ice in the Quaternary ice age (Figs. 14 and 16) suggests a representation of the form of the ring of upper westerlies which is in reasonable agreement with the proposed surface isobars. Clearly there were broad cold troughs over eastern North America and over Europe which were possibly more pronounced than the one over east Asia. The amplitude of the troughs and ridges was evidently less than now except over the Pacific.

The northern hemisphere circulation at the ice age maximum seems likely to have been centred near 80°N 50°W (*cf.* ice-covered area on Figs. 14 and 16). The existing circulation over the southern hemisphere has a similar order of eccentricity. The circulation would be strongest in the lower latitudes of the Atlantic sector. Both westerlies and Trade Winds would be confined to narrower zones and nearer the equator than at present, the Trades scarcely extending north of 20–25°N even in summer.

C. *Circulation During the Warm (Ice-Free) Epochs of Geological Time*

Reconstruction of the general circulation in ice-free epochs is much more speculative than for the ice age. We have no observational evidence to guide us as to the form of the circulation over a hemisphere in the absence of the maximum thermal gradient near the ice margin and without the inertia of ice which the play of the atmospheric circulation cannot readily remove.

A thermal gradient would still exist from equator to pole, and if the available solar radiation were stronger than now the poleward thermal gradient should be stronger than at present, *except* as regards the zone within 10–15° of latitude on either side of the ice margin.

As the ice margin shrank towards the pole, with the depression track and belt of upper westerlies accompanying it, another concentration of thermally driven upper westerly winds accompanied by another depression sequence might be expected to come to prominence in rather low latitudes. Two belts of westerlies, near 25 and 75°N, and an extra zone of middle latitude easterlies, in addition to narrow zones of polar easterlies and Trade Winds, are occasionally observed today over the North Atlantic and North Pacific. Analogous sequences are also suspected over the South Pacific at times when the main depression track moves into very high latitudes.

If the ice were to disappear, the depression sequence in the warmer latitudes would become the main one and would probably be transferred to rather higher latitudes, producing a hemispheric pressure distribution and prevailing winds not greatly different from now (*cf.* Fleagle's result[22] that the strongest thermal gradient on a uniform earth should be in middle latitudes).

It is possible, however, that the over-all thermal gradient from equator to pole would remain weaker than today after the albedo contrast at the ice margin had disappeared or because of increased moisture content, cloudiness and albedo in low latitudes. In this case, the weakened upper westerlies might be deformed by many ridges and troughs corresponding to differences of surface within each latitude zone; chaotic circulations with generally light and variable surface winds would result. Even the monsoons would probably develop only weak and complex circulations, since a fairly strong planetary circulation or an improbably simple geography appear to be prerequisites of orderly circulation patterns. Convection rains would probably be localized and sporadic, but violent. The total amount of moisture in the atmosphere would be greater than today (because of the warmer ocean surfaces); total precipitation would also be greater and, in spite of haphazard distribution in time, much more uniformly distributed over the world. Great rainfall would be offset by greater evaporation; deserts would occur as now, though possibly in less extreme form.

The seasonal shift north and south of the wind belts would probably be rather greater than at present though hardly exceeding 10–15° of latitude.

VII. Acknowledgment

The author wishes to thank the Director-General of the Meteorological Office, London, for permission to write this contribution to the book.

References

1. *Academia Sinica*, Staff Members of the Meteorological Institute, Peking: *Tellus*, **9**, 432 (1957); **10**, 58 (1958)
2. Ahlmann, H. W. *Geogr. J.*, **112**, 165 (1948)
3. Aldrich, L. B. *Smithson. misc. Coll.*, **69**, No. 10 (1919)
4. Ångström, A. *Geogr. Ann., Stockh.*, **17**, 242 (1935)

5. Arakawa, H. *Tokyo Met. Research Inst. Papers in Met. and Geophys.*, **7**, 1 (1956)
6. Banerji, S. K. *Indian J. Met. Geophys.*, **1**, 4 (1950)
7. Bergeron, T. *Quart. J. R. Met. Soc.*, **80**, 131 (1954)
8. Bjerknes, J. *U.G.G.I., Assoc. Mét., Procès Verb., Edinburgh* 1936, **2**, 106 (1939)
9. Bliss, E. W. *Mem. R. Met. Soc.*, **1**, No. 6, 87 (1926)
10. Brooks, C. E. P. *Met. Mag., Lond.*, **72**, 153 (1937)
11. Brooks, C. E. P. *Climate through the ages*, 2nd edn. 1949. London: Ernest Benn
12. Brooks, C. E. P., Durst, C. S., Carruthers, N., Dewar, D. and Sawyer, J. S. *Met. Off. Lond., Geophys. Mem.*, No. 85 (1950)
13. Budyko, M. I. *Atlas of heat balance*. 1955. Leningrad: Central Geophysical Observatory
14. Butzer, K. W. *Geogr. Ann., Stockh.* **39**, 48 (1957)
15. Charney, J. G. and Eliassen, A. *Tellus*, **1**, 38 (1949)
16. Crowe, P. R. *Trans. Inst. Brit. Geogr.*, **1949**, No. 15, 37 (1951)
17. Crowe, P. R. *Trans. Inst. Brit. Geogr.*, **1950**, No. 16, 23 (1952)
18. Deacon, G. E. R. *Quart. J. R. Met. Soc.*, **71**, 11 (1945)
19. Defant, A. *Geogr. Ann., Stockh.*, **6**, 13 (1924)
20. Dines, W. H. *J. Scot. met. Soc.*, **16**, 304 (1914)
21. Eady, E. T. 'Circulation of the atmosphere and oceans' in *The Planet Earth*. 1957. London and New York: Pergamon Press
22. Fleagle, R. G. *Quart. J. R. Met. Soc.*, **83**, 1 (1957)
23. Flohn, H. *Ber. dtsch Wetterdienstes U.S. Zone*, **18** (1950)
24. Flohn, H. *Geol. Rdsch.*, **40**, 153 (1952)
25. Flohn, H. *Erdkunde*, **7**, 266 (1953)
26. Flohn, H. *Ber. dtsch. Wetterdienstes U.S. Zone*, **22** (1955)
27. Hadley, G. *Phil. Trans.*, **39**, 58 (1735)
28. Haurwitz, B. and Austin, J. M. *Climatology*. 1944. New York: McGraw-Hill
29. Houghton, H. G. *J. Met.*, **11**, 1 (1954)
30. Humphreys, W. J. *Physics of the air*, 3rd edn. 1940. New York: McGraw-Hill
31. Knighting, E. *Met. Mag.*, **85**, 176 (1956)
32. Koch, L. *Medd. om Grønland*, **130**, No. 3 (1945)
33. Koteswaram, P. and George, C. A. *Indian J. Met. Geophys.*, **9**, 9 (1958)
34. Kraus, E. B. *Quart. J. R. Met. Soc.*, **80**, 591 (1954)
35. Kraus, E. B. *Quart. J. R. Met. Soc.*, **81**, 198 (1955)
36. Kraus, E. B. *Quart. J. R. Met. Soc.*, **81**, 430 (1955)
37. Kraus, E. B. *Quart. J. R. Met. Soc.*, **82**, 289 (1956)
38. Lamb, H. H. *Quart. J. R. Met. Soc.*, **81**, 172 (1955)
39. Lamb, H. H. *Met. Mag.*, **87**, 364 (1958)
40. Lamb, H. H. *Quart. J. R. Met. Soc.*, **85**, 1 (1959)
41. MacPherson, H. G. *Mon. Weath. Rev.*, Supplt. No. 39, 98 (1940)
42. Manley, G. *Quart. J. R. Met. Soc.*, **72**, 307 (1946)
43. Meinardus, W. *Nachr. Ges. Wiss. Göttingen*, 137 (1928)
44. Milankovitch, M. 'Mathematische Klimalehre und astronomische Theorie der Klimaschwankungen' in Köppen & Geiger's *Handbuch der Klimatologie*, I. A., 1930. Berlin: Borntraeger
45. Mintz, Y. *Univ. Calif., Dept. Met., Sci. Rep. No.* 3 (1953)
46. Montgomery, R. B. *Mon. Weath. Rev.*, Supplt. No. 39, 1 (1940)
47. Namias, J. *J. Met.*, **7**, 130 (1950)
48. Namias, J. *Mon. Weath. Rev., Wash.*, **83**, 155 (1955)
49. Palmén, E. *Quart. J. R. Met. Soc.*, **77**, 337 (1951)
50. Petterssen, Sv. *Cent. Proc. R. met. Soc.*, 120 (1950)

51. Phillips, N. A. *Quart. J. R. Met. Soc.*, **82**, 123 (1956)
52. Ramage, C. S. *J. Met.*, **9**, 403 (1952)
53. Ramaswamy, C. *Tellus*, **8**, 26 (1956)
54. Riehl, H. *Weather*, **9**, 335 (1954)
55. Riehl, H. *Tropical Meteorology*. 1954. New York: McGraw-Hill
56. Rossby, C. G. *J. Mar. Res.*, **2**, 38 (1939)
57. Rossby, C. G. *R. Met. Soc., Supplt. to the Quart. J.*, **66**, 68 (1940)
58. Rossby, C. G. 'The scientific basis of modern meteorology' in *U.S. Yearbook of Agriculture*, **1941**, 599 (1941)
59. Rossby, C. G. 'The scientific basis of modern meteorology' in *Handbook of Meteorology* (Berry, Bollay and Beers), Section VII, p. 502–529. 1945. New York: McGraw-Hill
60. Scherhag, R. *Met. Z.*, **51**, 129 (1934)
61. Scherhag, R. *Dtsch hydrogr. Z.*, **3**, 108 (1950)
62. Simpson, G. C. *Mem. R. Met. Soc.*, **3**, No. 23 (1928)
63. Simpson, G. C. *Quart. J. R. Met. Soc.*, **60**, 375 (1934)
64. Simpson, G. C. *Quart. J. R. Met. Soc.*, **83**, 459 (1957)
65. Starr, V. P. *J. Met.*, **5**, 39 (1948)
66. Sutcliffe, R. C. *Quart. J. R. Met. Soc.*, **65**, 519 (1939)
67. Sutcliffe, R. C. *Quart. J. R. Met. Soc.*, **82**, 385 (1956)
68. Sutcliffe, R. C. and Forsdyke, A. G. *Quart. J. R. Met. Soc.*, **76**, 189 (1950)
69. Sverdrup, H. U. *Oceanography for meteorologists*. 1942. New York: Prentice Hall
70. Sverdrup, H. U. *J. Mar. Res.*, **14**, 501 (1955)
71. Taulis, E. *Matér. Étude Calam.*, **33**, 3 (1934)
72. Wagner, A. *Klima-änderungen und Klimaschwankungen*. 1940. Braunschweig: Vieweg
73. Wexler, H. *Tellus*, **8**, 480 (1956)
74. Willet, H. C. *Mon. Weath. Rev.*, Supplt. No. 39, 126 (1940)
75. Willett, H. C. *Descriptive Meteorology*. 1944. New York: Academic Press
76. Willett, H. C. *J. Met.*, **6**, 34 (1949)
77. Lamb, H. H. and Johnson, A. I. *Geogr. Ann., Stockh.*, **41**, 94 (1959)

THREE

On the nature of certain climatic epochs which differed from the modern (1900-39) normal

INTRODUCTORY

Climatic changes during the last five or six thousand years appear, at some times, to have allowed sufficient vegetation for primitive men and animals to travel across what are now deserts in north Africa, central Asia and northern Mexico-south-western United States of America, and, at other times, to have cut off these routes of trade and migration. Within the last thousand years various categories of evidence suggest that there was, at first, rather little permanent ice on the Arctic seas and, later, such a great extension of this ice that grain growing was for centuries impossible in Iceland and the total evacuation of that country was considered; at the same time, the cod fishery almost disappeared even from the Faroe Islands. In the worst decades Scotland, as well as parts of Scandinavia and Iceland, experienced famine; upland farms and villages in England and Germany may have been abandoned partly for this reason.

The last hundred years, or rather more, have seen a significant warming over most of the world, particularly the Arctic. The limits of open water and of the cod fishery (cod population effectively checked by the 2° C. isotherm of water temperature), as well as those of very diverse biological species, have been displaced poleward in the Northern Hemisphere. Glaciers have shrunk. During about the same period, the levels of water bodies and the discharges of rivers in the lower latitudes (in both the arid and equatorial zones) have generally gone down materially, e.g., the Great Salt Lake of Utah, the Caspian Sea, the East African lakes and the Nile. Corresponding changes of mean annual rainfall have been reported, amounting in some places to 30-40 per cent; though India appears to have been more or less unaffected, and China and Japan show more complex variations (with rainfall minima about 1900 and 1940). Most of the trends ot the past hundred years have halted or show signs of reversal since 1940, though in China in 1960 extreme aridity was again reported.

HISTORICAL SURVEY

At least four climatic epochs since the Ice Age seem likely to repay more study by meteorologists than they have so far received : (*a*) the post-glacial climatic optimum (warm period culminating between about 5000 and 3000 B.C.); (*b*) the colder climatic epoch of the early Iron Age (culminating between about 900 and 450 B.C.); (*c*) the secondary climatic optimum in the early Middle Ages (broadly around A.D. 1000-1200 or rather longer); (*d*) the Little Ice Age (cold climate very marked between about A.D. 1430 and 1850).

The first step must be to build up knowledge of the world climatic patterns prevailing during these epochs. The following outlines can already be discerned:

POST-GLACIAL OPTIMUM. WARM EPOCH (CIRCA 5000 TO 3000 B.C.)

The distribution and general extent of land ice was probably not very materially different from now, and the world sea level similar to today.

The extent of ice on land, decreasing throughout the warm epoch, may have reached its minimum around 2000-1500 B.C.; i.e., after the main part of the warm epoch was over.

By soon after 4000 B.C. the world sea level had risen to about its present level (Godwin, Suggate and Willis, 1958), or possibly a few metres above (Brooks, 1949, p. 362; Fairbridge, 1961, p. 158). The rise over the previous 10-12,000 years from its minimum stand in the Ice Age can be primarily attributed to reduction of the ice sheets on land to somewhere near their present extent. Isostatic effects, however, altered the geography near the former ice sheets; there were extensive submerged lands and shallow seas for some thousands of years (see, for example, development of the Baltic and North Sea between about 8800 and 5000 B.C. in Zeuner, 1958, p. 50-3). Because of this, and because of rather higher ocean temperatures than now (1° C. in the tropical Atlantic (Emiliani, 1955) and probably several degrees in the Arctic (Brooks, 1949, p. 370), the present general sea level could have been attained at a time when the land ice was still slightly more extensive than now.

The Arctic Ocean, with much open water, was probably ice-free at least in summer, though not the channels of the Canadian Archipelago (Brooks, 1949, p. 143).

Fossil marine fauna (molluscs and edible mussels) and evidence of past vegetation and bog growth indicate much higher sea and air temperature than now quite generally in high latitudes north and south, e.g., at Spitsbergen (Brooks, 1949, p. 142, 362; Schwarzbach, 1959, p. 59, 153). Camel remains found in Alaska and tiger in the New Siberian Islands, approx. 75° N., are attributed to this period (Alissow, Drosdow and Rubinstein, 1956, p. 327) but probably imply temperate, not tropical conditions.

In the (present) temperate zone of the Northern Hemisphere temperatures were higher than now and there is evidence of a northward anomaly, especially before 5000-4000 B.C., of the atmospheric circulation.

The vegetation belts were displaced poleward and to greater heights above sea level than now. In Europe the summer temperatures can be estimated as prevailingly 2-3° C. higher than now (Schwarzbach, 1950, p. 153; Godwin, 1956), in North America rather less above present levels (Schwarzbach, 1961, p. 285). Winter temperatures, though possibly conditioned by anticyclones, can never have attained the severity now reached in air streams coming over the continents from the polar ice. The snow line was 300 metres above the present level in central Europe (Schwarzbach, 1961). Annual mean temperatures in Europe were about 2° C. higher than now (West, 1960). Since the fringe of the dry-climate landscape of the steppe reached Leningrad and the Volga Basin (Alissow *et al.*, 1956; see also Buchinsky, 1957, chapter 1), at least in the period up to about 4000 B.C., it seems safe to assume that the subpolar depressions and the axis of the main anticyclone belt were generally displaced north at that time in the European sector, perhaps by as much as 10° of latitude.

Later in the warm period there were considerable and long-lasting variations of rainfall, and it has been suggested that the climate of Europe became generally wetter after the development of an enlarged Baltic, perhaps as early as 5000 B.C. Depressions presumably tended to pass on more southerly tracks than formerly, gradually coming nearer to their present general latitudes. Milder, more oceanic winters would help maintain high annual mean temperatures.

In the Sahara and deserts of the Near East from about 5000-2400 B.C. there was an appreciably moister climate than now (Butzer, 1957, 1958).

The evidence, archaeological and zoological, is especially convincing as regards the early part of this period. Desiccation of the climate, possibly beginning well before 2400 B.C., might have a somewhat delayed effect because of the higher water table and presumably more extensive oases.

The high pressure belt presumed generally well north of the Mediterranean around 5000 B.C. and after. Africa and the Near East could come under the influence of broadened trade-wind and equatorial zones and more widespread summer (monsoon) rains. With this pattern winter rains in the latitude of the Mediterranean may also have occurred.

Gradually, the effects of the high pressure belt returning to lower latitudes seem to have been increasingly felt and, with increasing aridity in the region, by 3000 B.C. some of the animal migrations were cut off.

In Hawaii also the "climatic optimum" period gives evidence of greater rainfall than now in the (widened?) trade-wind zone.

In the southern temperate zone, a moister epoch, apparently rather warmer than now, was experienced though the temperature anomalies seem to have been less than in Europe. The evidence is largely from the extent and distribution of forest species in southernmost South America and New Zealand (Auer, 1958, 1960; Cranwell and von Post, 1936; Schwarzbach, 1950). Firm conclusions regarding the prevailing latitudes covered by the subtropical high pressure and west wind belts must await further work in other areas. (Work on the poor floras of the smaller islands in the southern temperate zone has, however, been able to throw no light on this matter, since no changes are apparent there.) It seems clear that in the earlier post-glacial period between about 7000 and 5000 B.C. Tierra del Fuego had had a rather dry, anticyclonic climate with prevailing west winds and limited forest extent on the west side only; New Zealand had a distribution more similar to that of today. During the warm-climate period which followed the forest spread in New Zealand warmth-loving species seem to have gained and wind directions appear to have been rather more variable than earlier (expanded equatoria and trade-wind zones?). The dates depend sufficiently on radio-carbon tests and can be confidently accepted for comparisons with the Northern Hemisphere (Auer, 1958).

Antarctica also experienced a warm period after the main Ice Age (when the Antarctic ice sheet had been several hundreds of metres thicker than now). Ahlmann (1944) tentatively, but doubtless rightly, identified this with the time of the post-glacial warm epoch in the northern and southern temperate zones.

The dating of the warmest epoch in the Antarctic as contemporaneous with that in the other climatic zones may be accepted as required by the results of radio-carbon dating of changes of world sea level (Godwin *et al.*, loc. cit.) and of the climatic changes in Tierra del Fuego, near 55° S.

In the Wohlthat Mountains, near 72° S.10° E., temperatures were so many degrees higher than now that there were considerable streams of running water and fluvial erosion of the landscape; between 600 and 1,890 metres above sea level lakes were formed which have subsequently frozen solid and remain as "fossils" (Ahlmann, 1944).

Flohn (1952, p. 171) estimates that annual temperatures in this epoch were 2°-3° C. higher than now in the Antarctic and in Tierra del Fuego and also on the Himalayan Mountains.

POST-GLACIAL CLIMATIC REVERTENCE. EARLY IRON AGE COLD EPOCH (CIRCA 900-450 B.C.)

Brooks (1949, p. 143) suggested that the sharp worsening of the climate of Europe, which came with floods and storms and advances of the Alpine glaciers between about 1400 and 500 B.C., following a much more gradual decline of temperature for centuries previously, implies and coincided with rather sudden re-formation of the "permanent" pack-ice cover on the Arctic Ocean north of 75°-80° N.

Regarding the recession in the temperate zone, most of the present glaciers in the Rocky Mountains south of 50° N. were formed about this time, certainly after

2000 B.C. (Matthes, 1939). In the Austrian Alps glaciers advanced to near the same limits which they regained, or more generally passed, around A.D. 1600 (Firbas and Losert, 1949). In Europe generally the most impressive feature is the evidence of a sharp increase of wetness.

There was a widespread re-growth of bogs after a much drier period (Godwin, 1954). This change ("recurrence surface" or *Grenzhorizont*) is still the most conspicious feature of peat bog sections all over northern Europe from Ireland to Germany and Scandinavia, represented by a change of colour from the black lower peat to the lighter upper layers. Lakeside dwellings in central Europe were flooded and abandoned (Brooks, 1949), and ancient tracks across the increasingly marshy lowlands in England and elsewhere in northern Europe were adapted to changed conditions or abandoned too (Godwin and Willis, 1959).

In Russia forest had spread farther south than in the warm epoch, advancing for instance along the lower Dnieper, and the species represented (beech, hornbeam, fir rather than oak) indicate some lowering of the summer temperatures. It is not clear whether any important dry period occurred in Russia, as it did farther west in Europe, between the end of the warmest epoch and the sharper Iron Age recession (Buchinsky, 1957).

In the Mediterranean and North Africa the climate seems to have been drier than during the climatic optimum, but not so dry as today. Rainfall was apparently not quite so rare as now in summer. Roman agricultural writers (e.g., Saserna) noted that around 100 B.C. the vine and the olive were spreading north in Italy to districts where the weather was formerly too severe: from this it would appear that the preceding centuries had had a cooler climate also in the Mediterranean.

The southern temperate and Antarctic zones had also entered a colder period by around 500-300 B.C. In southern New Zealand the evidence is consistent with prevailing westerly winds, but in Tierra del Fuego spread of the forest to cover the whole island on both sides of the watershed indicates quite frequent easterly winds and hence depression tracks on the whole in lower latitudes than now (Auer, 1960; Cranwell and von Post, 1936).

SECONDARY CLIMATIC OPTIMUM (CIRCA A.D. 1000 TO 1200)

This epoch appears to show most of the same characteristics as the post-glacial epoch both in the Northern Hemisphere and in the Antarctic, only in less degree, perhaps because of its shorter duration.

The Arctic pack ice had melted so far back that appearances of drift ice in waters near Iceland and Greenland south of 70° N. were rare in the 800s and 900s and apparently unknown between 1020 and 1200, when a rapid increase of frequency began. This evidence hardly supports Brooks' suggestion that the Arctic Ocean again became ice-free during this epoch, though "permanent" ice was probably limited to inner Arctic areas north of 80° N. and possibly not including the Canadian Archipelago (to judge from occasional exploits there by the Old Norse Greenland colonist).[1] From the evidence of early Norse burials and plant roots in ground now permanently frozen in southern Greenland, annual mean temperatures there must have been 2°-4° C. above present values. It seems probable that sea temperatures in the northernmost Atlantic were up by a similar amount.

In western and middle Europe vineyards extended generally 4°-5° latitude farther north and 100-200 metres higher above sea level than at present (Lamb, 1959). Estimates of the upper limits of the forests and of tree species on the Alps and more northern hills in central Europe range from 70 to 200 metres above where they now stand (Gams, 1937; Firbas and Losert, 1949). These figures suggest mean summer temperatures about 1° C., or a little more, above those now normal.

In North America archaeological studies in the upper Missisippi valley (approx. 45° N.) suggest a warm dry epoch, followed by a change to cooler, wetter conditions after A.D. 1300 (Griffin, 1961).

In lower latitudes Brooks (1949, p. 327, 355) names this as a wet period in central America (Yucatan) and probably in Indo-China (Cambodia). There is

1. Glaciological and other studies of Arctic ice islands, and their presumed growth when formerly part of the Ellesmere Land ice shelf, have not so far been reduced to an agreed time scale (Crary, 1960, p. 34; Stoiber *et al.*, 1960, p. 71). It seems most probable, however, that the ablation period in progress in the early 1950s began only about 40 years ago and that the total age of the ice is 620 years or less, implying growth during the Little Ice Age epoch and that net ablation prevailed before that, during the secondary climatic epoch, in the Canadian Archipelago.

evidence of greater rainfall and larger rivers in the Mediterranean and the Near East (Butzer, 1958, p. 12). There is some evidence of a moister period in the Sahara from 1200 or earlier, lasting until 1550 (Brooks, 1949, pp. 330-8).

In southernmost South America the forest was receding rapidly to western aspects only, indicating a drier climate than in the previous epoch and more predominant westerly winds.

On the coast of east Antarctica, at Cape Hallett, a great modern penguin rookery appears from radiocarbon tests to have been first colonized between about A.D. 400 and 700, presumably during a phase of improving climate, and to have been occupied ever since (Harrington and McKellar, 1958). This tends to confirm the earlier assumption of explorers of the Bunger Oasis in east Antarctica of a period of marked climatic improvement about a thousand years ago, since which there has been only a modest reversion.

THE LITTLE ICE AGE (CIRCA A.D. 1430-1850)

There is manifold evidence of a colder climate than now from most parts of the Northern Hemisphere.

The Arctic pack ice underwent a great expansion, especially affecting Greenland and Iceland, and by 1780-1820 sea temperatures in the North Atlantic everywhere north of 50° N. appear to have been 1°-3° C. below present values (Lamb and Johnson, 1959). Indirect evidence suggests that these (or even slightly lower) water temperatures were already reached by the 1600s.

Decline of the forests at the higher levels in central Europe between about 1300 and 1600 evidently had some catastrophic stages, especially after 1500, and Firbas and Losert (1949) believe this may have been the time of principal change of vegetation character at levels above 1,000 metres since the post-glacial climatic optimum. (In Iceland the relict woodland surviving from the climatic optimum virtually disappeared early in this epoch, doubtless partly by human agency.) Also near the Atlantic coast of Scotland eye-witness reports of the time (Cromertie, 1712) suggest widespread dying off of woods in the more exposed localities, presumably because of miserable summers and increased damage from salt-spray. In Europe around 50° N. it seems, however, that the prevailing summer temperatures were mostly about their present level (in the 1700s slightly above), though the winters were generally more severe.

Some notably severe winters also affected the Mediterranean. Glaciers advanced generally in Europe and Asia Minor, as well as in North America, and snow lay for months on the high mountains in Ethiopia where it is now unknown.

The Caspian Sea rose and maintained a high level until 1800. Records of the behaviour of the Nile suggest that this was a time of abundant precipitation in Ethiopia but very low levels of the White Nile, which is fed by rainfall in the equatorial belt: the equatorial rains were evidently either weak or displaced south.

The evidence generally points to an equatorward shift of the prevailing depression tracks in the Northern Hemisphere and more prominent polar anticyclones.

The Southern Hemisphere seems largely to have escaped this cold epoch until 1800 or after, though by then temperatures were possibly somewhat lower than today in some parts of the southern temperate zone. Between 1760 and 1830 the fringe of the Antarctic sea ice appears to have been generally a little south of its present position and the southern temperate rain-belt apparently also displaced south.

Recession followed after 1800-30 until 1900 or later. The rain zone and depression tracks moved north and there were great advances of the glaciers in the Andes and South Georgia, as well as some extraordinarily bad years for sea ice on the southern oceans (Aurrousseau, 1958; Findlay, 1884). This recession in the southern temperate and sub-Antarctic zones was, however, out of phase with the trend by then going on in the Northern Hemisphere. Since 1900 the temperature of the southern temperate zone as a whole may have been rising like that of other zones (Callendar, 1961); in the sub-Antarctic the rising trend began even later and may be out of phase with the latest trend in the Northern Hemisphere (Willett, 1950; Murray Mitchell, 1961).

SUMMARY OF THE HISTORICAL SURVEY

The first three epochs appear to demonstrate respectively: (*a*) climatic zones displaced towards high latitudes, equatorial/monsoon rain belt widened; (*b*) climatic zones displaced towards low latitudes, equatorial belt narrowed; (*c*) as (*a*) but in less degree.

These variations fit with the sequence of contractions and expansions of the circumpolar vortex proposed by Willett (1949), with minor modifications of date and extra detail thanks to recent additions to knowledge.

The last epoch appears to present a different pattern, with an equatorward shift of the climatic zones in the Northern Hemisphere accompanying a (probably smaller) poleward shift in the Southern Hemisphere, followed by return movements in both hemispheres during the nineteenth century.

Climatic fluctuations in the present equatorial, arid, temperate and polar zones have been such as accord with these changes.

The amplitude of the temperature fluctuations appears to have been much greatest in high latitudes, so that the meridional gradient of surface temperature, at least between 50° and 70° N. must have been materially less in the warm epochs than in the cold ones. It appears, however, that the temperatures on mountains even in low latitudes were raised 2°-3° C. in the warm epochs[1] and lowered by 1°-2° C. below present values during the Little Ice Age. This means that the possibility remains that the meridional (Equator-Pole) gradient of upper air temperature was actually less during the cold epochs, the surface temperatures in high latitudes being particularly unrepresentative at such times because of frequent strong inversions (Lamb and Johnson, loc. cit.).

Climatic trends in the Far East bear a rather complicated and partly inverse relationship to those elsewhere e.g., evidence of generally late cool springs in Japan A.D. 1000-1200, milder winters between about 1700 and 1900 than before or since (Arakawa, 1956, 1957; Lamb and Johnson, loc. cit.)]. From study of variations within the last two centuries Yamamoto (1956) describes how this inverse relationship tends to come about: (*a*) during periods of strengthened zonal circulation of the atmosphere (strengthened Siberian anticyclone and weak polar anticyclone in the Asian sector) Japan experiences more cold air from the continental interior in winter (and some Arctic outbreaks in the rear of depressions); (*b*) during periods of weaker zonal circulation (Siberian anticyclones weaker or displaced northwest, polar anticyclones covering more of northern

1. From Himalayan evidence, quoted by Flohn (1952). Evidence from other regions desirable.

Asia) the main cold air mass in winter streams west over central Asia towards Europe, and Japan comes more under the influence of Pacific anticyclones and mild oceanic air. However, farther north, the Okhotsk Sea develops more ice at such times, under the influence of the polar anticyclones, and this produces a tendency for poor summers in Japan.

Superimposed upon, and running through, the bold climatic phases and trends here defined many workers have found evidence of apparent periodic oscillations, particularly affecting rainfall but presumably also affecting the latitudes of the most frequent depression tracks over Europe and Asia.

A periodicity of 180-200 years has been suggested by variations in the Baltic ice and levels of the Caspian Sea (Betin, 1957), one of 400 years from Chinese data (Link and Linkova, 1959), one of about 600 years from recurrent regeneration layers ("Recurrence surfaces" or *Grenzhorizonte*) in the peat bogs in many parts of temperate Europe and a periodicity of 1,700-2,000 years from variations in the rivers, lakes and inland seas in European Russia and in central Asia.

There seems no doubt, however, that the four epochs described earlier are those which represent the greatest departures from present day conditions. If periodic variations of any agency influencing the Earth and its atmosphere be involved, it nevertheless seems that in these epochs some special conjunction of circumstances —possibly including external circumstances such as volcanic dust—must have come into play.

It may be significant that the two cold epochs more or less coincide with III and IV of the post-glacial world-wide waves of volcanic activity (I-IV) identified by Auer (1958, p. 229; 1959, p. 208). Radio-carbon dates of these volcanic phases are: I — around 7000 B.C. II — 3000-250 B.C.; III — around 500-0 B.C.; IV — around A.D. 1500-1800. Moreover III was marked by volcanic activity over both hemispheres, e.g., Kamchatka, Iceland, Andes and Tristan da Cunha (see also Thorarinsson *et al.*, 1959); whereas IV seems to have been largely in the Northern Hemisphere and equatorial zones, apart from the Southern Hemisphere eruptions of 1835 and certain later years. Thus the different climatic distributions deduced for these epochs correspond well with a difference that may reasonably be presumed in the geographical distribution of dust veils in the high atmosphere.

METEOROLOGICAL INVESTIGATIONS OF CHANGES IN THE GENERAL ATMOSPHERIC CIRCULATION

BY SURFACE PRESSURE MAPS BACK TO 1750

Monthly m.s.l. pressure charts have been constructed in the British Meteorological Office, covering as much of the world as possible, for each January and each July back to the earliest years for which usable observation data could be found. The internal consistency checks provided by a network of observing stations, some in each area having long series of observations, have made it possible, after tests for probable error of the isobars, to reconstruct the pressure field for a worthwhile area of Europe back to 1750. Pressure distribution over the North Atlantic Ocean from as early as 1790 can be established within a tolerable error margin (standard error ± 2.5 mb. in January, ± 1.0 mb. in July) by using 40-year means. The method, sources of data and tests used have been published elsewhere (Lamb and Johnson, 1959).

Fig. 1 and 2 show the 40-year average m.s.l. pressure in January and July respectively for the earliest possible period over the Atlantic Ocean (1790-1829) compared with the modern normal charts based upon the *Historical Daily Weather Maps* (1900-39). Solid lines are used for the isobars where the pressure values can be regarded as known within the error margins mentioned above, broken lines are used where the general pattern of the pressure field is reasonably certain but the values are not good enough for useful measurements to be based upon them.

January

Average pressure gradients have increased in January from the period around 1800 to the present century [cf. Fig. 1 (*a*) and (*b*)].

In Fig. 3 a limited selection of pressure difference indices of circulation intensity in January are presented. From these, and others not shown, it is seen that the increase of intensity of the zonal circulation since the middle or earlier part of the nineteenth century is a world-wide phenomenon, affecting at least the westerlies and trade-wind zone in the North Atlantic and the southern westerlies. The peak intensity of the zonal

1a

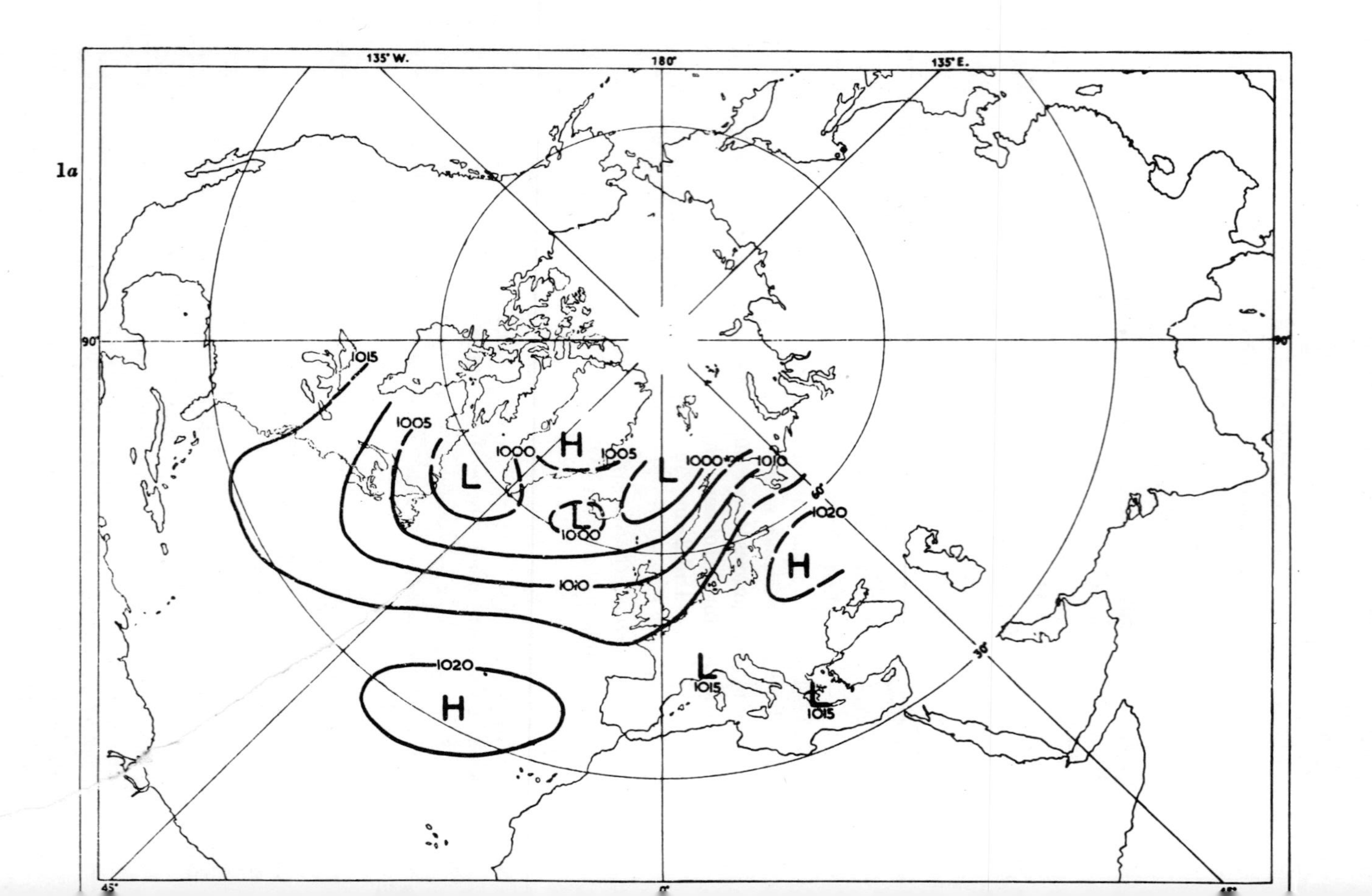

135° W.
180°
135° E.
90°
90°
45°
0°
45°
1015
1005
1000
H
1005
1000
1010
L
L
L
1000
1020
H
1010
1020
H
L
1015
L
1015
60°
30°

1b

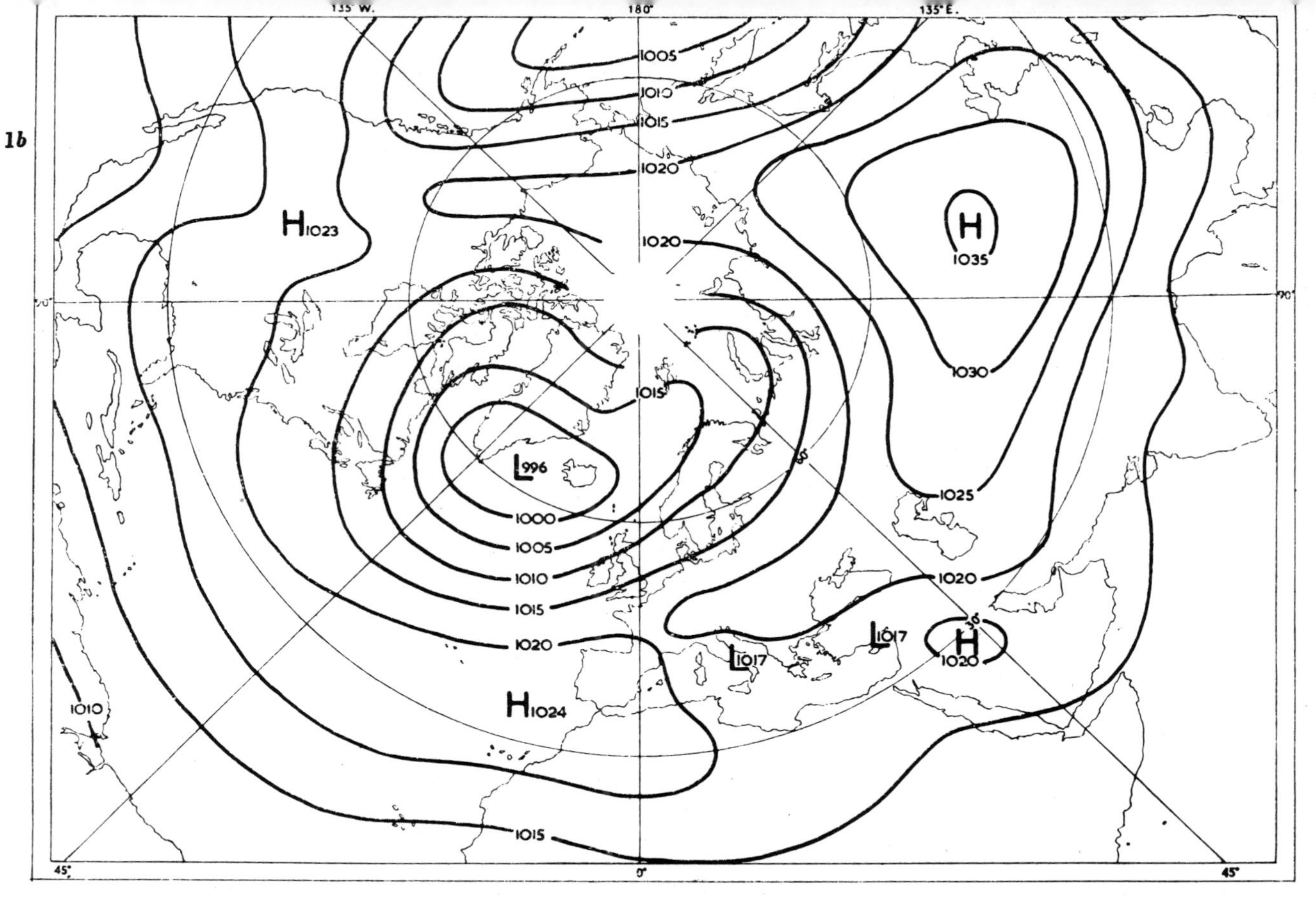

FIG. 1. Average m.s.l. pressure for January : (*a*) 1790-1829; (*b*) 1900-39.

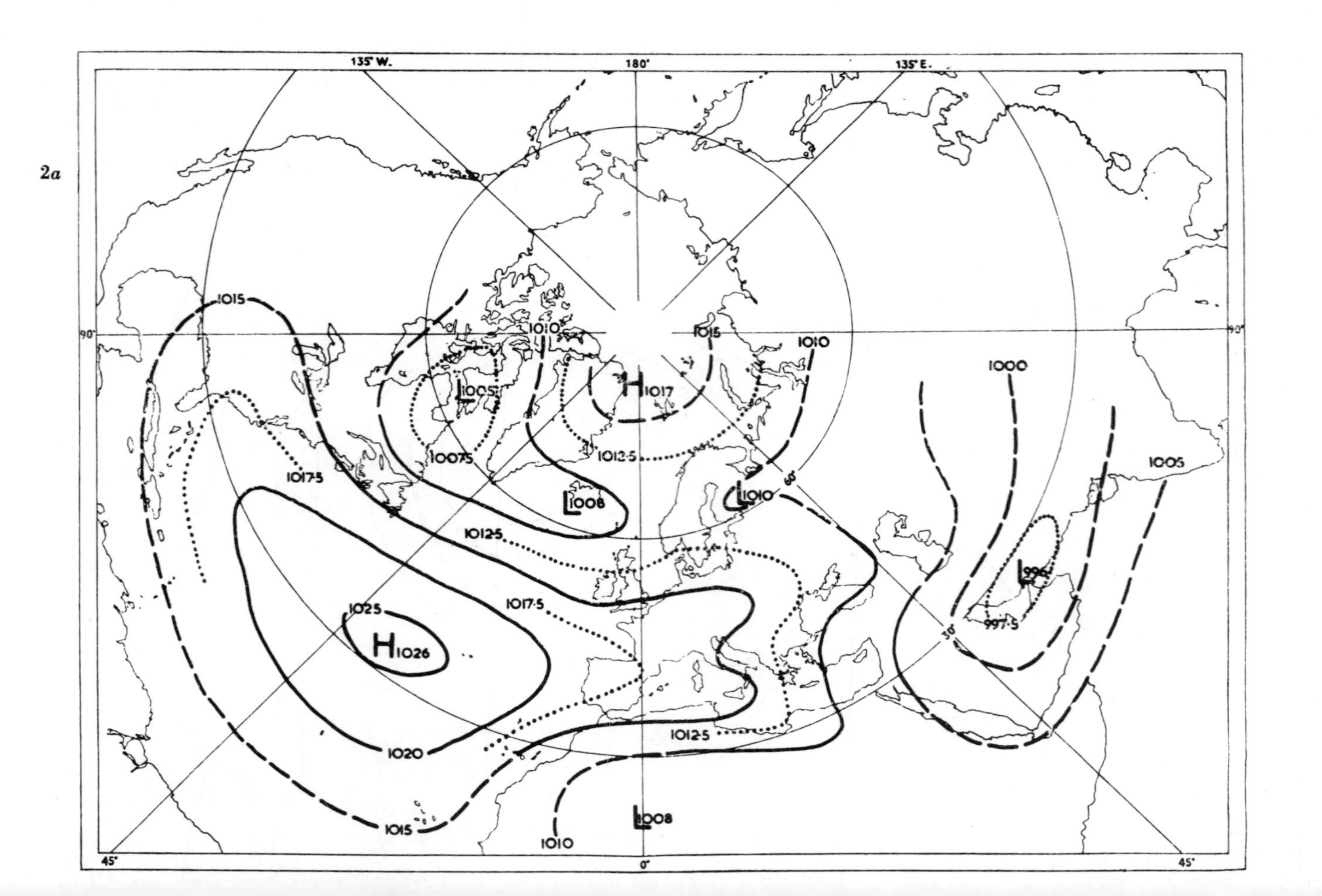

135° W.
180°
135° E.
90°
90°
45°
0°
45°
60°
30°
1015
1010
1005
1007.5
1015
1010
H 1017
1000
1012.5
1017.5
1005
L 1008
L 1010
1012.5
L 996
1017.5
1025
997.5
H 1026
1012.5
1020
1015
L 1008
1010

2a

2*b*

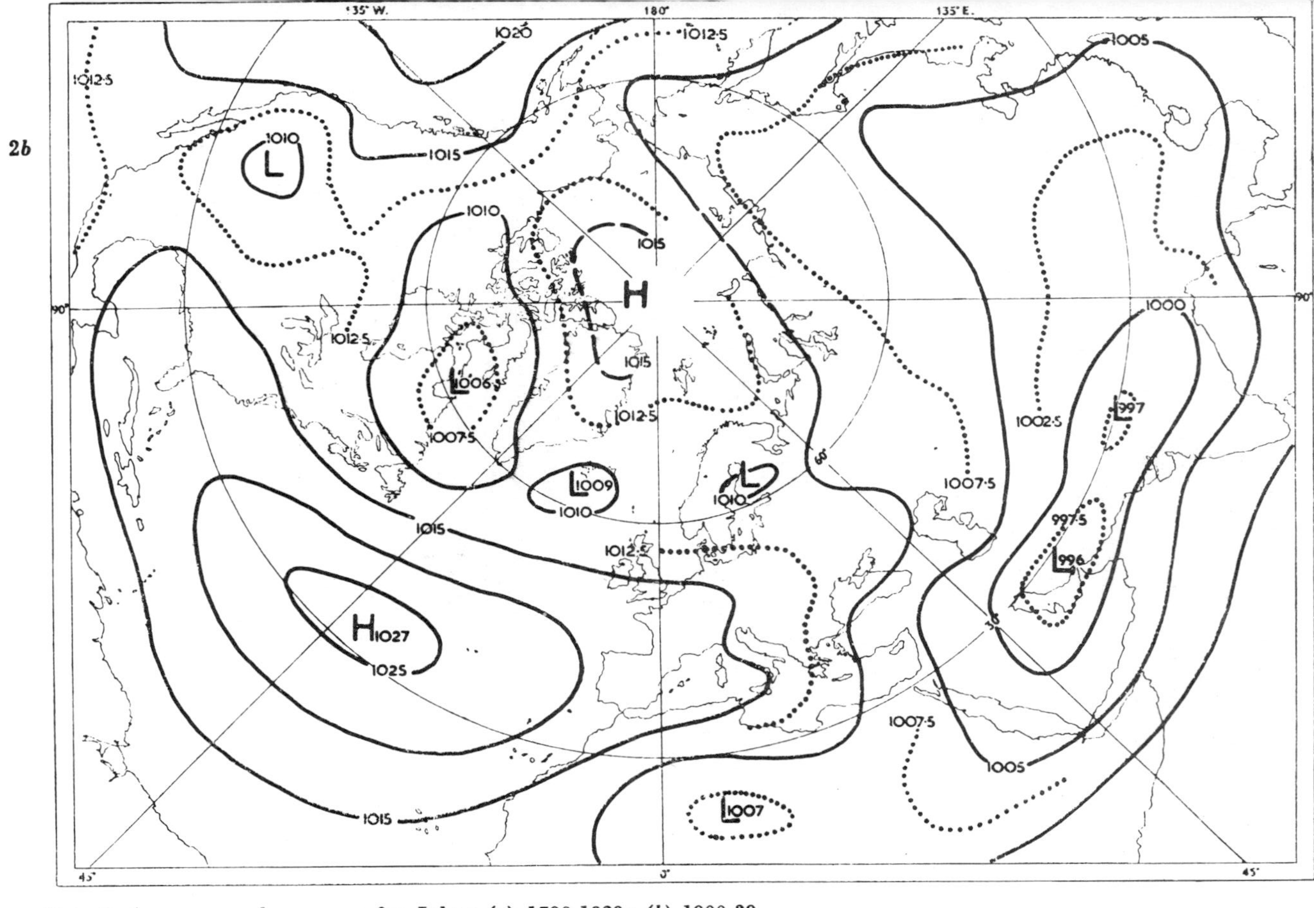

FIG. 2. Average m.s.l. pressure for July : (*a*) 1790-1829 ; (*b*) 1900-39.

circulation so far was reached about 1930 in the North Atlantic and 1910 in the Southern Hemisphere. Over the North Atlantic the increase of the zonal circulation from around 1800 to 1930 appears to amount to 5-10 per cent. Changes in the extent of Arctic ice (for which the North Atlantic is virtually the only outlet) appear, however, to amplify circulation changes in this sector.

It is an advantage of the map method that indices of circulation vigour can be measured at points where the main air streams are best and most regularly developed. Comparison of numerous correlation coefficients between measures of the same air stream taken at different points have demonstrated that such indices are the most representative (Lamb and Johnson, 1959). The Northern Hemisphere indices in Fig. 3 have been chosen in this way, but, for the earliest years, and in the Southern Hemisphere, it is still necessary to make measurements only near where there happen to be observing stations. The monthly mean pressure gradient between 50° and 60° N. for westerlies over the British Isles, used in Fig. 3 (*c*) to cover a longer period than any of the indices in Fig. 3 (*a*) or (*b*), is an index linked with the overall pressure range between Azores maximum and Iceland minimum in January by a correlation coefficient of about +0.6 (1800-79, +0.62; 1880-1958, +0.56—both statistically significant beyond the 0.1 per cent level). It is reproduced here because it shows the increase of vigour of the westerlies from a generally lower level in the eighteenth century.

The period around 1790-1830 was evidently one of rather notable minimum strength of the zonal circulation in January, though there had been another minimum earlier, probably before 1750.

The variations in the mean strength of the North Atlantic westerlies nicely parallel the changes of mean January temperature in Britain and central Europe. The mean January temperature of central England (Manley, 1953) between about 1740 and 1850, was for instance, over 1.5° C. lower than between 1900 and 1940. Since this type of temperature trend is typical for the colder half of the year, it is reasonable to suppose that other months have also partaken in the change of strength of the North Atlantic westerlies.

The mean meridional component, which is much weaker than the mean zonal component, of the circulation (meridional component measured by pressure differences along 55° N.) does not appear to have shared

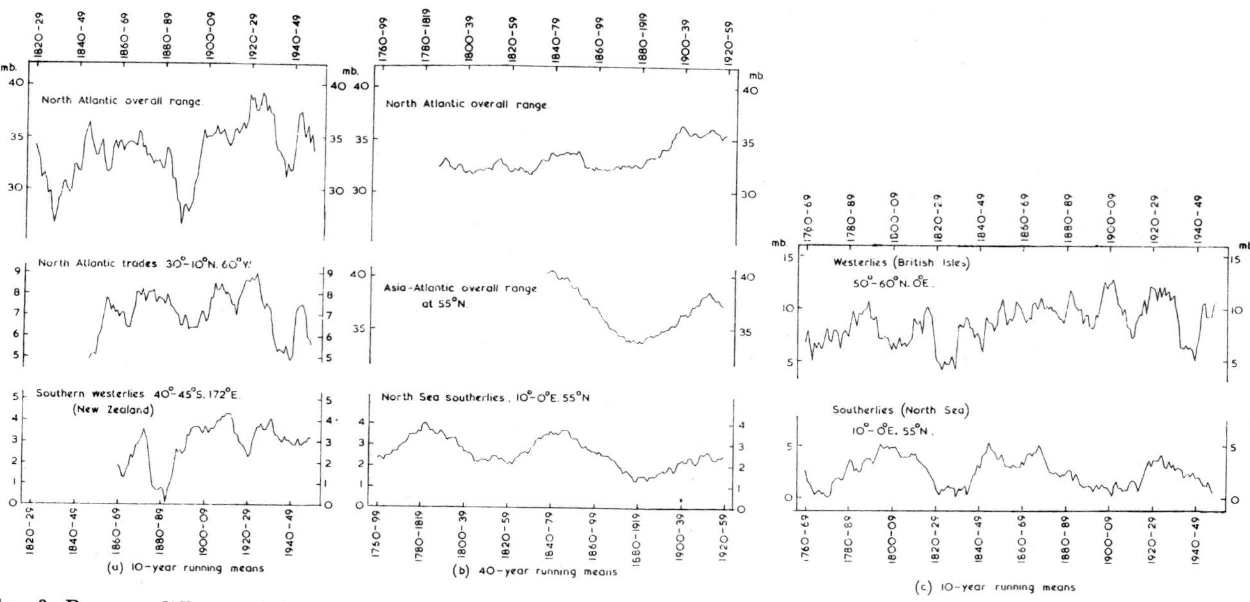

FIG. 3. Pressure difference indices of circulation intensity in January.

the increasing trend of the zonal circulation in January, but seems rather to show a long-term fluctuation with a possible period of around 60 to 70 years.

The importance of considering the meridional circulation and the zonal circulation separately in connexion with the recent warming of the Arctic has been further demonstrated by Petterssen (1949) and by Wallén (1950, 1953) who discovered that between 1890 and 1950 the frequency of northerly meridional situations decreased and that of southerly meridional situations increased markedly in the region of the Norwegian Sea and Scandinavia; since 1950 northerly meridional situations have once more become prominent. This discovery might be related to changes of wave-length (and displacement of the preferred positions for troughs and ridges) in the upper westerlies of which we shall give further evidence later.

Variations of the meridional component of the circulation, especially the winter southerlies over the North Sea, must be linked in some way with the occurrence of blocking anticyclones, which is also subject to variations possibly with periods of 60-90 years. Since no persistent trend is found in the meridional component, the generally colder winters of the period around 1800 and earlier are mostly to be explained by weakness of the mean westerly flow towards Europe rather than by blocking, which was only really prominent at long intervals both in the epochs of weak and of stronger westerlies.

July

Changes in the July circulation from 1790-1829 to 1900-39 (Fig. 2) are much less obvious than those in January, though Europe seems to have had a weaker and more anticyclonic pressure field in the earlier period.

The changes are better seen from the trends of the intensity indices shown in Fig. 4. (Following the principle of measuring pressure gradients where the main air streams are best and most regularly developed, the most representative indices of the July circulation are not found at the same points as those used for January.) The general nature of these curves is an increase of intensity from low values around the middle of the nineteenth century to high values in the twentieth century. A major peak intensity of such indices generally seems to have been passed between 1900 and 1950—mostly in

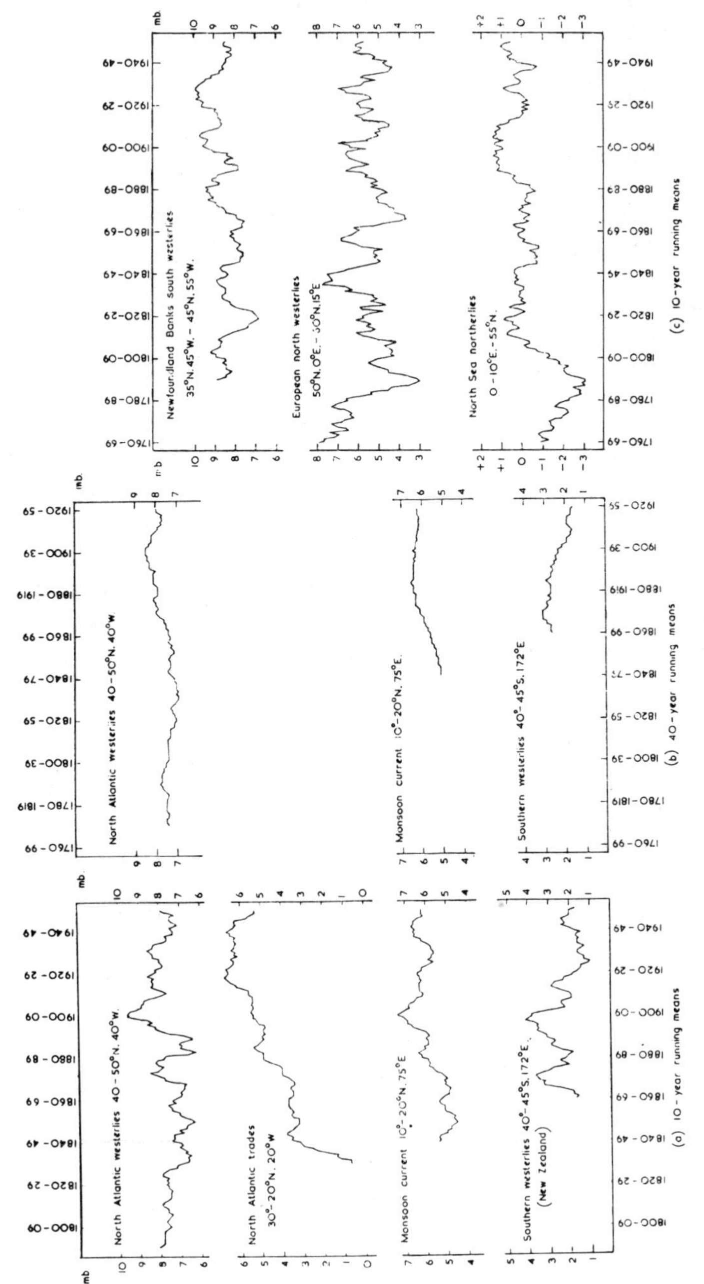

FIG. 4. **Pressure difference indices of circulation intensity in July.**

the decades 1900-09 or 1920-39—but again appears earlier in the Southern Hemisphere around 1890-1920 (1897-1906 New Zealand, 1908-17 Chile).

The rather stronger July circulation in the Northern Hemisphere before 1800-50 seems to have shown different patterns from those prevailing in the present century. Hints of rather lower pressure in the Labrador region (east of the North American cold trough) and of higher pressure over central and northern Europe are developments that might be expected to accompany the persistence of a cold surface (with some permafrost and remnants of ice and snow) in somewhat lower latitudes than now occurs.

The mean meridional components of the circulation, illustrated in Fig. 4 (*c*) by the pressure difference between 0° and 10° E. at 55° N. (northerly wind component over the North Sea), in July appear to show a rising trend. This is apparent also over the China Sea and is probably involved in the increasing gradient for south-westerly winds over the Newfoundland Banks [Fig. 4 (*c*)]. The North Sea index rises from the 1790s to the present century; if there are any real oscillations superimposed, the period seems to be 70-90 years—between peaks around 1820 and 1900 and between minima in the 1780-90s, the 1850s and 1940s—and the rising trend may be still continuing.

Summary

Increases of strength of the zonal circulation have been found in January and July over widely separated parts of the globe, apparently being quite general from around the middle of the last century and culminating around 1930 in the Northern Hemisphere and 1900-10 in the Southern Hemisphere. The trend of some indices suggests that an overall increase of energy may have been going on since well before 1850 in July as well as January. Possibly the rather stronger summer circulation over the North Atlantic and neighbouring longitudes in the late 1700s than in the mid-1880s should be regarded as a local difference associated with the presence of some persistent snow and ice in rather lower latitudes before, say, 1830 than at any time since. Increased strength of the general circulation has probably occurred in most months of the year. The increase from *circa* 1800 to 1930 in the strength of the zonal circulation over the

North Atlantic in January amounts to between 5 and 10 per cent, but in general is probably less than this.

A general rise in the winter temperatures in Europe accompanied the increased vigour and prevalence of the westerlies. Summer temperatures showed a much smaller, and not statistically significant, fall.

Changes of average latitude of the main zones of the atmospheric circulation have also been studied. They seem to show a general equatorward displacement, especially of the sub-polar depression track, in winter and summer, by 2-4° of latitude in those periods and regions where sea ice has attained an abnormally great extent—e.g., around 1800 in the North Atlantic and around 1900 near Chile. A progressive equatorward trend of the northern and southern high pressure belts in the Atlantic sector in January during the present century is so far unexplained.[1]

A tendency for increased ice on the Arctic seas in this sector since about 1940 may be a consequence of this. In July the trend seems to have been the other way till about 1930. Over the Indian Ocean and Australian sectors of the Southern Hemisphere the main pressure belts have all moved 2°-4° south in January and north in July during the present century,[2] displacements whose trend seems to follow that of the intensity of the (monsoon) pressure gradients developed over Asia, especially the winter northerlies and summer southerlies over eastern Asia, passing its extreme point and reversing broadly around 1930.

AN IMPORTANT AND SEVERE STAGE IN THE CLIMATIC CHANGE SINCE 1800

Regarding the recent period of climatic recovery from the Little Ice Age and strengthening atmospheric circulation, with warming of most latitude zones and increasing aridity in the desert zone (see Butzer, 1957*b*), the particularly strong Northern Hemisphere circulation

1. Willett (1961) has lately reported on an index of solar activity which shows a highly significant negative correlation with the latitude (but no relation with the intensity) of the strongest upper westerlies across North America in January over the period 1900-60. A smaller negative correlation coefficient between relative sun-spot number and the latitude of the westerlies was also obtained. Hence the extremely dlsturbed sun in recent sun-spot cycles may have some bearing on this equatorward trend of the pressure and wind zones in the North Atlantic.
2. The January trend affecting summer rainfall in Australia was first reported by Kraus (1954), who does not, however, seen to have been aware of the reverse tendency in the southern winter.

of the 1920s and 1930s and of the decade 1900-09, at least as regards the sector between North America and Europe, has already attracted the attention of meteorologists (see Wagner, 1940; Scherhag, 1950; Lamb and Johnson, 1959). The peculiar characteristics of the 1830s do not, however, seem to have received notice, perhaps because it has not previously been possible to present circulation maps. The mean pressure distributions for January and July for each decade since 1750 can now be presented and those for 1830-39 are shown here in Fig. 5.

This decade stands out from the series 1750 to date in several respects:

1. Highest pressure generally over Europe and the Mediterranean.
2. Most northerly position of the high pressure belt in this sector.
3. Lowest pressure in Gibraltar, evidently with easterly winds and probably a still greater low pressure anomaly to the south and south-west.
4. Very high temperatures at Gibraltar (unhomogenized series but positive anomalies of 2°-4° C. in both winter and summer months appear common in the 1830s).
5. Fragmentary reports of an abnormal climatic régime at Madeira, tending to warmth and summer drought, and at Malta, where the persistent (summer and winter) drought raised public alarm, particularly between 1838 and 1841—incidentally leading to the institution of regular rainfall measurements.

It would probably be worth while to devote effort to establishing fuller information about the climate (and displacements of the normal climatic zones) during this period, particularly over North Africa and perhaps generally over as much of the world as possible.

At present, it seems relevant to point to the following circumstances:

1. A general upward trend of intensity of the zonal circulation was probably already well under way, and may have been so since before 1750 [see British Isles curve in Fig. 3 (*c*)]. This is also suggested by a study of the North Atlantic trade winds from 1827 onwards, using ships' logs, by Privett and Francis (1959): it appears, moreover, that the 1830s were a decade of strong trades, somewhat above the smoothed trend.
2. The 1830s more or less coincided with pronounced peaks in summer and winter (1820-33 and 1838 in

January, 1830-39 in July) of Scandinavian blocking anticyclones—just possibly a periodic phenomenon with perioditicies of 60-90 years associated with solar events (see Scherhag, 1960, p. 91). There were some exceptionally high monthly mean pressures in the January of this period at Trondheim and St. Petersburg (though St. Petersburg also had a few very low ones), with exceptionally strong, and prevalent, westerlies to the north and easterlies to the south.

3. Iceland and Greenland records suggest that enormous quantities of Arctic ice were broken up during the 1830s and drifted away into the Atlantic, followed by a period 1840-54 when ice was hardly ever seen near Iceland and when the permanent ice had retreated greatly both east and west of Greenland.
4. Sydney and Adelaide had long dry periods about this time—Sydney from the 1820s to the early 1840s, Adelaide through the 1840s and possibly earlier, implying prevalence of far southern positions of the anticyclone belt and depression tracks in that sector of the Southern Hemisphere. In Chile increasing rainfall in the Santiago district from 1820 onwards (after a long very dry epoch) has been taken as a sign of the temperate and subpolar depression belt returning northwards.
5. The Antarctic sea ice seems also to have been more erratic in the 1830s and after than in the preceding decades. In 1832, 1840-44 and 1855 enormous amounts of ice broke away into latitudes between 60° and 40° S. but seem to have left the higher latitudes unusually ice-free.

The Arctic ice never regained the extent which it apparently had before 1840. The circulation maps also make it doubtful whether any truly analogous patterns have occurred in recent years with those before 1840—a point which may be significant for long-range forecasting.

CONSIDERATION OF THE PROBABLE UPPER AIR CIRCULATION IN THE PERIOD AROUND 1800

Figs. 6 and 7 display the longitudes of lowest and highest m.s.l. pressure over the North Atlantic in January and July from 1790 to the present time. The latitudes used

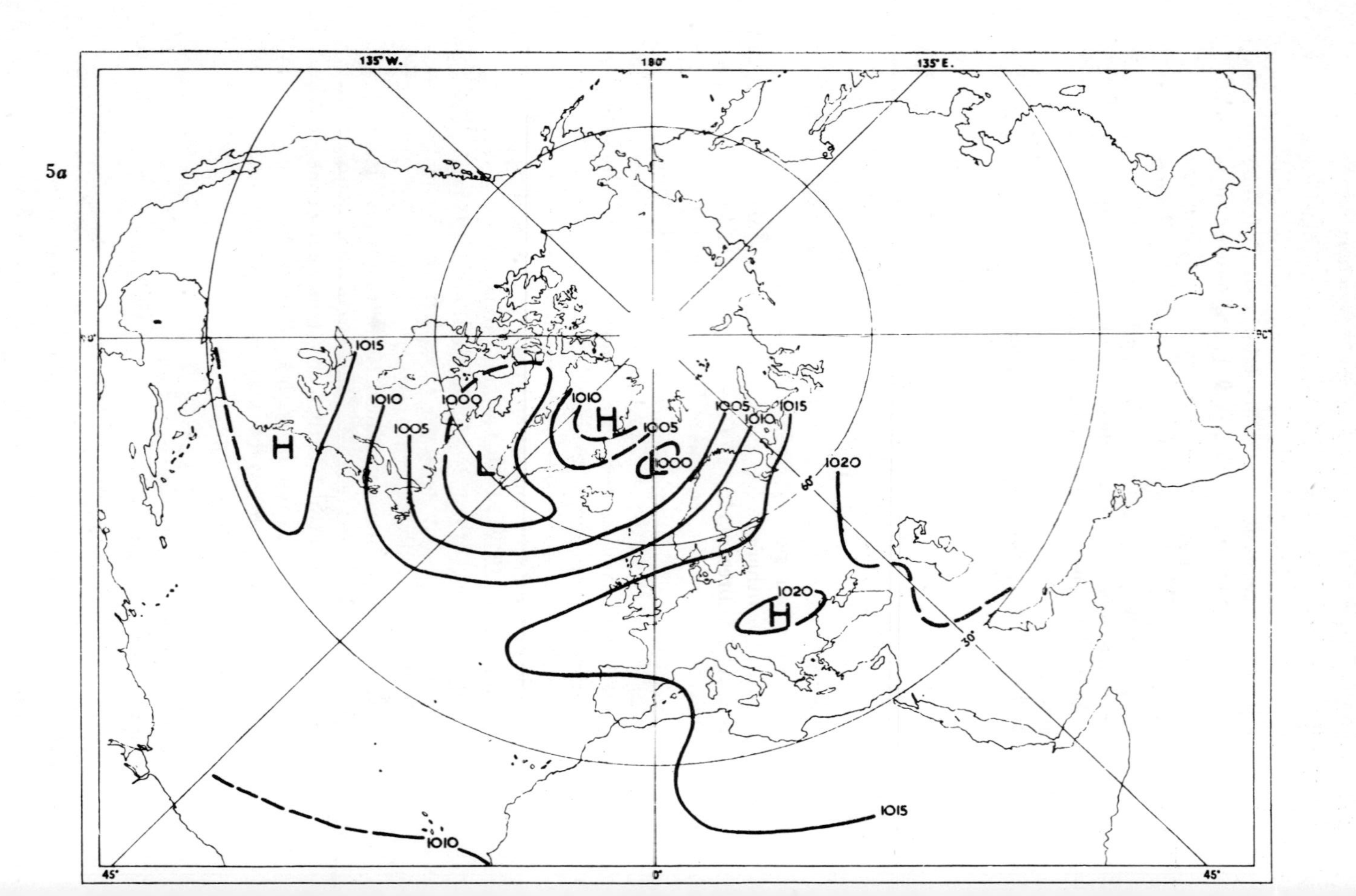
135° W.
180°
135° E.
45°
0°
45°
90°
60°
30°
1015
1010
1005
1000
1010
1005
1000
1005
1010
1015
1020
1020
1015
1010
H
L
H
H
H

5a

5b

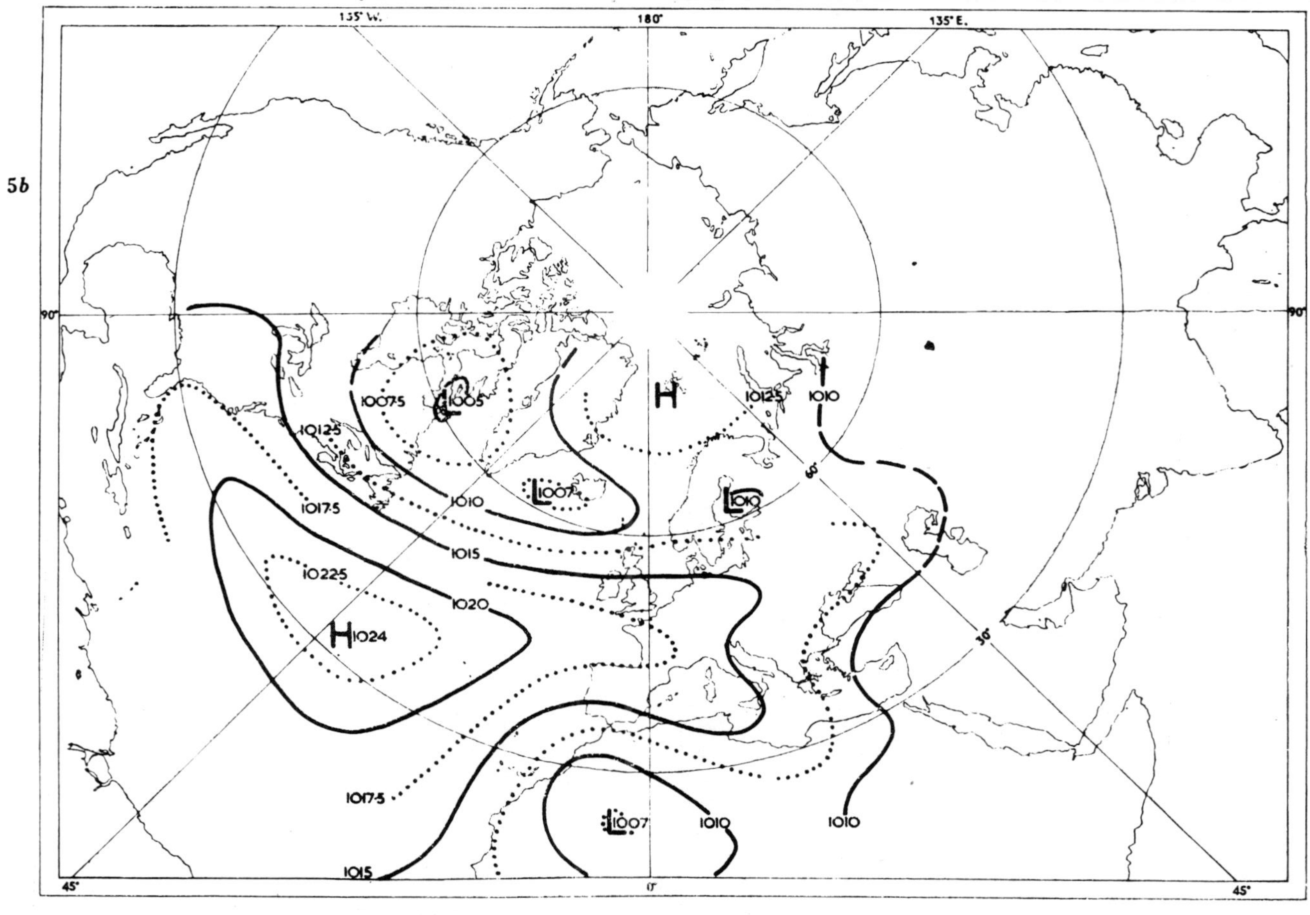

FIG. 5. Average m.s.l. pressure for 1830-39 : (a) January; (b) July.

were chosen (*a*) to make use of the most reliable portions of the isobaric charts and (*b*) to be where the identifiable features are related to the prevalent cyclogenetic and anticyclogenetic effects east of upper troughs and ridges respectively.

The wave length L of a standing wave is taken to be expressed by the Rossby formula

$$U = \frac{\beta L^2}{4\pi^2}$$

where U is the prevailing zonal velocity of the upper westerlies and β is the rate of change of the Coriolis

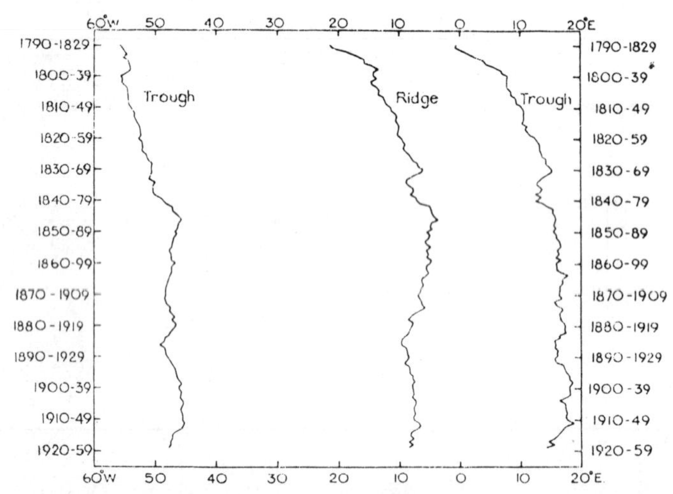

FIG. 6. Longitudes of the semi-permanent surface pressure troughs and ridges at 45° N. in the Atlantic sector in January (40-year running means).

parameter with latitude at the latitude of the mainstream of the westerlies.

Both Figs. 6 and 7 show that the longitude spacing of surface systems generally increased and decreased at times when the indices of circulation intensity were increasing and decreasing respectively. This is particularly clear with the spacing between the West Atlantic trough and mid-Atlantic ridge which are closest to the mainstream of the upper westerlies: the spacing of these surface features should correspond to about half a wave length. This result appears to give qualitative confirmation of the changes of circulation intensity found from the surface pressure gradients. But both in January and

July the change of wave length is surely too great (implying at 25 to 30 per cent change of intensity) to be accounted for wholly in this way. It seems therefore

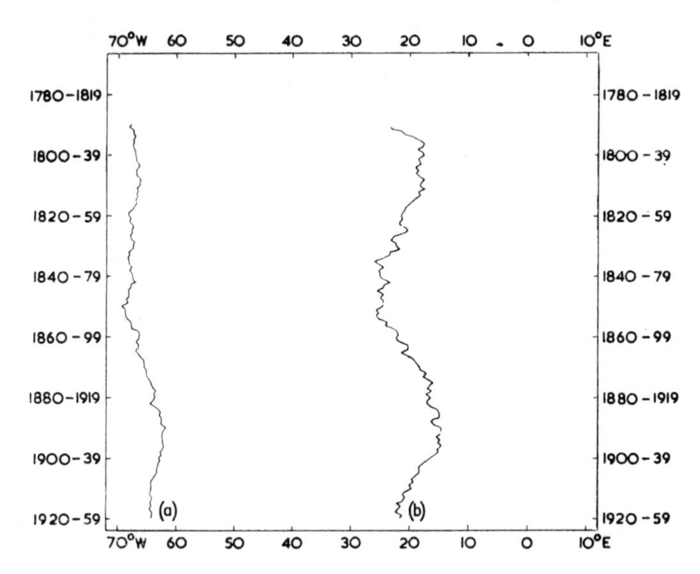

FIG. 7. Longitudes of the semi-permanent surface pressure troughs and ridges in the Atlantic sector in July (40-year running means) : (*a*) longitude of trough at 55° N. ; (*b*) longitude of ridge at 55° N.

that some slight change of latitude of the strongest upper westerlies must also have taken place ; in particular, a poleward displacement, of a few degrees of latitude from the times of weak circulation around 1800-50 to the epoch of strongest circulation in the present century seems to be implied.

The consistency of these trends suggests that the surface patterns, and in particular the longitudes of certain features, may be used judiciously to indicate probable changes in the main tropospheric westerlies aloft. This principle is the basis of the experimental investigations described in this and the following section.

A likely first approximation to the 1,000-500 mb. thickness patterns prevailing over the North Atlantic in January and July around A.D. 1800 was obtained (Fig. 8) by considering the average sea-surface temperatures observed between 1780 and 1820 (Lamb and Johnson, 1959) and shifting the mean thickness isopleths from their modern positions by the same amount as the sea-surface isotherms. Broadly this preserved nearly saturated adiabatic equilibrium with the sea-surface temperature, except for the highest thicknesses in January and the lowest thicknesses in July where vertical stability prevails over some parts of the Atlantic—these exceptions were, however, at the edges of the region over which surface pressures could be mapped.

Over the neighbouring land regions some slight equatorward displacement of the thickness values in the period around 1800 would be implied if a join-up with those over the ocean is to be achieved. Such a displacement might have been produced either by the dynamic effects of modified or southward-displaced upper westerlies or, more directly, by a small reduction of the effective insolation.

The latter suggestion gains *a priori* plausibility because Wexler (1956), in an attempt to explore the possibility of explaining Ice Age phenomena (precipitation pattern and atmospheric circulation) in terms of a persistent 20 per cent reduction of the insolation due to volcanic dust, obtained estimated anomalies of the 700 millibar and deduced surface pressure patterns which amounted to a remarkable qualitative prediction of the pressure charts subsequently constructed by Lamb and Johnson (1959) from actual data for the period around A.D. 1800. In particular, Wexler predicted as features of the January pattern an elongated polar trough and intensified frontal activity along the Atlantic coast of the United States, higher pressure over Greenland and more prominent cold northerly flow over the Norwegian Sea and North Sea affecting the coasts of Scandinavia and Britain.

Wexler moved the modern normal insolation isopleths by distances sufficient to reduce the amount of insolation by 20 per cent. Over the relatively cloud-free snow-covered interior of the continent he assumed the 1,000-700 mb. thickness values to be controlled by the insolation and moved the thickness lines by the same amount, so as to coincide with the same insolation.

Applying Wexler's argument in reverse to the 1,000-500 mb. thickness distribution around A.D. 1800, we see in Fig. 8 (*a*) and (*b*) that a reasonable join-up with the thickness isopleth positions over the North Atlantic could be achieved if the isopleths over North America (and continental Eurasia and Africa) were shifted by an amount to correspond with a 5 per cent reduction of insolation or rather less—possibly with any reduction between 0 and 5 per cent or a little over. (This seems not unreasonable in view of the 5 to 10 per cent reduction of circulation vigour over the North Atlantic in winter and the smaller reductions found at other seasons and places.) The only regions which did not fit were: (*a*) the coastal region near Newfoundland and Labrador, where a greater reduction of mean thickness over the sea (and neighbouring land) may reasonably be attributed to colder water and more ice; (*b*) western and central Europe, where greater reductions of thickness seem to be required and may perhaps be taken as dynamic, i.e., linked with the other evidence of a shorter wave length and more western position of the quasi-permanent trough in the upper westerlies.

Figs. 9 and 10 show the 500 mb. patterns derived by using these thickness patterns and 1,000 mb. contours corresponding to the actual pressure fields.

Since sea temperatures 1780-1820 were available for the North and South Atlantic Ocean, it seemed worth while to apply a similar experiment to the great ocean region as a whole, excluding areas disturbed by strong water currents, strong upwelling and zones of intense cloudiness (as in the equatorial and subpolar rain-belts). The zones of strong water currents and of upwelling are only fringe regions of the ocean but their delineation is unavoidably somewhat uncertain and arbitrary. Over the broad remaining regions of the ocean, where both positive and negative anomalies occurred, it seems likely that the general (overall average) level of surface-water temperature and of 1,000-500 mb. thickness is controlled by the amount of insolation actually penetrating the atmosphere to the surface. The results of trying the obviously crude assumption that this was the whole explanation of shifts of sea temperature (and thickness) isopleths since 1800 were: (*a*) over the North Atlantic between 30° and 55° N., including the fringes where cold currents were probably expanded—an indicated reduction of insolation in 1780-1820 by 7 or 8 per cent (almost certainly too large); (*b*) over the North Atlantic between 30° and 55° N., omitting the fringes —a reduction of 3 to 4 per cent; (*c*) over the North and South Atlantic between 50° N. and 40° S., omitting the fringes and the equatorial rain-belt—a reduction of 0.7 to 1.5 per cent.

The result under (*c*) is possibly too small because the most extensive region of colder surface north of 50° N.

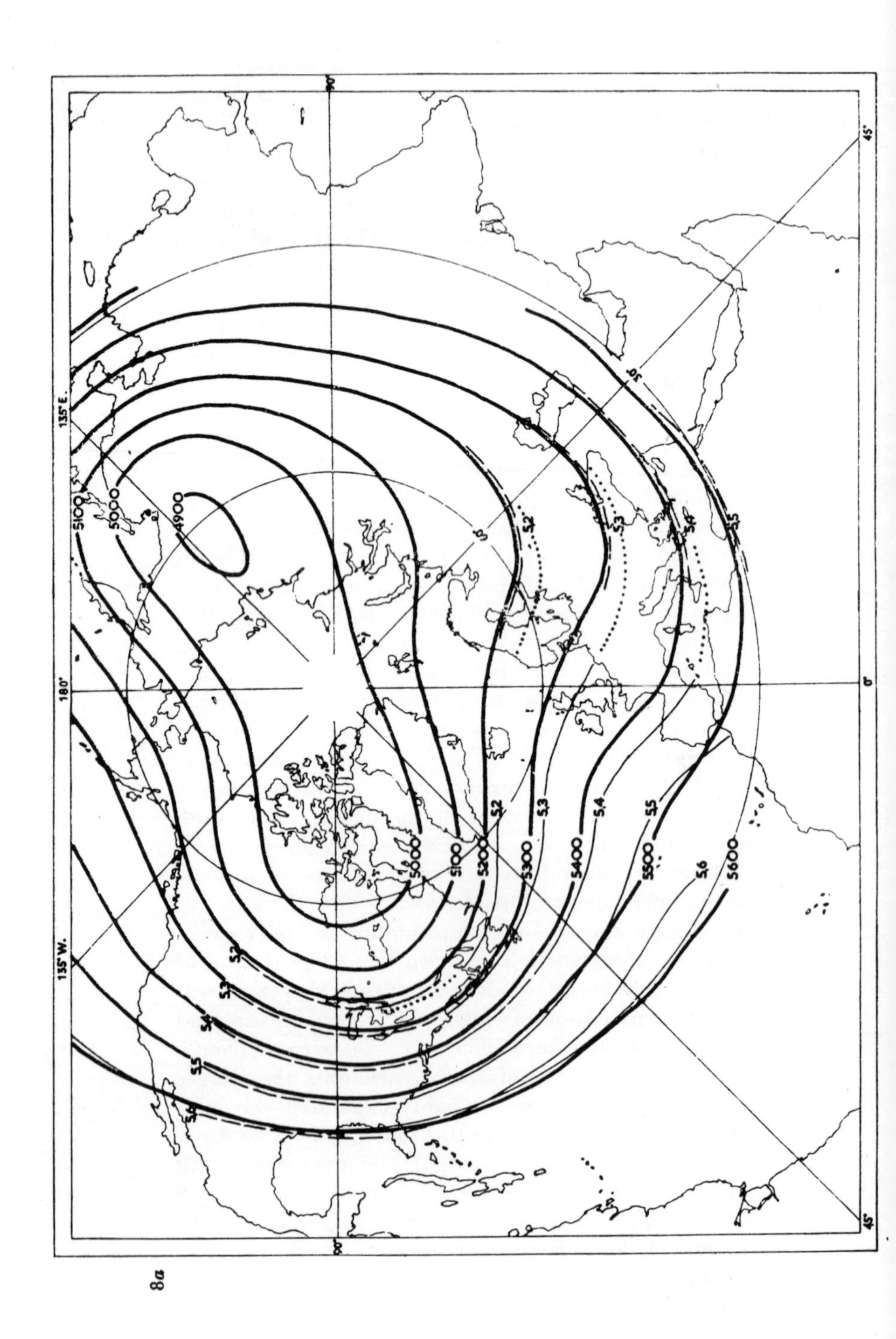
135° E.
180°
135° W.
90°
0°
45°
4900
5000
5100
5200
5300
5400
5500
5600
5,2
5,3
5,4
5,5
5,6

8a

8b

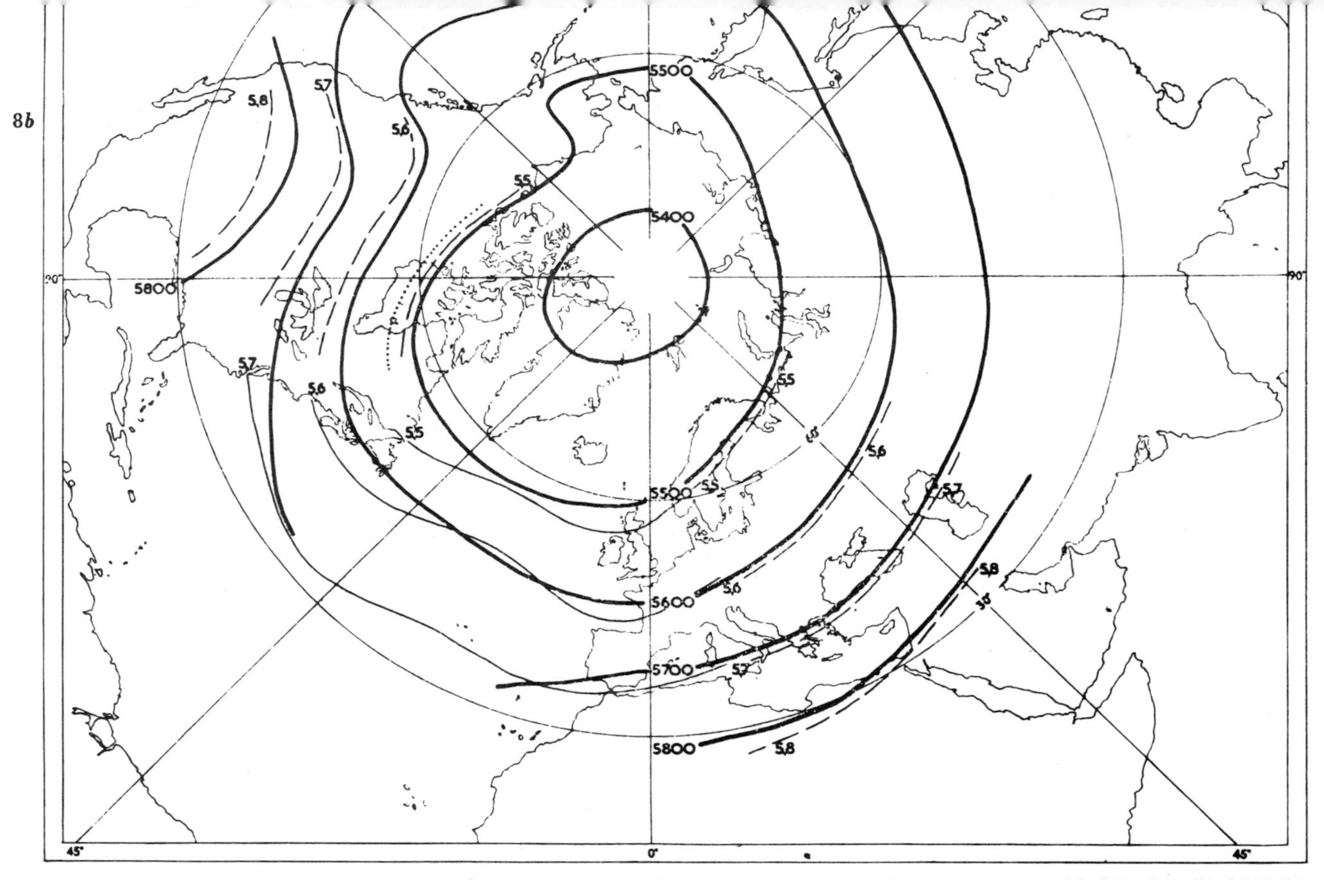

FIG. 8. Average 1,000-500 mb. thickness : (*a*) January ; (*b*) July. Bold lines averages for recent years : (*a*) 1950-58 ; (*b*) 1949-57. Narrow lines suggested for 1780-1820 from sea temperatures. Broken lines suggested for about 5 per cent reduction of insolation.

9a

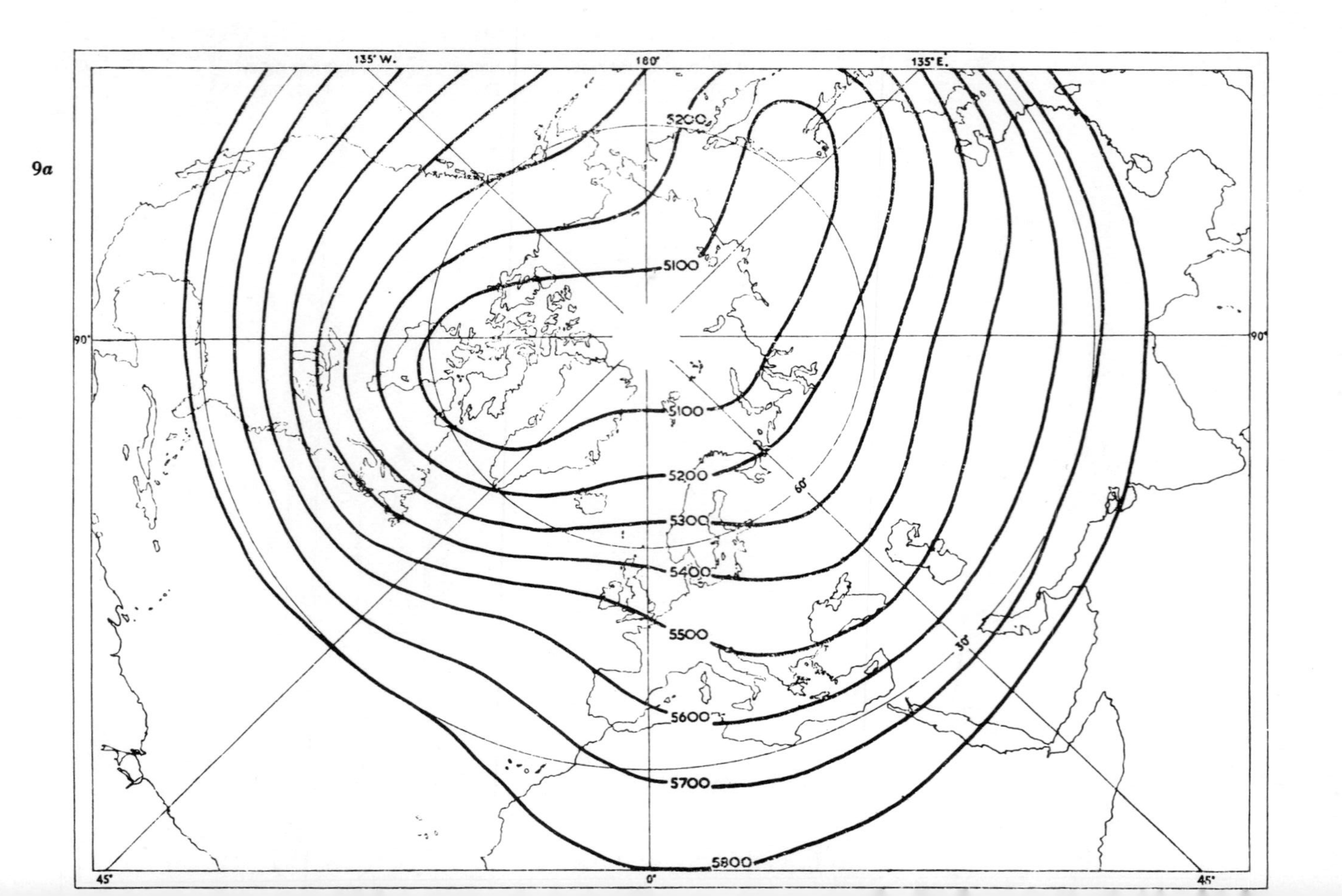

135° W.
180°
135° E.
90°
90°
45°
0°
45°
60°
30°
5200
5100
5100
5200
5300
5400
5500
5600
5700
5800

9b

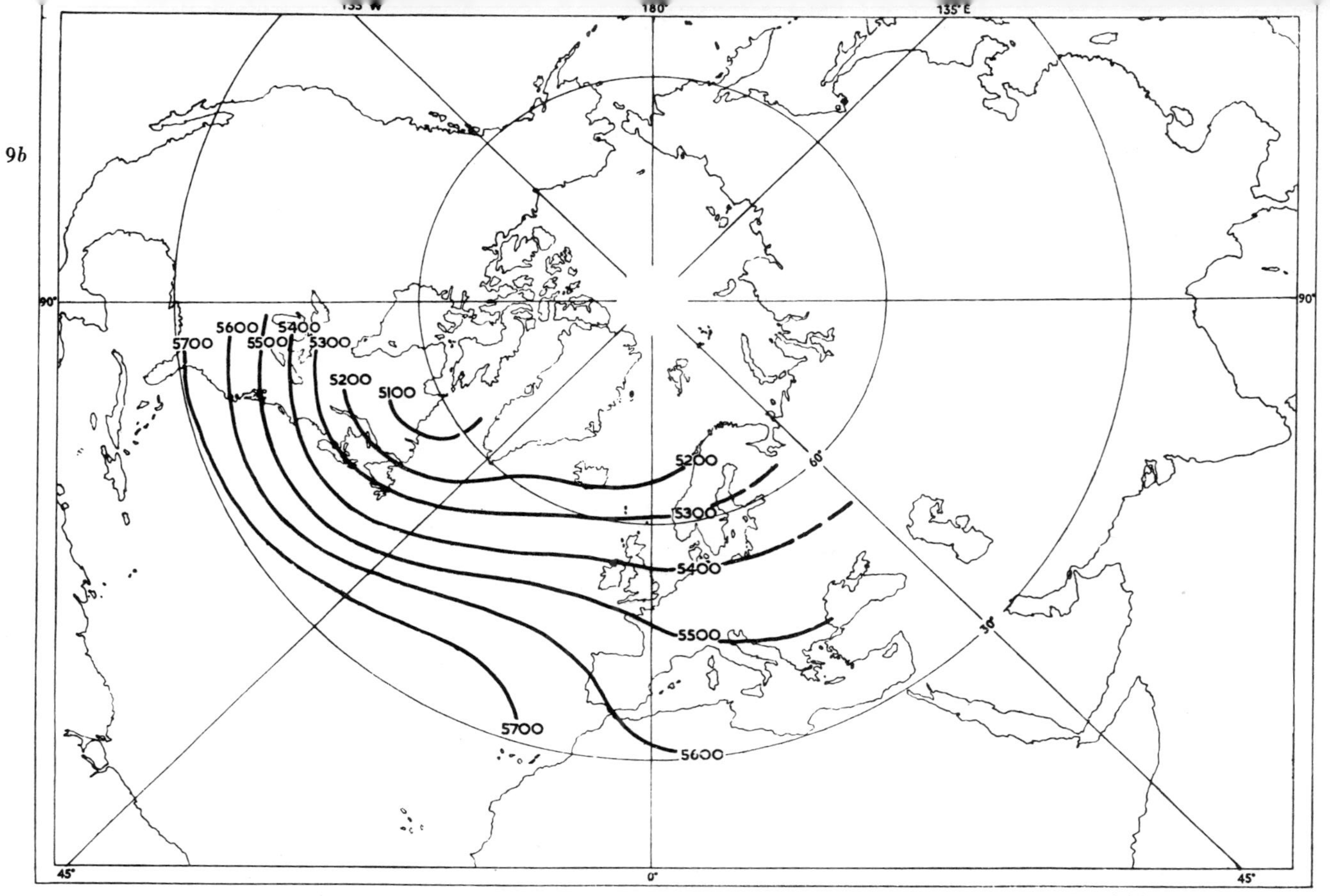

FIG. 9. Average 500 mb. contours for January : (*a*) 1949-58 ; (*b*) 1780-1830. (Based on Figs. 1 (*a*) and 8 (*a*).)

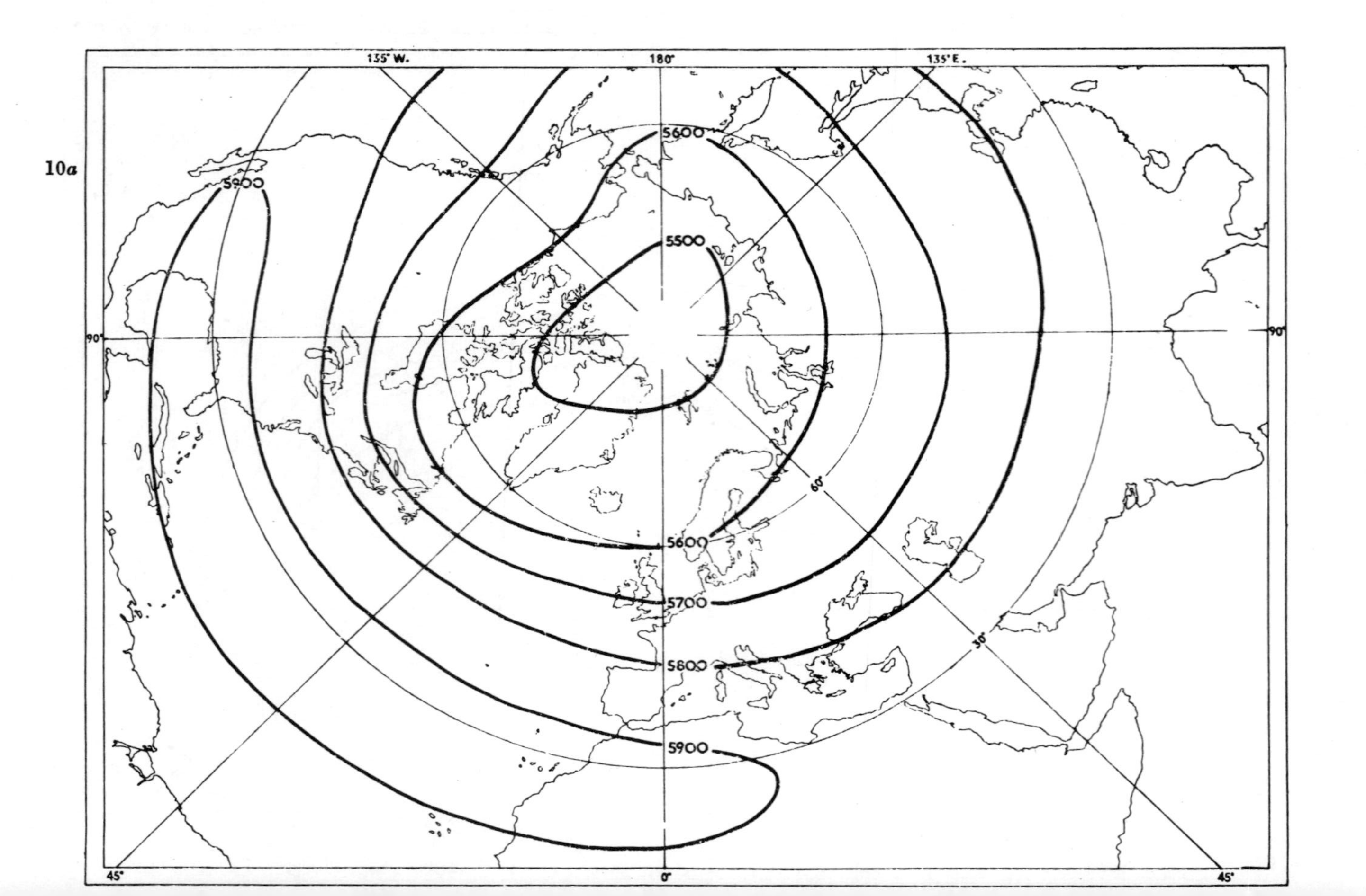

135° W.
180°
135° E.
90°
90°
45°
0°
45°
60°
30°
5900
5600
5500
5600
5700
5800
5900

10*a*

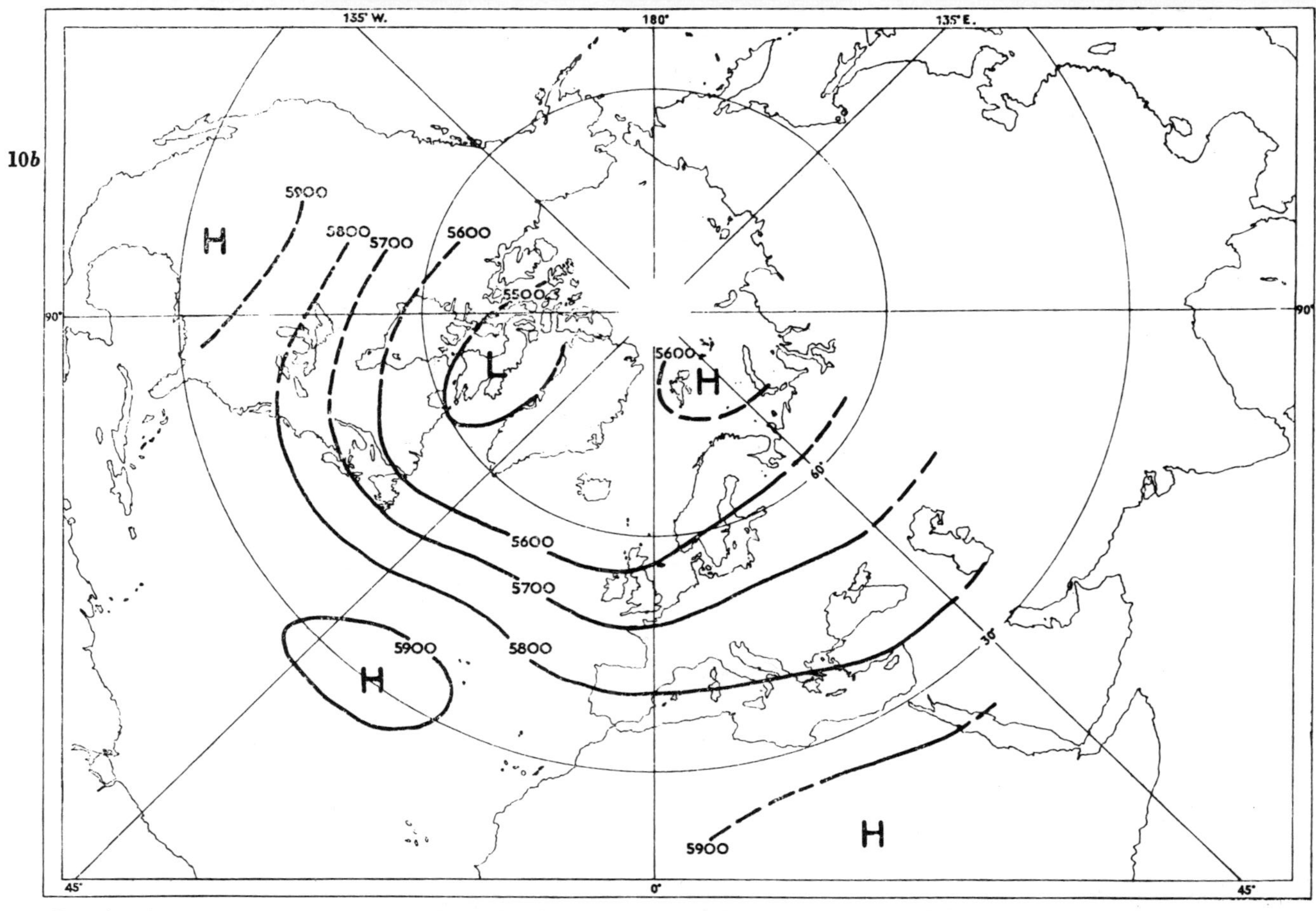

FIG. 10. Average 500 mb. contours for July : (*a*) 1949-58 ; (*b*) 1780-1830. (Based on Figs. 2 (*a*) and 8 (*b*).)

is excluded and apparently other cold areas near 40° S. We may guess that anomalies in the great Pacific Ocean were smaller, though on the whole in the same sense.

Summing up it seems therefore that there is a case for supposing a small reduction of, say, 1 to 2 per cent in the average available insolation over the surface of the globe during the epoch 1780 to the 1820s compared with the present century. Over the Northern Hemisphere the reduction may have been rather over 2 per cent. We notice, however, that the greatest displacement of the isopleths was over the North Atlantic Ocean, so that the increased Arctic ice and spread of cold water north of 50 °N. was playing perhaps the most immediately important part in modifying the atmospheric circulation pattern at that time. It seems further to be implied by the 500 mb. changes in Figs. 9 and 10 that the circulation, although perhaps generally rather weaker around 1800, was locally strengthened where the cold surface over the continents and the Labrador current reached rather lower latitudes than today. Other features indicated were a shortened wave length[1] and large amplitude waves.

AN EXPERIMENT IN THE SYSTEMATIC TREATMENT OF DOCUMENTARY WEATHER RECORDS SINCE A.D. 800

Efforts are being made to extend our pictures of the monthly mean atmospheric circulation over Europe still farther back. Several decades before 1750 can be covered by numerous well kept registers of wind and weather —e.g., on board navy ships berthed for a month or more in various harbours from the Baltic and Iceland to the Mediterranean (and possibly farther afield). Assembly of this data takes time and could perhaps profitably be pursued in different countries. It is known that there

1. Betin (1957) has noticed an interesting variation of climatic behaviour in Europe which seems likely to be related to changing wave length and most frequent ridge and trough positions. Over the eighty years of decreasing ice between about 1870 and 1950 there was a negative correlation coefficient between Baltic ice and the level of the Caspian Sea, which is fed by rainfall in the Volga Basin, whereas the longer term trends of both since 1550 run parallel. Presumably between 1870 and 1950 cyclonic or anticyclonic conditions over the Baltic tended to cover the Volga Basin too, whereas for a long period previously this was not the case.

were drastic climatic vagaries in the decades that can be covered, particularly the 1690s.

A wealth of manuscript information from still earlier times regarding the character of particular months and seasons exists in state, local, monastic, manorial and personal accounts and chronicles. Compilations have been made by meteorologists and others in many countries, so that by now it is possible to attempt numerical assessment of various phenomena, though much care is needed and special techniques have to be devised to watch and allow for changes in the fullness of reporting.

As a first attempt at systematic use of this material to reveal something about the changes in the prevailing atmospheric circulation from the warm climate period of the early Middle Ages right through the Little Ice Age to the present day, the reports from different places in Europe between 45° and 55° N. and between Ireland and Russia were used. This is a particularly suitable region for study because it is always affected by the behaviour of the mainstream of the zonal circulation aloft and because reports are most abundant there. One can commonly compare contemporary events in the Mediterranean, Scandinavia and elsewhere. Immediate objects in view were to establish the climatic sequence in Europe more firmly, and in more detail, and to discover how far different longitudes underwent similar experiences.

The most reliable surface weather indications in the early manuscripts relevant to this study were thought to be:

1. Severity or mildness of the weather prevailing in the main winter months of December, January and February. The effects upon landscape, transport and the agricultural economy are likely to have been reported in all important cases. It should be possible to identify confidently the persistent spells: mild winter by rains, flooding and thunderstorms even in continental regions, also by early or out-of-season flowering of plants; severe winters by frozen rivers, lakes and seaways, and by many sorts of privation and damage.
2. Raininess or drought in summer. Again the effects upon the landscape and upon agriculture are reasonably sure to have achieved mention in all outstanding cases. Wet summers produce flooding and ruined crops, though highly coloured accounts of individual

> thunderstorms may occur in otherwise good summers. Dry summers are known by parched ground and dwindling rivers, whilst the grain crops are usually good; forest fires are also particularly liable to occur. The rain character of a summer is surer of faithful recording than the temperature, since an oppressive heat wave might well be the only recorded reference to temperature in an otherwise poor summer.

Since long spells of weather of set character persisting from July to August are one of the most prominent features (Lamb, 1953) of the climate of temperate Europe (early recognized in the Saint Swithin and Seven Sleeper legends), and since the circulation patterns involved presumably correspond to the quasi-stationary pattern attained at the climax of the summer heating of the hemisphere in the individual years, July and August only were used as the time unit for summer.

The compilations available included: Buchinsky's (1957) for the Russian plain (references especially to the Ukraine, the Moscow region and Poland); Hennig's (1904), chiefly covering central Europe and Italy, but also including references to other places between Ireland and Poland; Easton's (1928) regarding winters in western (and central) Europe between Scandinavia and the Mediterranean; Vanderlinden's (1924) for Belgium; an unpublished collection kindly made available by D. J. Schove for the British Isles, including use of C. E. Britton's chronology of early time (1937) and original sources. Amplifying evidence from vine harvests in Luxembourg (Lahr, 1950), Baden (Muller, 1953) and ice on the Baltic (Betin and Preobazenskij, 1959) was also considered.

Crude numerical indices were then defined and applied to the years in groups of not less than a decade (thus eliminating uncertainties in early times regarding the exact year of a particular occurrence). Data for some groups of years appear full and self-consistent from quite early times—e.g., remarkable warmth and dryness of central European summers between A.D. 988 and 1000—but a complete sequence of decade characteristics can hardly begin before A.D. 1100. So as not to make too great demands in terms of approximately uniform standards of reporting only the simple indication of excess of mild or cold, wet or dry for individual decades is here attempted (Fig. 11). Half-century means of

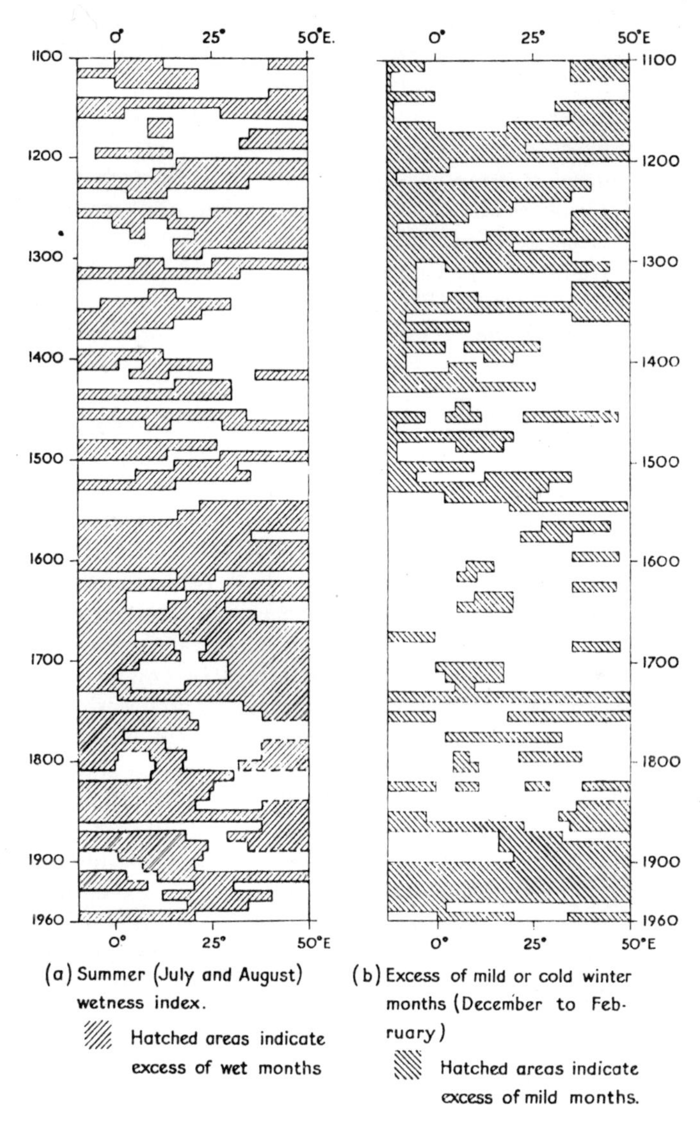

Fig. 11. Summer wetness index and winter mildness (or severity) in different European longitudes near 50° N. by decades from 1100 to 1959.

the following indices appeared, however, to give reliable numerical values from an earlier date, and have been tentatively extended back to A.D. 800.

1. Winter severity index. The excess number of unmistakably mild or cold winter months (December, January and February only) over months of unmistakably opposite character per decade—excess of cold

months counted negative. (Unremarkable decades score about 0. Extreme decade values of the index in Europe range from about +10 to —20.)

2. Summer wetness index. Each month (July and August only) with material evidence of drought counted 0, unremarkable months 0.5, months with material evidence of frequent rains and wetness counted 1. (Unremarkable decades score about 10. Extreme decade values of the index in Europe range from about 4 to 17.)

For the epoch since regular weather observations became available, these were preferred for identifying notably wet or dry, mild or severe months.

The earliest and longest records here used are a daily weather register from Hesse 1621-50 (Lenke, 1960), central England temperatures from 1680 to 1952 (Manley, 1953, and private communication), rainfall in England and Wales from 1727 (Nicholas and Glasspoole, 1931) and in Holland from 1735 (Labrijn, 1945).

The problem of welding the earlier and later series of months considered notable into a single series was tackled by studying overlap periods of several decades for which both instrument measurements and descriptive chronicles were to hand. The overall numbers of months marked as displaying noteworthy anomalies remained satisfactorily steady between 1100 and 1550 at about one-third of all the winter months and 40 per cent of the Julys and Augusts. (The frequency of months noted in the Russian chronicles was an exception, being fairly steadily about half that for more western longitudes and tending to concentrate on months of disastrous severity: index values obtained from this source were therefore doubled to assimilate them to the others.) Rather higher frequency of months noted as extreme between about 1550 and 1700 was thought more likely due to the peculiar climate of that time than to relaxed criteria of extreme weather. The criteria adopted in using the instrument records of the period since 1680 to 1800 therefore were: (*a*) winter months counted as mild or severe if the temperature anomaly exceeded the standard deviation from the longest period mean; (*b*) Julys and Augusts counted as wet or dry if the rainfall measured was within the highest or lowest quintile.

The possibility of a slight "change of zero" in the 1700s or early 1800s must, however, still be borne in mind. With this reservation Fig. 11 displays the course of the summer and winter climate of Europe in different longitudes near 50 °N., by decades, from 1100 to 1959.

All longitudes are not always affected by the same anomalies at the same time. Correlation coefficients between the winter index values in Britain and Germany and in Britain and Russia 1100-1750 were respectively +0.45 and +0.31 : these both appear statistically significant at the 1 per cent level, but in both cases coefficients with reversed sign were found in some centuries during this period.

Comparisons of the winter severity index in Europe with an indicator of winter character in Japan—the freezing dates of Lake Suwa (Arakawa, 1954)—produced no significant correlation coefficients.

There seems (Fig. 11) to have been more tendency for like character of the winters, and of the summers, in all European longitudes between 1150 and 1250—in the case of the winters as late as 1350 or after—and since 1850 than at most other times. These have been the periods of most predominance of mild winters, presumably with westerly winds sweeping far across Europe, and good summers. The predominance of mild winters, greatest between 1150 and 1300, but also noteworthy in certain earlier and later periods (Fig. 12 also), was punctuated by individual decades with cold winters everywhere in Europe near 50° N. There were roughly half-century intervals between the decades with most mild winters, also between those with most cold winters—perhaps another suggestion of a periodicity in the occurrence of blocking anticyclones over North Europe.

Between 1550 and 1700 all hints of this oscillation are lost owing to the heavy preponderance of cold winters, especially in Russia and Britain. This distribution suggests that the westerlies were weak and that northerly windstreams over the Russian plain and over the Norwegian Sea were important—the latter would tend to explain the very rapid worsening of the ice situation in Iceland and Greenland waters, especially after 1550. Preponderance of wet summers (Julys and Augusts) in all European longitudes near 50° N. between 1550 and 1700 is also noticeable.

Examining the smoothed trends of summer wetness and winter severity indices presented by the running five-decade (half-century) average values in Fig. 12,

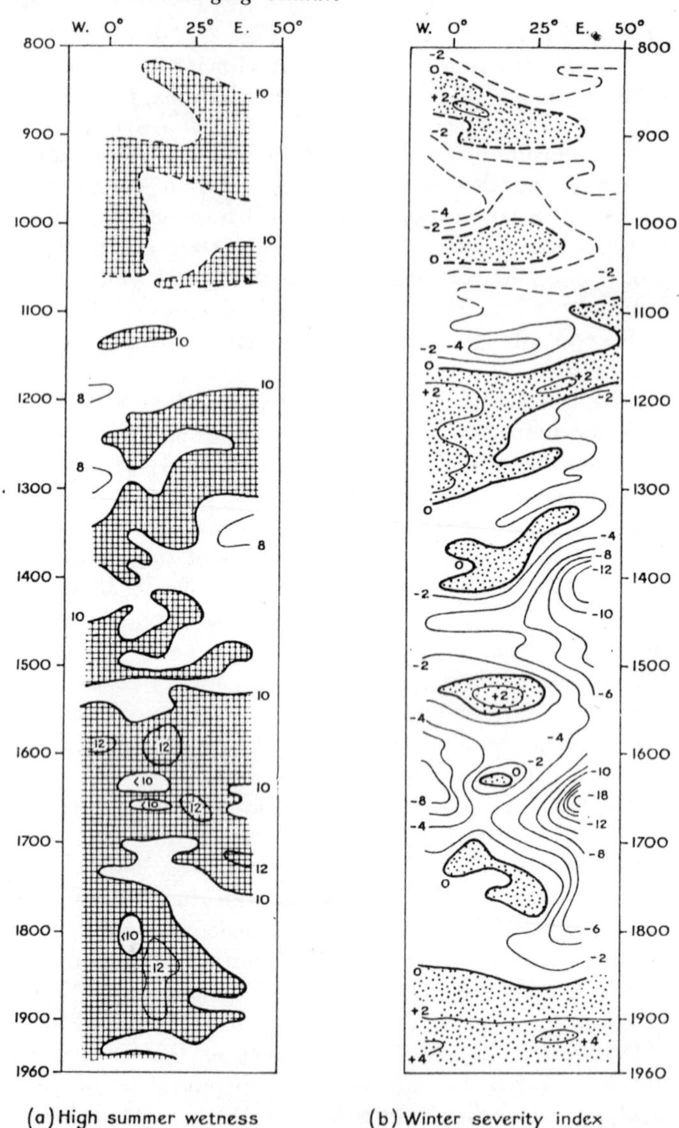

(a) High summer wetness index.

(b) Winter severity index

Fig. 12. Summer wetness and winter severity indices in different European longitudes near 50° N. (overlapping half-century means) from 800 to 1959. Cross hatching indicates excess of wet Julys and Augusts. Dots indicate excess of mild Decembers, Januarys and Februarys.

one apparently discovers a general westward progress across Europe of a region of maximum summer wetness between 1250 and 1400-1500 and a corresponding eastward progress during the climatic recovery between about 1700 and 1900. Also shown is a general westward retreat from about 1200 onwards of the predominance of mild winters and a return movement (more clearly seen from the isopleths for predominance of cold winters withdrawing east) between 1700 and 1900. There are complexities of detail which tend to obscure these trends, but summer and winter sequences—the one of temperature, the other of a different element—appear to run parallel during both the climatic decline preceding the Little Ice Age and the recovery afterwards. Moreover the fact that any semblance of an orderly progression should be revealed by such primitive data may seen surprising and possibly justifies one in disregarding complexities.

Viewed in this light, the epochs 1550-1700 and about 1000-1200 appear as times of standstill, when the trend was halted and whatever fluctuations went on affected all European longitudes alike. These are perhaps properly regarded as the culminating periods respectively of the Little Ice Age and of the warm climate (secondary optimum) before it.

Fig. 12 even suggests a still earlier period, between 800 or earlier and 900, of eastward spread across Europe of a region of predominantly mild winters and dry summers. Six to ten notably severe winters seem to have occurred rather earlier, between 764 and 860, mostly still more remarkable in the eastern Mediterranean (ice on the Adriatic, the Bosphorus, Dardanelles and Nile); there was apparently only one more similar occurrence afterwards—in 1011—until the 1600s.

Severe winter weather in Europe is related to a westward and southward shift (or expansion) of the cold trough in the upper westerlies normally found nowadays over eastern Europe; mild winter weather is similarly closely related to the East Atlantic warm ridge (Fig. 9). Wetness of the summers depends not only on proximity to the depression track (around 62° N. in this sector nowadays), but tends to be most pronounced in the region of the upper cold trough normally discernible over Europe and immediately east thereof (Fig. 10).

Westward and eastward movements of the features displayed in Figs. 11 and 12 before and after the Little Ice Age are such as might accompany respectively shortening and lengthening of the waves in the upper westerlies downstream from a more nearly anchored ridge in the vicinity of the Rocky Mountains.

The experiment was therefore tried of measuring the apparent longitudinal displacements of the features identified on Figs. 11 and 12, with the following results:

Winter: in 1550-1700 maximum winter mildness some 20°-30° longitude west of today's and in 1150-1300 once more about today's position.

Summer: in 1550-1700 greatest predominance of wet Julys and Augusts 15°-30° longitude farther west than in recent times; before 1300 farther east then nowadays.

Table 1 summarizes measurements, and directly derived estimates, of parameters relating to the circulation over the North Atlantic sector.

The latitude of the strongest flow at the 500 mb. level is taken as the middle of the zone of closest packed isopleths in the neighbourhood of the point of inflexion (between trough and ridge) in mid-Atlantic. The latitude of the depression track is taken over the eastern Atlantic between about 20° W. and 10° E., in order to be related to the 500 mb. measurement yet more indicative of weather in temperate Europe.

The longitude of the European upper trough is measured in 45°-55° N., the same latitude zone to which the summer wetness and winter severity indices (Figs. 11 and 12) apply. The estimates of wave length, and of change of wave length from the modern normal, allow for a smaller sympathetic westward or eastward movement of the cold trough near the Atlantic margin of North America.

These measurements appear to admit the solutions in terms of change of latitude and/or intensity of the main circulation features which are outlined in the following paragraphs:

LITTLE ICE AGE CULMINATING PERIOD 1550-1700

SUMMER

Either flow weakened by about 30 per cent or strongest flow shifted south by 5° or more. The likeliest solution, following the indications regarding intensity changes and latitude shifts on the charts around 1800 and earlier, including fragmentary charts for the 1690s, appears to be southward shift of the main flow by 4°-5°, with only

Table 1. Key parameters of the atmospheric circulation, North Atlantic sector

	Modern normal 1900-39 (1949-58 500 mb. values)	Extreme years in the early 1940s (partly after Scherhag)	Little Ice Age culminating period 1550-1700	Early Middle Age warm epoch 1000-1200
Summer (July)				
Latitude of strongest 500 mb. flow	48° N.	50°-52° N.		
Departure from modern normal	—	+3°		
Longitude of European trough at 500 mb.	10°-20° E.	15°-20° E.	0°-10° W.[1]	
Departure from modern normal	—	Slight +	—15° to 30°	+10
Wave length change implied (°longitude)	—	+6°	(—10° to 20°)[2]	(+5° to 10°)
Wave length (°longitude)	78°	84°	(65°-70°)	(83°-88°)
Latitude of depression track	62° N.	65° N.		
Departure from modern normal	—	+3°		
Winter (January)				
Latitude of strongest 500 mb. flow	60° N.	55°-60° N.		
Departure from modern normal	—	—3°		
Longitude of European trough at 500 mb.	40°-50° E.	25°-33° E.	10°-20° E.[1]	
Departure from modern normal	—	—15°	—20° to 30°	Slight
Wave length change implied (°longitude)	—	—10° to 15°	(—20°)	
Wave length (°longitude)	120°-130°	110°	(100°-110°)	
Latitude of depression track	68° N.	65° N.		
Departure from normal	—	—3°		

1. Values read off the charts for the period around 1800.
2. Values in parentheses are derived estimates; all other values measured from the charts and diagrams.

trivial, if any, weakening of the summer circulation in the North Atlantic sector.

Main depression track was 57°-60° N. over the eastern Atlantic sector, possibly rather south of 57° N. over the ocean itself, but reaching 60° N. over Russia.

There should have been also a change in prevailing wave number, five to six waves having been normal around the hemisphere, possibly at times a good fit with a five-wave pattern which might become correspondingly firmly established. (The modern normal wave length is intermediate between that required for a four- and a five-wave pattern.)

Using the indications of Fig. 10 (*b*), we may judge the likeliest positions for summer cold troughs in middle latitudes in a five-wave pattern during the Little Ice Age epoch as (*a*) near 60°-70° W.; (*b*) 0°-10° W.; (*c*) 60°-70° E.; (*d*) 130°-140° E.; (*e*) 130° W.

WINTER

Either flow weakened by about 30 per cent or strongest flow shifted south by 5° or more. The likeliest solution seems to be that the flow was in general weakened over the North Atlantic by 5-10 per cent in winter and the mainstream shifted south by 3°-5°.

Main depression track was 63°-65° N. It is obvious from the charts around 1800 that this position of the main depression track allowed for a scatter with many more depressions than now entering the Mediterranean.

There should have been a change of wave-number around the hemisphere from the twentieth-century predominance of three-wave patterns at the times of most vigorous winter circulation, especially in January, to one where four-wave patterns were commoner, often even at the peak intensity of the winter circulation. (This is a feature which has tended to reappear in recent years, in the weaker and southward displaced circulations in several winters of the 1940s and 1950s.)

Using the indications of Fig. 9 (*b*), we may judge the likeliest positions for winter cold troughs in middle latitudes in the Little Ice Age epoch as: (*a*) 80°-90° W.; (*b*) 10°-20° E.; (*c*) 110°-130° E.; (*d*) more variable in position, but probably tending to be near enough to North America at times to reduce the Rocky Mountains warm ridge to insignificance. (This is a suggestion which might explain an apparent tendency even in the nineteenth century for severe winters to occur simultaneously in western and eastern North America and Europe.)

EARLY MIDDLE AGES WARM EPOCH 1000-1200

SUMMER

Either flow 30 per cent stronger than now or strongest flow shifted north by 3° to 5° from the modern normal. The likeliest solution seems again to be that the main anomaly was one of latitude position.

Main depression track over the eastern Atlantic was 65°-67° N. Presumably there was considerable similarity with 1959 and the best summers of the 1930s and 1940s in Europe (1933-35, 1941-43, 1945, 1947, 1949); the marked aridity of the 1100s in Europe probably means that the depression track was then a degree or two still farther north, passing near the east coast of Greenland and generally near 70° N. in the European sector. This would be consistent with the suggestion of little floating ice on the Arctic seas south of 80° N. and an anticyclone belt over Europe, whilst Mediterranean summer droughts should have experienced more breaks than nowadays.

WINTER

The evidence suggests a more northerly position of the depression track than now, perhaps allowing the same wave length as nowadays with a rather weaker atmospheric circulation. If we assume that a depression track in the Barents Sea was common owing to the less extent of ice, there may have been periods when a two-wave pattern was attained at the climax of the winter circulation vigour. The cold belt across Europe near 50° N. (Figs. 11 and 12) in the winters of the 1100s would then be most readily attributed to easterly winds with a long land track, as would also occur in other years and decades when blocking anticyclones were prominent. This pattern would probably imply more rain-giving depressions in the Mediterranean than normal in the winters of the twentieth century, but also less extreme cold than at those times when northerly outbreaks over Russia and the Norwegian-Greenland Sea were commoner (e.g., around A.D. 800 and 1600.

Botanical studies, which already suggest an important increase of total rainfall in northern Europe around 1200-1300 and a drier time between 1700 and 1800 (anticyclonic summers and winters in central eastern Europe indicated by the charts of 1750-1800), may be able to add more firm indications of the prevailing temperatures, rainfall and latitudes of depression tracks in different centuries. Further evidence might also come from similar studies of documentary records of seasonal weather character in the latitudes of the Mediterranean and northern Europe and in the Far East, whilst archaeological studies in the Americas may have a part to play.

TENTATIVE GENERAL CONCLUSIONS

The climates of the different epochs here discussed are amenable to interpretation largely in terms of (*a*) intensity changes and (*b*) latitude shifts of the main limbs of the zonal circulation, accompanied by appropriate changes of wave length and trough positions in the belt of westerlies. The latitude and longitude changes must have had direct consequences in modifying climates in every latitude zone and have perhaps been more conspicuous than the changes of circulation strength.

There is some evidence for supposing that both the circulation in general and the radiation available were weakened during the Little Ice Age A.D. 1430-1850 by a few per cent in the Northern Hemisphere and perhaps by about 1-2 per cent over the world, most probably due to volcanic dust. Correspondingly, it might be reasonable to suppose that the circulation in general, and (more doubtfully) the radiation available, were slightly above their twentieth-century strength in the early Middle Ages (especially 1000-1200), though it would be safer to assume that they were not far different from modern values. Possibly the chief difference between the modern situation and that of the early Middle Ages warm epoch and of the major post-glacial climatic optimum around 5000-3000 B.C. lies in the duration of these warm epochs and the sea temperatures consequently attained in the Atlantic and Arctic.

As the energy of the circulation increased (at least between 1800 and recent decades) the Northern Hemisphere circulation seems in general to have shifted poleward, perhaps mainly controlled by the displacement of the main thermal gradient accompanying the shrinking Arctic ice and winter snow cover on land.

It is clear that the extended Arctic ice and cold water

of the period around A.D. 1800 and earlier modified the Atlantic sector circulation, causing peculiarly great latitude shifts there and even local strengthening of the circulation and thermal gradients near the southern extremities of the extended cold troughs—in an epoch when over wider regions the energy was reduced.

Correspondingly, in the early Middle Ages warm epoch, when the energy generally available may be supposed to have been greater (if only because of higher sea temperatures), the circulation seems to have been not always stronger than now (and possibly sometimes weaker) in northern Europe. The likeliest reason for this seems to be the remoteness at that time of the Arctic ice limit. Indeed, the patterns of that time may have some bearing upon what would happen in various latitudes if the Arctic ice were artifically disposed of.

When the general atmospheric circulation increases in energy the strongest (most disturbing) effects should be expected in those sectors where a broad quasi-permanent ice or cold-water surface has protruded farthest towards low latitudes. At times very strong circulations and very abnormal patterns might then be produced and become very variable from year to year if the protrusion of Arctic ice were to break up or shrink rapidly. The peculiar climatic course of the 1830s in the North Atlantic and neighbouring regions should probably be viewed in this light. The decade was one of extreme variations between persistent blocking and intense zonal circulations, most strongly developed in unusually high latitudes, so that the low values of some of the intensity indices in that decade may be misleading —indices taken in what are at most other times the best positions being just then unrepresentative.

Wexler has pointed out that any long-period changes in the insolation available should produce a much quicker response over the great land masses than in the oceans and regions of quasi-permanent ice. This seems to be supported by our study of the state of the general circulation around 1800, when a trend towards increasing energy may (according to some indications) have been already under way for about a century, and we observe a peculiarly great equatorward displacement of the circulation over the North Atlantic Ocean.

Peculiar instability of the climate in the Atlantic-European sector at various times between 1250 and 1550, with harsh alternations of wet and dry, warm and cold years in various (especially eastern) parts of Europe in the 1300s and (especially) 1400s, may perhaps be regarded as a phenomenon of the trend towards colder climate and increasing areas of snow and ice surface crudely corresponding to the vicissitudes of the 1830s during the recovery trend.

Clearly general trends of circulation strength must be judged by measures of the circulation in many different parts of the world and allowance made for passing phases in which misleading effects arise in regions affected by persistent ice or cold water—especially the North Atlantic.

To judge the position of the most recent decades in relation to longer-term trends it may be necessary to consider whether the appearance of rhythmic changes of wave position, wave length and circulation intensity affecting Europe—rises to maxima around 1100 and 1900-30 and a minimum around 1650—represents some long-period oscillation. So far the evidence seems against this, since the fluctuation was probably asymmetric in time—the decrease spread over 300-500 years, the recovery nearly complete in 150-200 years—and the Southern Hemisphere was probably not affected. Nevertheless there is a good deal of evidence that the general circulation has for the time being fallen away from its maximum intensity around 1900-30—evidently not due to volcanic dust—and the trend of the North Atlantic circulation towards lower latitudes in winter (and probably other seasons) needs watching and explaining. In this connexion the case made out for solar weather relationships by Willett (1949, 1961) and Baur (1956, 1958) cannot be ignored.

BIBLIOGRAPHY

AHLMANN, H. W. 1944. Nutidens Antarktis och istidens Skandinavien, *Geol. Fören. Stockh. Föhr.*, vol. 66, p. 635-654.

ALISSOW, B. P.; DROSDOW, O. A.; RUBINSTEIN, E. S. 1956. *Lehrbuch der Klimatologie.* Berlin, Deutscher Verlag der Wissenschaften.

ARAKAWA, H. 1954. Five centuries of freezing dates of Lake Suwa in central Japan, *Arch. Met., Wien*, B, vol. 6, p. 152-166.

——. 1956. Climatic change as revealed by the blooming dates of the cherry blossoms at Kyoto, *J. Met.*, vol. 13, p. 599-600.

——. 1957. Climatic change as revealed by data from the Far East, *Weather* (London), vol. 12, p. 46-51.

AUER, V. 1958. *The Pleistocene of Fuego-Patagonia.* Part II : *History of the flora and vegetation.* Helsinki. (Suom. Tiedeakat., Geologia-Geographica.)

——. 1959. *The Pleistocene of Fuego-Patagonia. Part III : Shoreline displacements.* Helsinki. (Suom. Tiedeakat., Geologia-Geographica.)

——. 1960. The Quaternary history of Fuego-Patagonia, *Proc. Roy. Soc.*, B, vol. 152, p. 507-516.

AURROUSSEAU, M. 1958. Surface temperatures of the Australian seas, *J. and Proc. Roy. Soc. N.S.W.* (Sydney), vol. 92, part IV, p. 104-114.

BAUR, F. 1956. *Physikalisch-statistische Regeln als Grundlagen für Wetter- und Witterungs-Vorhersagen*, vol. I. Frankfurt am Main, Akademische Verlagsgesellschaft.

——. 1958. *Physikalisch-statistische Regeln als Grundlagen für Wetter- und Witterungs-Vorhersagen*, vol. II.

BETIN, V. V. 1957. Ice conditions in the Baltic and its approaches and their long-term variations. *Gosudarst. Okeanogr. Inst. Trudy*, vol. 41, p. 54-125.

——. 1959. Variations in the state of the ice on the Baltic Sea and Danish Sound, *Gosudarst. Okeanogr. Inst. Trudy*, vol. 37, p. 3-13.

BRITTON, C. E. 1937. A meteorological chronology to A.D. 1450, *Geophys. Mem., Lond.*, no. 70. London, Meteorological Office.

BROOKS, C. E. P. 1949. *Climate through the ages.* 2nd ed. London, Ernest Benn.

BUCHINSKY, I. E. 1957. *The past climate of the Russian Plain.* 2nd ed. Leningrad, Gidrometeoizdat.

BUTZER, K. W. 1957*a*. Mediterranean pluvials and the general circulation of the Pleistocene, *Geogr. Ann., Stockh.*, vol. 39, p. 48-53.

——. 1957*b*. The recent climatic fluctuation in the lower latitudes and the general circulation of the Pleistocene, *Geogr. Ann., Stockh.*, vol. 39, p. 105-113.

——. 1958. Studien zum vor- und frühgeschichtlichen Landschaftswandel der Sahara, *Abh. math.-nat. Kl. Akad. Wiss. Mainz*, no. 1.

CALLENDAR, G. S. 1961. Temperature fluctuations and trends over the earth, *Quart. J. roy. met. Soc.*, vol. 87, p. 1-12.

CRANWELL, L. M.; VON POST, L. 1936. Post-Pleistocene pollen diagrams from the Southern Hemisphere. I : New Zealand, *Geogr. Ann., Stockh.*, vol. 18, p. 308-347.

CRARY, A. P. 1960. Arctic ice island and ice shelf studies, *Scientific studies at Fletcher's Ice Island, T-3 : 1952-1955. Geophysics Research Papers* (no. 63), vol. III, p. 1-37. Boston, Air Force Cambridge Research Center. (AFCRC-TR-59-232(3) ASTIA document no. AD-216815.)

CROMERTIE, George Earl of. 1712. An account of the mosses in Scotland, *Phil. Trans. Roy. Soc.*, vol. 27, p. 296-301.

EASTON, C. 1928. *Les hivers dans l'Europe occidentale.* Leyden, E. J. Brill.

EMILIANI, C. 1955. Pleistocene temperatures. *J. Geol.*, vol. 63, p. 538-579.

FAIRBRIDGE, R. W. 1961. Eustatic changes in sea level, *Physics and chemistry of the Earth*, vol. 4, p. 99-185. New York, London, Pergamon.

FINDLAY, A. G. 1884. *Directory for the South Pacific.* 5th ed. London, Richard Holmes Laurie.

FIRBAS, F.; LOSERT, H. 1949. Untersuchungen über die Entstehung der heutigen Waldstufen in den Sudeten, *Planta* (Berlin), vol. 36, p. 478-506.

FLOHN, H. 1952. Allgemeine Zirkulation und Paläoklimatologie, *Geologische Rundschau* (Stuttgart), vol. 40, p. 153-179.

GAMS, H. 1937. Aus der Geschichte der Alpenwalder, *Zeitschrift des deutsch. und österreich. Alpenvereins* (Stuttgart), vol. 68, p. 157-170.

GODWIN, H. 1954. Recurrence surfaces, *Danmarks Geologiske Undersögelse. II : Raekke* (Copenhagen), no. 80.

——. 1956. *History of the British flora.* Cambridge, University Press.

——; SUGGATE, R. P.; WILLIS, E. H. 1958. Radio-carbon dating of the eustatic rise in ocean level, *Nature, Lond.*, vol. 181, p. 1518-1519.

GODWIN, H.; WILLIS, E. H. 1959. Radio-carbon dating of pre-historic wooden trackways, *Nature, Lond.*, vol. 184, p. 490-491.

GRIFFIN, J. B. 1961. Some correlations of climatic and cultural change in eastern North American prehistory, *New York Academy of Sciences, Symposium on solar variations, climatic changes and related geophysical problems.* (Publication pending.)

HARRINGTON, H. J.; MCKELLAR, I. C. 1958. A radio-carbon date for penguin colonization of Cape Hallett, Antarctica, *N.Z. J. Geol. Geophys.*, vol. 1, p. 571-576.

HENNIG, R. 1904. Katalog bemerkenswerter Witterungsereignisse von den ältesten Zeiten bis zum Jahre 1800, *Abh. preuss. met. Inst.* (Berlin), vol. II, no. 4.

KRAUS, E. B. 1954. Secular changes in the rainfall regime of southeast Australia, *Quart. J. roy. met. Soc.*, vol. 80, p. 591-601.

LABRIJN, A. 1945. Het klimaat van Nederland gedurende de laatste twee en een halve eeuw, *Kon. Nederl. Met. Inst., Meded. Verh.* ('s Gravenhage), vol. 49, no. 102.

LAHR, E. 1950. *Un siècle d'observations météorologiques appliquées à l'étude du climat luxembourgeois.* Luxembourg, Bourg-Bourger Verlag.

LAMB, H. H. 1953. British weather around the year, *Weather*, vol. 8, p. 131-136, 176-182.

——. 1959. Our changing climate, past and present, *Weather*, vol. 14, p. 299-318.

——; JOHNSON, A. I. 1959. Climatic variation and observed changes in the general circulation, *Geogr. Ann.* (Stockholm), vol. 41, p. 94-134.

LENKE, W. 1960. Klimadaten 1621-1650 nach Beobachtungen des Landgrafen Herman IV von Hessen, *Ber. dtsch. Wetterdienstes*, no. 63.

LINK, F.; LINKOVA, Z. 1959. Méthodes astronomiques dans la climatologie historique, *Studia geoph. geod.* (Prague), vol. 3, p. 43-61.

MANLEY, G. The mean temperature of central England, 1698-1952, *Quart. J. roy. met. Soc.*, vol. 79, p. 242-261.

MATTHES, F. E. 1939. Report of committee on glaciers, *Trans. Amer. geophys. Un.*, part I, p. 518-520.

MÜLLER, K. 1953. *Geschichte des badischen Weinbaus.* Laar in Baden, von Moritz Schauenburg.

MURRAY MITCHELL, J. 1961. Recent secular changes of global temperature, *New York Academy of Sciences, Symposium on solar variations, climatic changes and related geophysical problems.* (Publication pending.)

NICHOLAS, F. J.; GLASSPOOLE, H. 1931. General monthly rainfall over England and Wales, 1727 to 1931, *Brit. Rainf.*, p. 299-306.

PETTERSSEN, S. 1949. Changes in the general circulation associated with the recent climatic variation, *Geogr. Ann.* (Stockholm), vol. 36, p. 212-221.

PRIVETT, D. W.; FRANCIS, J. R. D. 1959. The movement of sailing ships as a climatological tool. *The Mariner's Mirror.* vol. 45, p. 292-300. (Quarterly journal of the Society for Nautical Research, London.)

SCHERHAG, R. 1950. Die Schwankungen der allgemeinen Zirkulation in den letzten Jahrzehnten, *Ber. dtsch. Wetterdienstes, U.S. Zone*, no. 12, p. 40-44. (Bad Kissingen).

——. 1960. *Einführung in die Klimatologie.* Braunschweig, Westermann.

SCHWARZBACH, M. 1960. *Das Klima der Vorzeit.* Stuttgart, Ferdinand Enke.

——. 1961. The climatic history of Europe and North America, in : *Descriptive palaeo-climatology* (Nairn). New York, London, Interscience Publishers.

STEVEN, H. M. 1959. *The native pinewoods of Scotland.* Edinburgh, Oliver & Boyd.

STOIBER, R. E. ; LYONS, J. B. ; ELBERTY, W. T. ; MCCREAHAN, R. H. 1960. Petrographic evidence on the source area and age of T-3, *Scientific studies at Fletcher's Ice Island, T-3 : 1952-55. Geophysics Research Papers* (no. 63), vol. III, p. 78, Boston, Air Force Cambridge Research Center. (AFCRC-TR-59-232(3) ASTIA document no. AD-216815.)

THORARINSSON, S. ; EINARSSON, T. ; KJARTANSSON, G. 1959. On the geology and geomorphology of Iceland, *Geogr. Ann.* (Stockholm). vol. 41, p. 135-169.

VANDERLINDEN, E. 1924. Chronique des événements météorologiques en Belgique jusqu'en 1834, *Mém. Acad. R. Belg.*, 2e série, vol. 5.

WAGNER, A. 1940. *Klima-änderungen und Klimaschwankungen.* Braunschweig, Vieweg.

WALLÉN, C. C. 1950. Recent variations in the general circulation as related to glacier retreat in northern Scandinavia, *Geofis. pura appl.* (Milan), vol. 18, p. 3-6.

——. 1953. The variability of summer temperature in Sweden and its connection with changes in the general circulation, *Tellus*, vol. 5, p. 157-178.

WEST, R. G. 1960. The Ice Age, *Advanc. Sci., Lond.*, vol. 16, p. 428-440.

WEXLER, H. 1956. Variations in insolation, general circulation and climate, *Tellus*, vol. 8, p. 480-494.

WILLETT, H. C. 1949. Long-period fluctuations of the general circulation of the atmosphere, *J. Met.*, vol. 6, p. 34-50.

——. 1960. Temperature trends of the past century, *Royal Meteorological Society, Centenary Proceedings*, p. 195-206.

——. 1961. Review of " Atlas of planetary solar climate with sun-tide indices of solar radiation and global insolation " (Bollinger), *Bull. Amer. met. Soc.*, vol. 42, p. 303-304.

YAMAMOTO, T. 1956. On the climatic change in Japan and its surroundings. *Proceedings Eighth Pacific Science Congress 1953, Quezon City, Philippine Islands*, vol. 2A, p. 1113-1128.

ZEUNER, F. E. 1958. *Dating the past.* 4th ed., London, Methuen.

FOUR

Mapping methods applied to the study of climatic variations and vicissitudes*

Climate is not invariant, even over periods that matter to living people. Among some people an impression of constancy may have been gained from the view of our climate expressed by Italian visitors, whether 2,000 or 500 years ago. That is because the relative difference between the Italian and English climate has probably remained about the same. One also needs to consider what would be the views of a 'traveller through time' who knew this country well 2,000 years ago, or even 20 to 40 years ago, and came back today. In some respects he could notice changes.

Maps – or rather map sequences, presenting, as it were, a set of snapshot pictures of our weather and wind circulation taken at different times – look like making a great contribution to the study and understanding of this problem. This is a case in which maps, far from being for immediate impact only, constitute a serious research tool for prolonged study and from which measurements of fundamental quantities (gradients, flow, position and orientation) can be made.

Map methods and statistical methods are complementary, though they may with advantage be married together and used conjointly. Statistical methods are adapted to describing briefly all that is necessary about a collective (population) of observations that is randomly distributed with respect to some central line, and they may be able to do this on the basis of even a 10 per cent or smaller sample. As is well known, this is particularly useful in the study of the distribution of errors in experimental measurements. Map methods serve to throw light upon the law (or influences) that controls a particular non-random geographical distribution. Maps may be used to search for the factors that control the distribution or to illustrate them when found. To do this, however, something approaching a 100 per cent survey of the distribution may be necessary unless the governing law is a simple one. For research inevitably a strong discipline is required. Hitherto the necessary rules that must be followed in mapping distributions if intelligible results are to be obtained have not been as clearly evolved as in statistics. This is essential. Routines alone, however, will not solve problems. For either mapping or statistical treatments to be fruitful the problems must be clearly conceived and correctly posed.

Analysis of climatic variations has been furthered (Lamb and Johnson, 1959, 1961) by defining certain basic standard procedures in presenting the data on maps. The practices evolved could have wide applicability not only to weather phenomena but probably to phenomena of all kinds where the geographical distribution is

* Lecture given in St John's College, Oxford on 3 October 1963 at the Oxford Symposium on Experimental Cartography and reproduced here by kind permission of the Delegates of the Clarendon Press.

intelligible and important. The greatest gain is to be reaped in cases, like that here described, where the distribution is governed by physical laws and processes that are at least partly understood. When the data are particularly sparse, as in parts of the present study, representation of the probable distribution over wide intervals in the data may still be successful in so far as physical processes determine a field that is free of sharply localized features.

When the requirements defined below are observed, mapping methods can make a great contribution to clear thinking about fundamental problems of causation and interrelationship. The procedures described are also convenient in practical use in indicating a definable standard of reliability of the map.

Basic requirements in mapping climatic elements or other phenomena which vary with time

1. The maps must relate to some datum period, such as a particular span of years, which should in all cases be specified.

This requirement applies to climatic maps and tables alike, but has seldom been observed hitherto. Table 1 below is a sample array of climatic data for different recent periods and shows how the content may be affected by the period chosen.

TABLE 1. *Sample differences between recent periods of years.*

Period	*Average number of weeks in the year with sea-ice at the coasts of Iceland*	*Av. daily max. temp. in London (Kew) in January* (° C)	*Av. daily min. temp. in London (Kew) in January* (° C)	*Av. daily max. temp. in London (Kew) in July* (° C)	*Av. daily max. temp. at Toronto in July* (° C)
1871–1900	9	6·0 (43° F)	1·2 (34° F)	21·7 (71° F)	20·3 (69° F)
1901–1930	4	7·4 (45° F)	1·8 (35° F)	22·4 (72° F)	20·9 (70° F)
1921–1950	1·5	6·9 (44° F)	2·1 (36° F)	22·7 (73° F)	21·5 (71° F)
1950–1959	4	6·5 (44° F)	2·1 (36° F)	21·7 (71° F)	21·9 (71° F)

2. The datum period must be long enough to cover a reasonable sample of shorter-term or random variations about the prevailing mean condition.

3. All elements or aspects of the climate mapped, and all parts of the map, should relate to the same period of years.

This stipulation is essential if the maps are to have any clear meaning as regards understanding of related events in terms of cause and effect, i.e. in terms of physical processes (for instance, rainfall in continental regions varying partly with prevalence of winds from the ocean).

4. Numerical estimates of the margin of probable error are likely to be required and their distribution over the area surveyed should be mapped and understood, as in all other scientific methods and experiments.

The vicissitudes of climate

Climate depends not only on the net gain or loss of energy in the balance of incoming and outgoing radiation, which are subject to regular and steady seasonal changes, but upon the vagaries of the circulations of the air and oceans which transport and therefore redistribute heat. Thus one year differs from another even in the great Saharan, Asian and Australian deserts and in the remotest central parts of Antarctica. Hence the need is widely recognized of assessing and mapping climatic risks – for example

(*i*) the frequency of particularly heavy falls of rain or snow;

(*ii*) the maximum (gust) wind speed, or the greatest and least annual rainfalls, to be expected at any given place once in 10, 20, 50, 100 or 1,000 years.

Maps of climatic risks of these kinds, and the statistical assessments on which they are based (see, for example, Brooks 1950 pp. 201–229 on 'Climatic Accidents'; also Court 1953), have been among the most useful developments in climatology in the

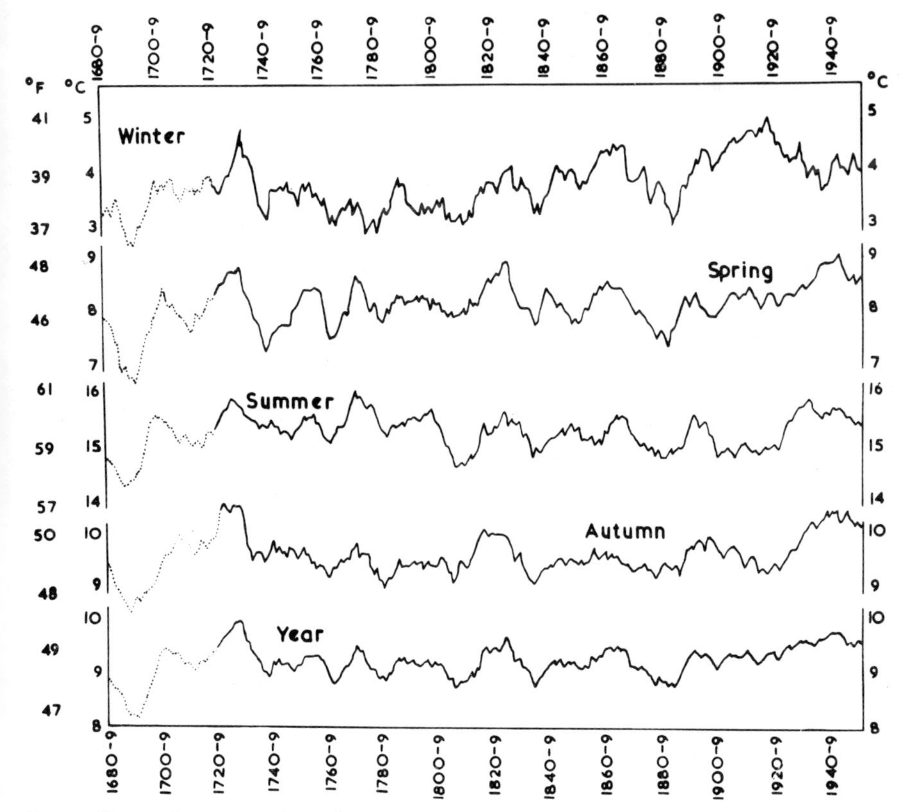

FIG. 1. Seasonal average values of air temperature in central England since 1680: 10-year running means. (By courtesy of Professor G. Manley (1961).)

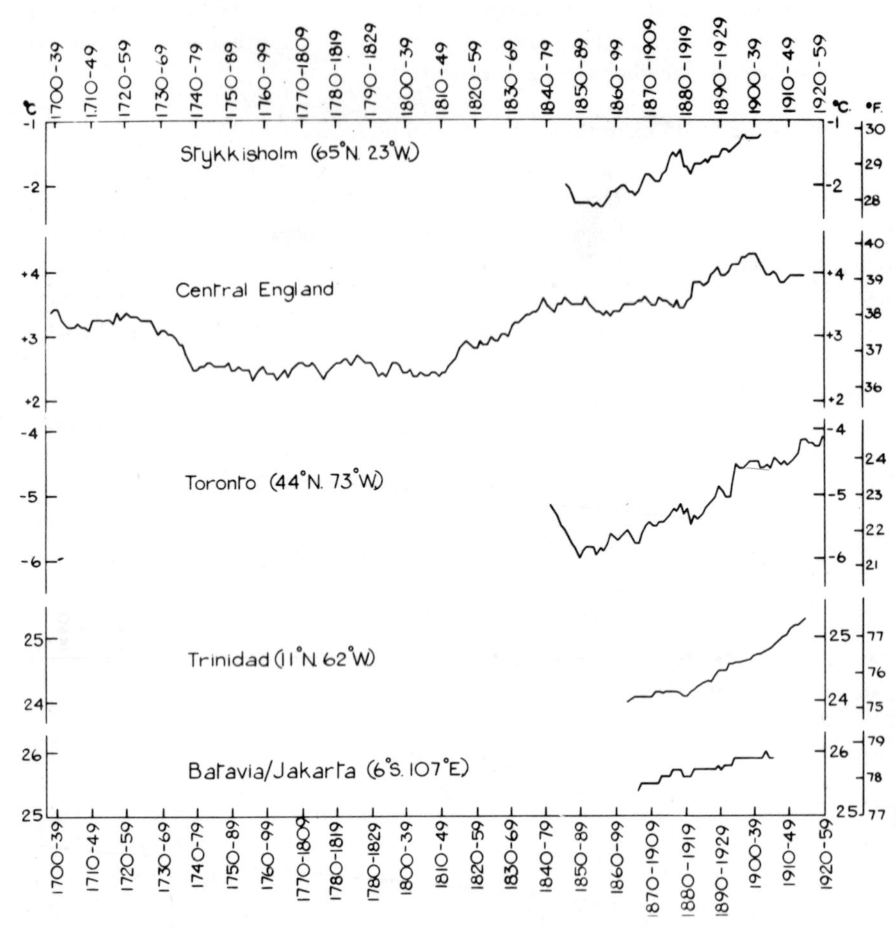

FIG. 2. Average air temperatures at places in Iceland, England, Canada and the tropical zone: 40-year running means.
(*a, above*) January.
(*b, opposite*) July.

last 30 years and are much used in the planning of engineering, industrial and agricultural projects. They also enter into military calculations.

The frequency assessments, however, customarily ignore trends and may ignore unrepresentativeness of the sample period studied – the 'reference period'. They are only valid within some term of years over which the climate remains effectively unchanged. Recent experience demonstrates that

(*i*) frequencies should never be stated as the number of recurrences to be expected in any period much longer than the reference period whose statistics were studied.* (Frequencies within any particular shorter interval of time are,

* This danger is sometimes concealed by statements given in terms of the 'return period'. If an event has occurred h times in N years, it appears to have a 'return period' of N/h years (which is shorter than the reference period). Use of this return period depends on the assumptions

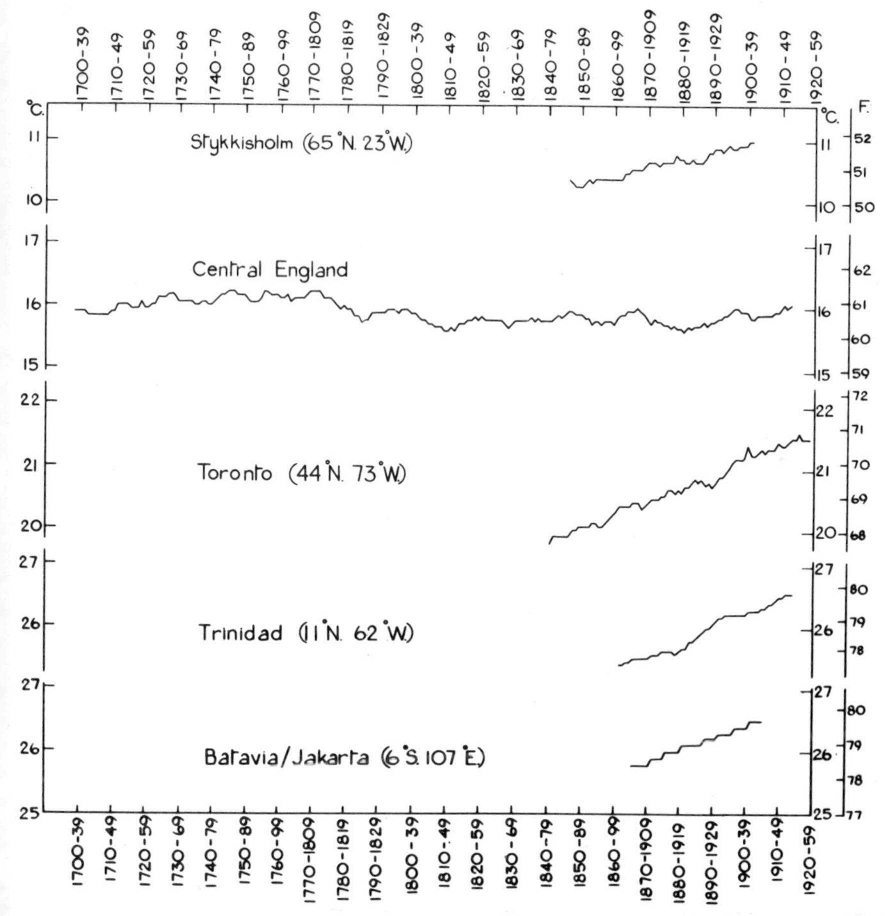

of course, subject to the incidence of variations related to the variance in the individual years.)

(*ii*) when the reference period consulted is short (a few years or even a decade or two), gross errors may arise in applying the same frequencies as predictions of future liability to the same phenomenon. Moreover, the margin of probable error in these cases cannot be assessed without knowledge of either the physical processes producing change or, at least, of a longer sample of previous history.

Two examples will illustrate the reality of these difficulties.

(*a*) that the average time interval between occurrences quoted is representative of the frequency over much longer periods of time, (*b*) that the reference period actually studied was long enough to be relevant to the length of the forecast period required, and (*c*) that the recurrences are governed by independent factors such that variations in the frequency effectively follow the laws of chance.

The third assumption in particular is seldom fully satisfied in meteorology, and assumptions (*a*) and (*b*) need scrutiny in every case.

Until 1954 insurance rates for shipping on the North Atlantic were based upon the known frequency of tropical hurricanes in the first 30 years of this century, averaging 5·7 a year. Heavy losses in 1954 prompted further inquiry, which showed that the frequency in each decade since 1930 had averaged 8 to 10 a year and that this applied also to the period 1887–96.

The winter of 1962–63 produced a lower average temperature in central England than any since 1740 – i.e. for 223 years. If the spacing indicated by this sample of years were typical, and the natures of successive years were quite unrelated, the expectation of experiencing two such winters running would be once in 223^2 (i.e. about 50,000) years. This is clearly not the correct solution to the real problem, since the last 50,000 years have seen both an ice age and an epoch warmer than now. Moreover, the immediately preceding 200 years before 1740 produced 5 or more winters of about the same severity; and there were 4 or 5 not much less severe within one decade, including the successive winters of 1694 and 95, 1697 and 98.

Survey of climatic fluctuations and changes

Ahlmann (1949) was one of the first to draw attention in this country to a notable change of world climates within our own times, such that one decade and even one century may differ significantly from another. Significance in this connexion may, and should, be assessed not only according to the conventional statistical measures of magnitude (as related to the standard deviation) but also in terms of the extent of the adaptations which the climatic changes provoke in the ranges of fauna and flora and in the human economy.

Figs. 1–7 illustrate the changes that have occurred in the average values of temperature and rainfall and things affected such as the extent of glaciers and the levels of rivers, lakes and inland seas. The longest available homogenized series of temperature observations are for central England (Manley 1958, 1961) and indicate (Fig. 1) progressive warming from the late-seventeenth to the present century, though with many fluctuations superimposed. Figs. 2(*a*) and (*b*) illustrate the rising trends over various shorter ranges of time of 40-year averages of temperature in January and July in Iceland, England, Canada and the tropics: among these samples only the level of July temperature in England has remained sensibly constant. Fig. 3 shows the results of computations of temperature changes over the whole world by J. M. Mitchell (1963). General melting and recession of glaciers (Fig. 4) in most parts of the world has accompanied the warming. World sea-level itself is estimated to have risen by about 1 cm. per decade since 1890, partly as a result of water gained from the glaciers and partly due to thermal expansion of the water.

Average rainfalls in sample regions are shown in Fig. 5. The figures for Southice at 82° S. on the Antarctic ice-cap in the Atlantic sector are derived from glaciological work by Lister (1959) on the Transantarctic Expedition. Changes at the South Pole appear similar to this. Those in the highest northern and southern latitudes increased up to some time in the present century, probably because warmer seas put more vapour into the air and, as we shall see, because of intensified transport by the winds. Intensification of the prevailing west-wind belts in the temperate zones and of the arid zone anticyclones turns out to be the probable explanation also

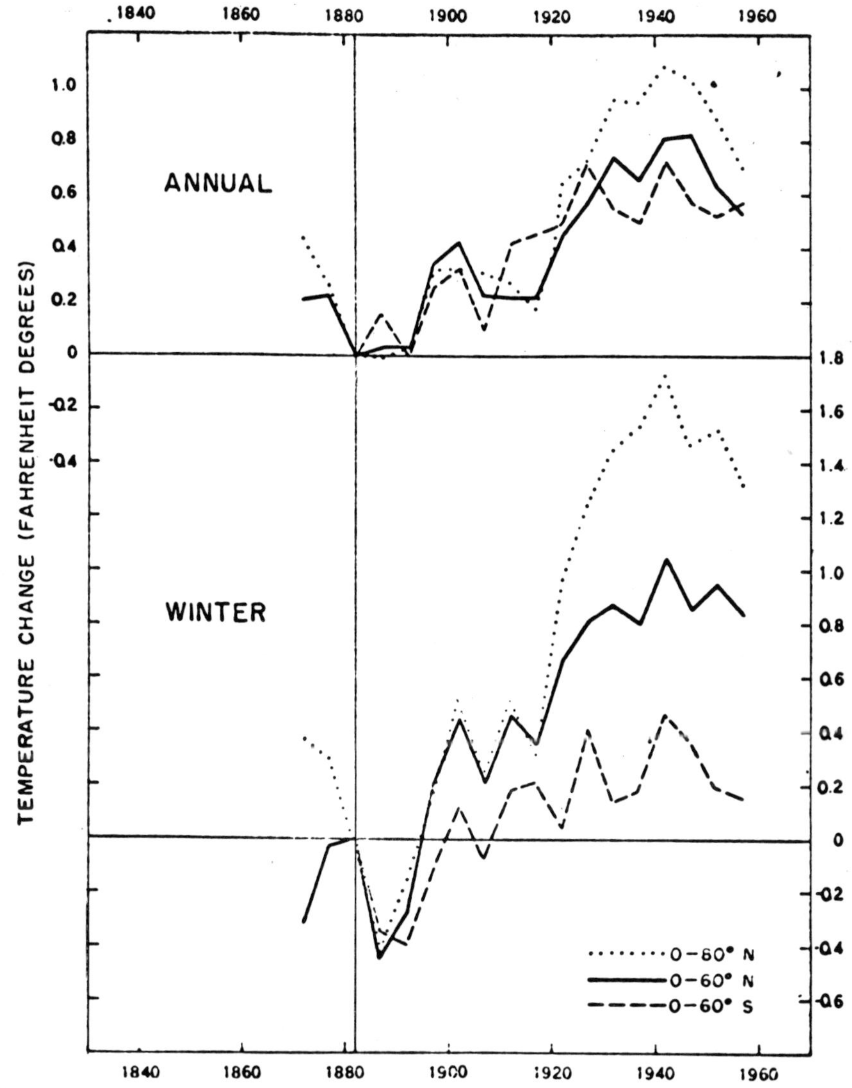

FIG. 3. Trends of mean temperature (5-year means) in northern and southern hemispheres (after J. M. Mitchell, jr.).

of low rainfall during the early part of the present century in the eastern parts of the continents and in most of the tropical/equatorial zone (Kraus 1958, 1963) and of a rainfall maximum in temperate lands exposed to westerly winds from the oceans. Most of the trends referred to in this article show signs of reversal since 1940.

Very long records of yearly rainfall in the Santiago district of Chile and of snow accumulation at Byrd Station 80° S in the Pacific sector show opposed trends (Fig. 6), which hint at position shifts with time of the sub-Antarctic belt of travelling storms and most abundant rainfall in the South Pacific. So we see the necessity of distinguishing between rainfall changes due to changes of intensity of the circulation and others due to shifts of main features of the circulation. There may additionally be long-term changes in the over-all rain yield over the world (or large parts of it) due to changes of sea and air temperature, evaporation rates and atmospheric moisture capacity.

Temperature changes may usefully be submitted to a similar analysis, in which circulation maps are needed to resolve intensity and position changes. A confusing feature of the long-term temperature changes observed in Europe is that, unlike surrounding regions, part of central Europe including Austria, Bohemia and

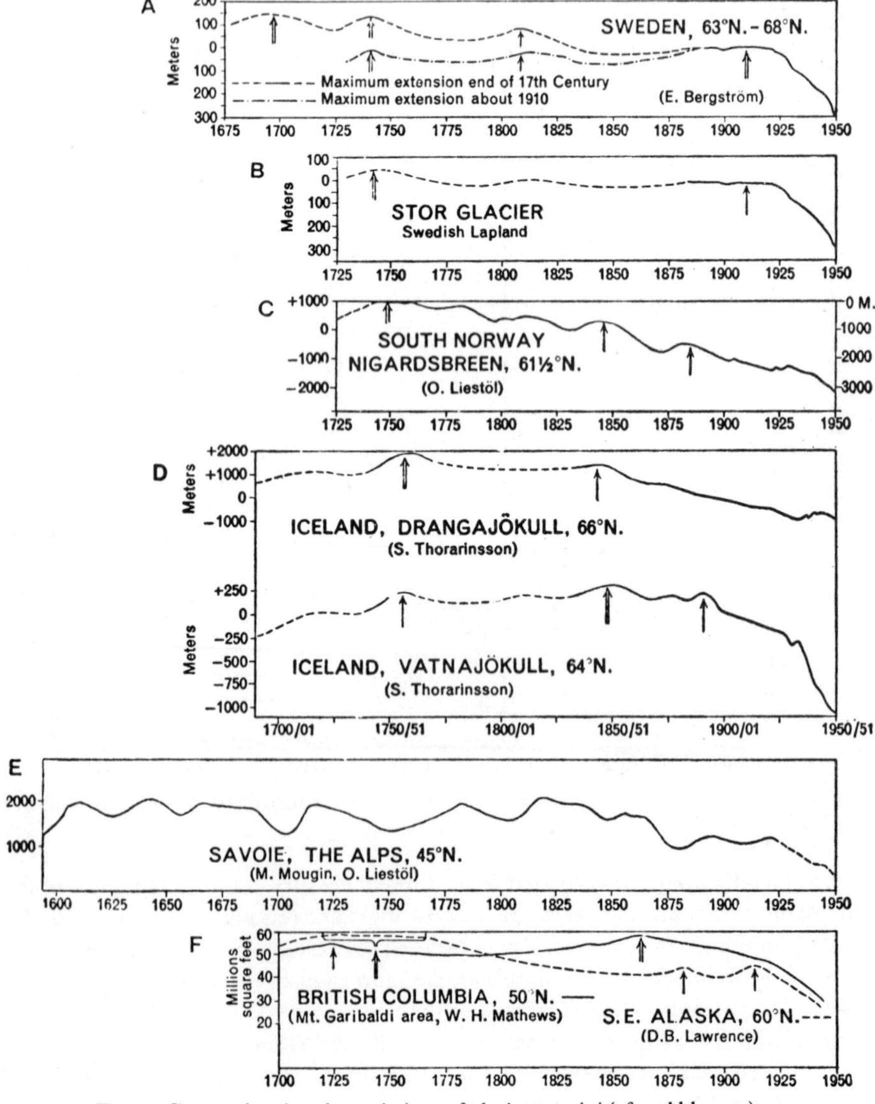

FIG. 4. Curves showing the variations of glacier termini (after Ahlmann).

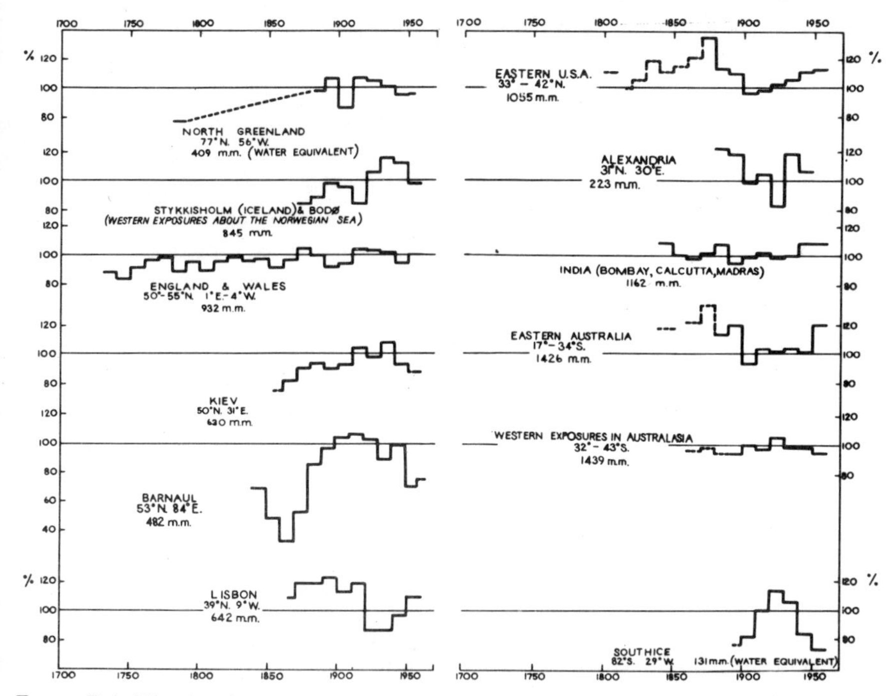

FIG. 5. Rainfall – decade averages as percentages of the 1900–39 average annual totals (quoted under the name of each place or area).

Bavaria seems to have had a warm epoch at the end of the eighteenth and in the early nineteenth century (Steinhauser 1961). This now appears likely to have been due to a configuration of the wind circulation giving southerly Alpine Föhn winds rather commonly just at that time – a topographical accident, unrepresentative of wider regions.

The levels of lakes in the U.S.A. and Sweden, of the Caspian Sea and of the annual discharge of the river Nile (Fig. 7) respond to the rainfall trends already described, least rainfall occurring in regions east of the great mountain ranges in the prevailing west-wind zone of temperate latitudes and in the arid and tropical zones during those recent decades when the anticyclone belt and the temperate westerlies were most strongly developed. Lake Chany east of Omsk in Siberia (55° N 78° E) shows the same trend (Dzerdzeevsky 1961). The trend of the level of the Dead Sea, however, differs and evidently responds to partly independent variations of the cyclonic activity in the eastern Mediterranean. The variations of water surface levels depicted in Fig. 6 have displaced shore lines in some places by several kilometres.

Mapping of climatic changes is to this extent linked with revisions of the actual maps of topography. There would be more extensive differences between the vegetation or land-use maps of one epoch and another, though in those cases the changes are not only due to climate. From now on changes in the levels of many lakes, and even of the Caspian Sea, may be due more to direct human manipulation than to climate.

The simplest form of map presentation of a geographical shift due to climatic change is illustrated by the normal – i.e. in this case, the commonest – positions of the limit of Arctic sea-ice (pack-ice) at its seasonal maximum extent in April around 1800 and in the present century (Fig. 8). Significant shifts of the average positions of the isotherms of sea-surface temperature have also occurred since 1800 (Lamb and Johnson 1959) as world air temperatures have risen and the Arctic ice receded. In these matters also there is evidence of some reversal since about 1940–50. In mid-February 1963 the ice in the Norwegian Sea and Barents Sea was actually the most extensive ever fully surveyed, probably resembling some of the worst years before 1840 (though certainly exceeded in the 1690s).

The recent widespread change of trends means that neither extrapolation nor a no-change hypothesis can be used with any confidence as a guide to the future.

No reasonable forecast can be made without some understanding of the physical processes at work. The dominant physical processes cannot be identified and surveyed unless the data on all aspects of the climate are arranged by period. To make the matter intelligible one must consider the distinctive total climate of a particular year or epoch.

The approach to interpretation of climatic changes

Arrangement of the observational data on maps (and, ideally, on vertical cross-section diagrams) is necessary to obtain a view of the spatial relationships and extent of the processes at work, corresponding to the time relationships already examined by graphs such as Figs. 1–7. Even where space relationships have been surmised (as in the previous section) these should be verified as reasonable by map studies – for instance, studies of short-term (including day-to-day) variations.

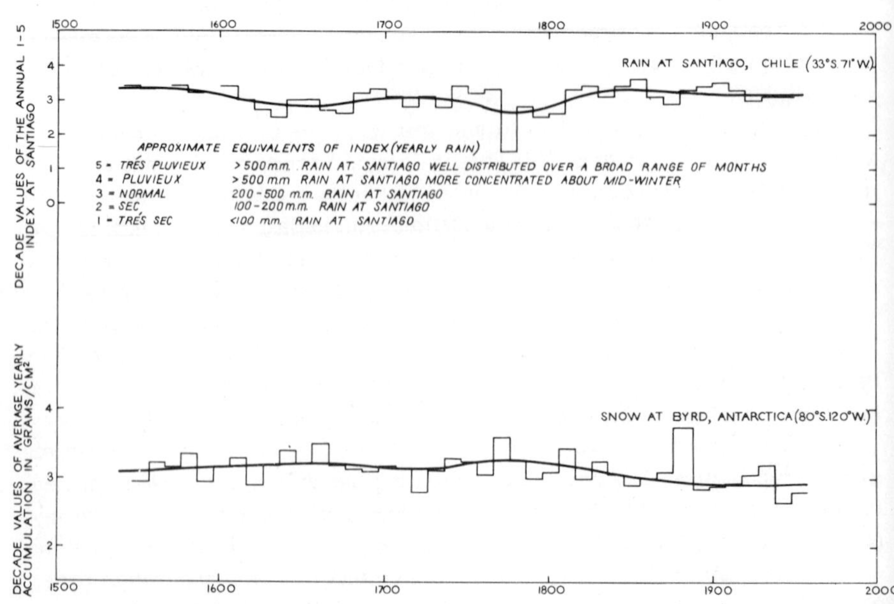

FIG. 6. Rain at Santiago and snow at Byrd Station, Antarctica since 1547.

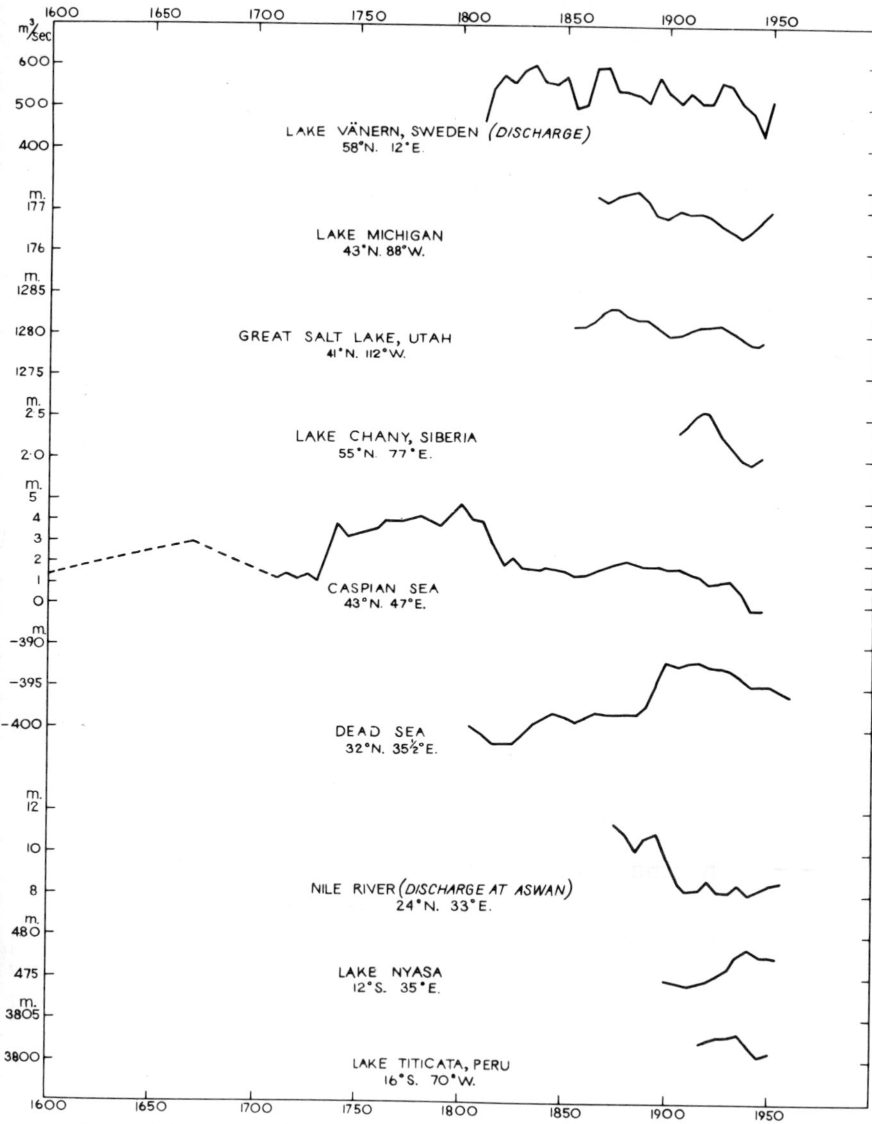

FIG. 7. Lake and river levels (10-year mean values plotted at 5-year intervals).

Principal virtues of the map method are

(*i*) to spot doubtful or erroneous data, through manifest inconsistencies between neighbouring observations;

(*ii*) to provide an analysis of the size, shape and position of the phenomena under examination;

(*iii*) from (*ii*) to arrive at a tentative identification of the physical factors responsible – e.g. location of heat sources and sinks over land and sea, prevalent air motions in the horizontal and vertical planes;

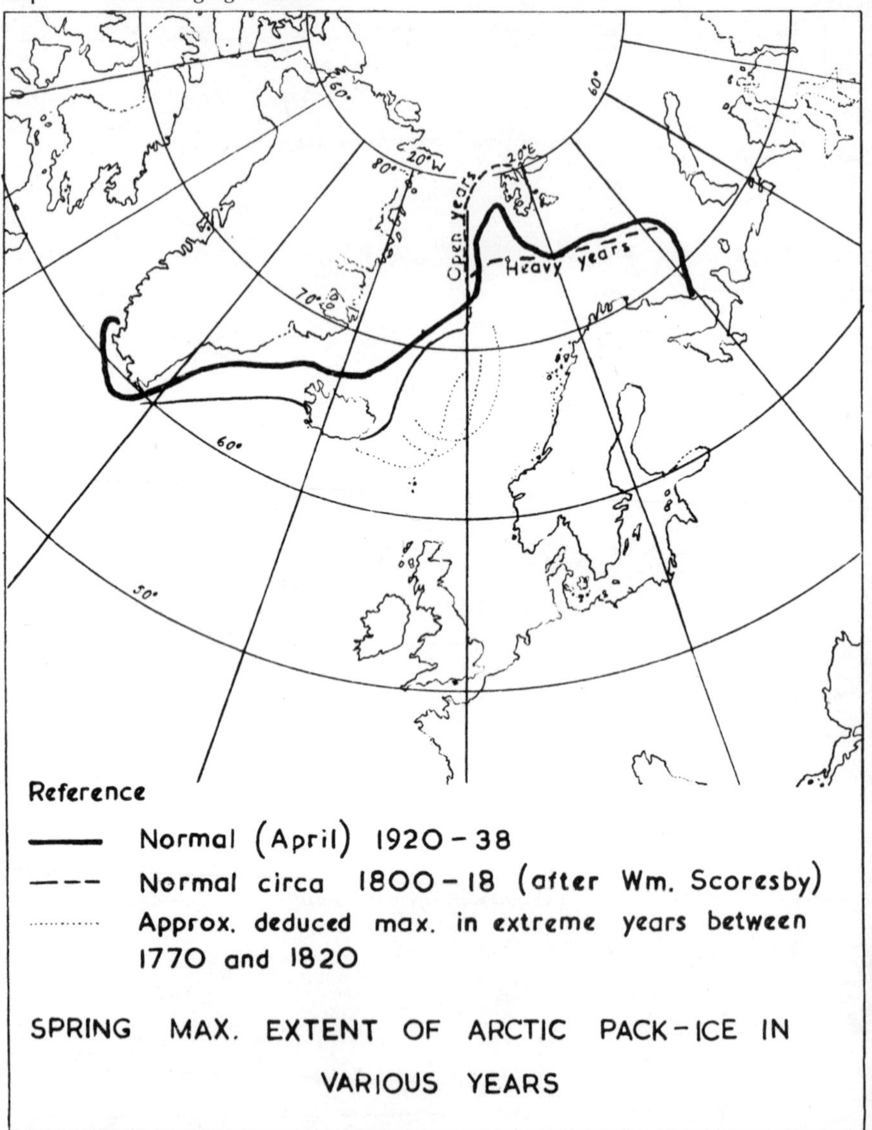

FIG. 8. Average extent of the Arctic pack-ice at the spring maximum in various years.

(*iv*) in the case of the general circulation of the atmosphere, measurements made over the oceans where the main airstreams are most strongly and regularly developed are simpler to interpret than measurements confined to the actual points where observations happen to be available on land. Moreover the mainstreams of the circulation change their positions relative to any particular observing station.

Because the changes of the external radiation supply are regular and seasonal, subject to only minute variations from one year to another, the fundamental element for study of climatic variations is the circulation of the atmosphere and the accompanying circulation of the oceans. These constitute the mechanism of the climatic differences, arising through differences in the transport of heat and moisture, differences in albedo occasioned by cloudiness and snow and differences in the thermal condition (heat storage) of the surface in various regions. Thus, circulation maps (e.g. Figs. 15 and 17 later) are the most useful tool by which to obtain a unified view of what is going on.

Diagrams in which one axis represents time and the other a space dimension either in the vertical or in some horizontal direction are also useful. An example is given later in Fig. 16.

Ideally the circulation should be studied in three dimensions, because the most massive currents are in the upper air. But the development and steering of the depressions and anticyclones which control weather at the surface and set the pattern of surface winds is determined by the flow of the upper winds. This means that, although adequate upper air observations are only available for the period since about 1940, a related and meaningful view of the circulation can be got at the surface from maps of the pressure distribution at sea level.

The instantaneous distribution of atmospheric pressure in a horizontal plane represents a field of force which sets the air in motion. At most points this force is nearly balanced by other forces which act upon the moving air, particularly that due to earth rotation. As a result, the air, except in the friction layer near the ground, normally moves nearly along the isobars and at speeds which vary with the strength of the pressure gradient. The winds near the surface blow at a reduced speed and generally at an angle of 15 to 35° to the isobar toward the low pressure side. This close relationship between barometric pressure and wind means that the field of barometric pressure can be used to provide a survey of the wind pattern. The relationship is still apparent on monthly mean maps, as recognized in the maps of 'average pressure and winds' in physical atlases. Use of averages for time-intervals of the order of a month is inevitable, if the quantity of data to be analysed in climatic studies is to be manageable.

In the upper air at heights between about 2 and 15–20 km. there is a single great circumpolar vortex of westerly winds over either hemisphere, which carries most of the momentum of the atmospheric circulation. This produces developments at the surface which determine a fairly simple flow pattern of the main windstreams even at the surface – polar easterlies, temperate westerlies and trade winds in low latitudes, though with distinctive curvature around individual 'cells' of low and high pressure mostly centred over the oceans. The corresponding smoothness of the pressure field, especially over the oceans, means that there is some hope of mapping the main features even where the network of available observations leaves wide gaps – as first demonstrated over the great expanses of the Southern Ocean (Lamb 1956).

Variations in the distribution of atmospheric pressure were for long a curiously neglected item in the investigation of reported climatic changes. This neglect was all the more unfortunate because the barometer was one of the earliest meteorological instruments developed to a reasonably satisfactory state, and the problems of exposure of this instrument to secure comparable readings were relatively simple and soon solved. Moreover, the welter of apparently unrelated facts of temperature and rainfall changes – rainfall being particularly subject to intricate and very local distribution patterns – was bewildering, at least until the general warming in the first half of this century provided a common feature.

None of the space relationships of rainfall changes hinted at in an earlier section

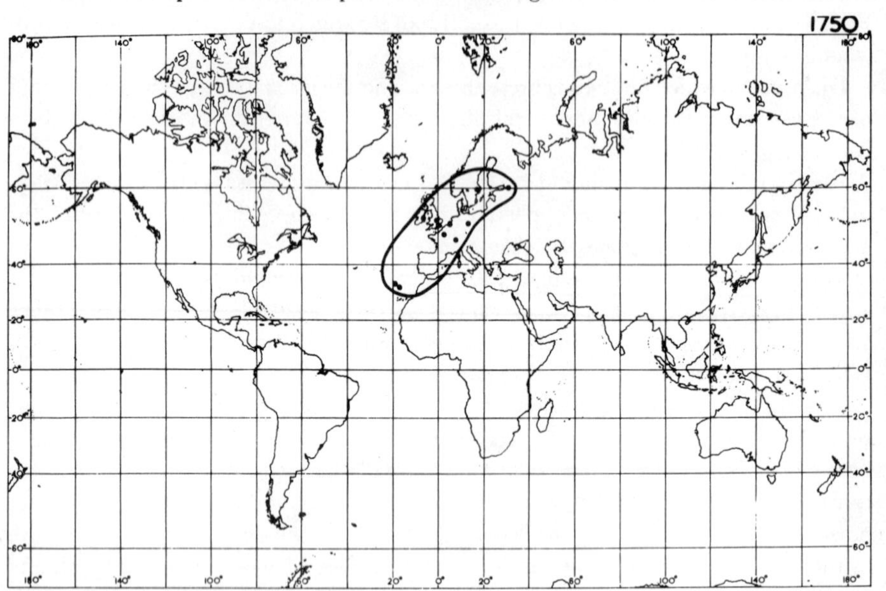

FIG. 9. Growth of the world network of available observations of barometric pressure and of reliable 10-year mean isobars:
(*a, above*) 1750–59.
(*b, below*) 1850–59.
(*c, opposite*) 1950–59.

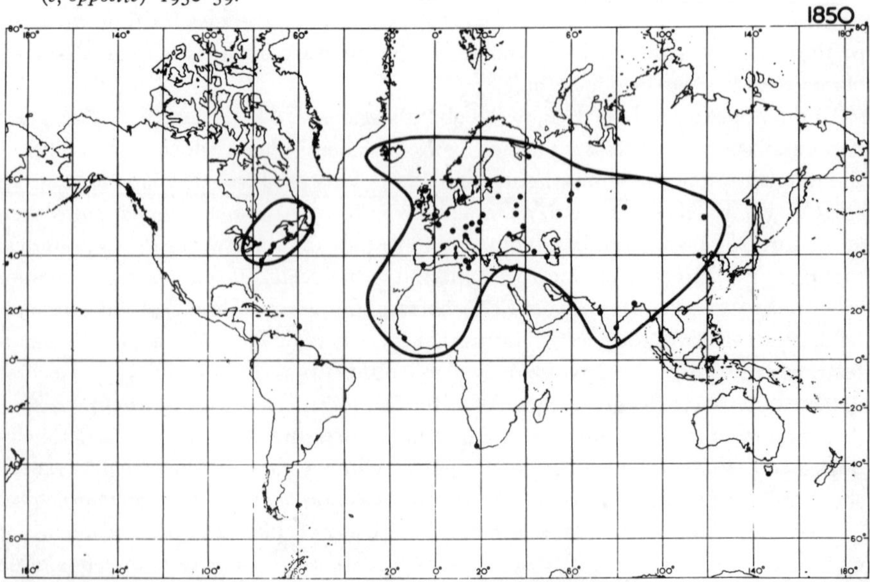

of this paper was noticed until the first discoveries about changes of the large-scale wind circulation had been made (Defant 1924, Wagner 1940, Petterssen 1949, Scherhag 1950). These first studies of circulation changes covered only the years since about 1880. There were many indications, from the winter temperatures in Europe, from the glaciers and so on, that this was far too short a period either to show the origins of the warming or the nature of the epoch of colder climate from which the world was emerging.

The writer has been able to reconstruct the nature of the atmospheric circulation over a useful part of the world back to 1750 by following the principles laid down earlier in this article.

Development of the series of pressure maps

Fig. 9 shows the network of observations available for analysis of the atmospheric circulation in three sample decades, the 1750s, 1850s and 1950s. Long series of pressure observations at or near a single place, which had been scrutinized for homogeneity by meteorologists of an earlier generation and only needed adjustment ('reduction') to M.S.L. and standard gravity, were the backbone of the maps. The continuing series which began earliest in various parts of the world were:

Trondheim 1762–
Paris 1764–
Edinburgh 1769–
London 1787–
St Petersburg/Leningrad 1822–
Ekaterinburg/Sverdlovsk 1836–
Barnaul (Siberia) 1836–
Toronto 1840–
Hobart 1841–
Madras 1841–
Cape Town 1842–
Stykkisholm (Iceland) 1846–
Rio de Janeiro 1851–
Mauritius 1853–
Auckland (New Zealand) 1854–
Adelaide 1857–
Trinidad 1862–
Ponta Delgada (Azores) 1865–

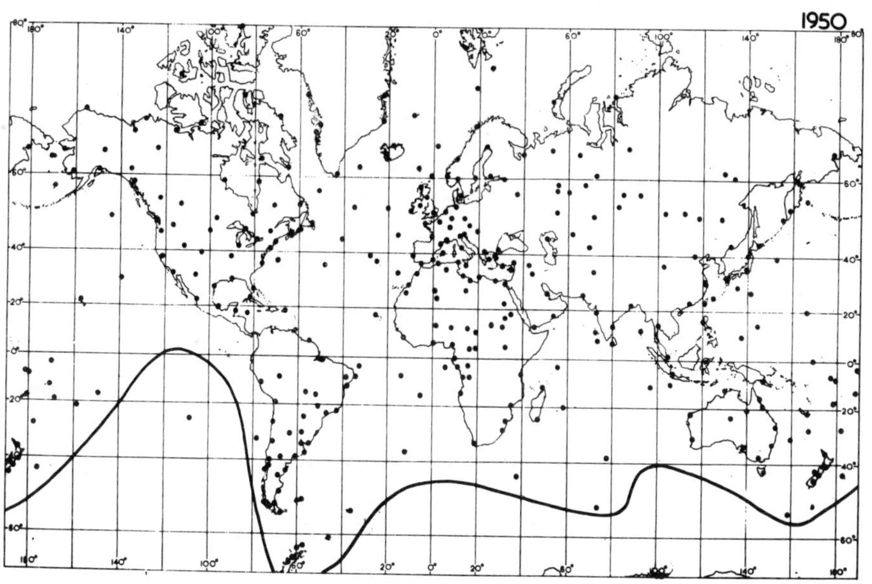

The maps themselves with values for these places plotted made it possible to establish the quality of, and corrections to be applied to, other early observation records of some length, notably:

London 1723–64, 1774–81
Berlin 1729–70
Udine 1803–42
Palermo 1791–1856
Gibraltar 1822–
Archangel 1813–31
St Petersburg/Leningrad 1769–83
Irkutsk 1836–44
Nikolaevsk on Amur 1855–85
Peking 1841–55
Cambridge, Mass. 1742–79, 1780–89, 1790–1812, 1840–88
Salem, Mass. 1786–1820
New Bedford, Mass. 1813–50
Providence, Rhode Island 1831–60

Other observation series in early years in some important outlying regions could apparently be accepted on internal evidence of good quality and because their implications for the pressure map appeared reasonable and consistent with other indications of the map. These included:

British Navy ships wintering in the Canadian Arctic from 1820 onwards
Reykjavik (Iceland) 1823–37
West Greenland stations 1833–51
São Miguel, Azores 1840s
St Helena 1841–45
Falkland Islands 1859–68, 1875–77

Use was made of the special features of smoothness, and relatively small variations in time, of the field of annual mean pressure in arriving at these assessments. Back to the 1780s the number of available pressure observations in Europe meant that the network was close enough for the pressure values themselves to be used to indicate particular corrections, including the probable height above sea level of the barometers, at a few stations where there were uncertainties.

Monthly mean pressures at M.S.L. were plotted for each January and each July from 1750. Where the network was sparse and the isobar direction indeterminate, observed frequencies of different wind directions wherever available were also plotted as wind roses on the maps. Supplementary information about temperature, rainfall, frequencies of rain, snow, thunder, etc. at many places, and about sea-ice, was entered as marginal notes, since these items might be supposed to go with prevalence of certain windstreams and isobar patterns.

Isobars were then drawn on the working charts over the widest area for which the patterns of wind-flow, cyclonicity, etc. appeared to be implied by the observational information. At this stage, over very large areas the analysis of such maps is really no more than an elaborate construction of hypothesis. The reliability and possibilities of using the maps for actual measurements of position and strength of the main windstreams require to be established by test. The tests devised were simulation tests.

The first analysis of the monthly mean pressure distributions for 20 recent years was made on charts with only skeleton data (Test Charts, series A) similar in kind, amount and distribution to that available in 1780–1820. The process was repeated with a data network equivalent to that of another period, 1821–35 (Test Charts, series B). Only after that was the final analysis of charts for the 20 recent years made from complete data. The test area comprised eastern North America, the North Atlantic and Europe, for which there was enough evidence to attempt an analysis even for the earliest period. Comparison of the test charts with the final charts made it possible to survey the errors arising with reduced observational evidence as in 1780–1820 and 1821–35.

Figs. 10(*a*) and (*b*) show for January and July respectively the distribution of 'analyst's bias' – i.e. the departures of the 20-year average pressures derived from the Test Chart series A from the 20-year averages given by analysis of full data for the same years. All the charts were analysed by the same hand. It was considered satisfactory to use areas of the map where the bias did not appreciably exceed 1 mb. in January or half a mb. in July, a higher standard being required in July to avoid possible distortions of the weaker pressure gradients then prevailing. This meant that the analysis was satisfactorily free from bias over the whole width of the North Atlantic in January between the observation networks of Europe and the American seabord. In July it was not satisfactory without further refinement. The analysis of the whole series of July charts from 1750 was therefore adjusted to eliminate the bias of nearly 2 mb. near Bermuda and over 1 mb. in mid-Atlantic south of Iceland. Comparisons of the average pressures for each decade in the regions affected before and after adjustment of the individual charts verified that the bias had been reduced to under half a mb.

The geographical distribution of the incidence of random errors was then studied by measuring differences between pressures shown on the individual charts of the Test Series A and of the final analysis with full observational coverage for the same January or July. Figs. 11(*a*) and (*b*) show plotted values of the standard errors derived for various points on the map. The standard error (σ) was derived by the expression

$$\sigma = \sqrt{\{\Sigma x^2/(n-1)\}}$$

where x stands for the errors on the individual maps and n for the number of values available for test – i.e. in this case 20, the number of January or July charts in the test series. Random errors may be reduced if only the averages of groups of years are used, since the standard error (σ_M) of the mean of y years is given by

$$\sigma_M = \sigma/\sqrt{y}$$

The isopleths (full lines) on Figs. 11(*a*) and (*b*) and their numbered values indicate the distribution of standard errors of 10-year mean pressures, being rather under a third ($1/\sqrt{10}$) of the corresponding errors for the individual maps.

It was considered that standard errors not exceeding 2·5 mb. would be generally acceptable for the analysis of the North Atlantic and comparable regions of the world. This could be taken to mean that errors exceeding 5 mb. would occur at the limits of the accepted analysis only about once in twenty maps. With the weaker

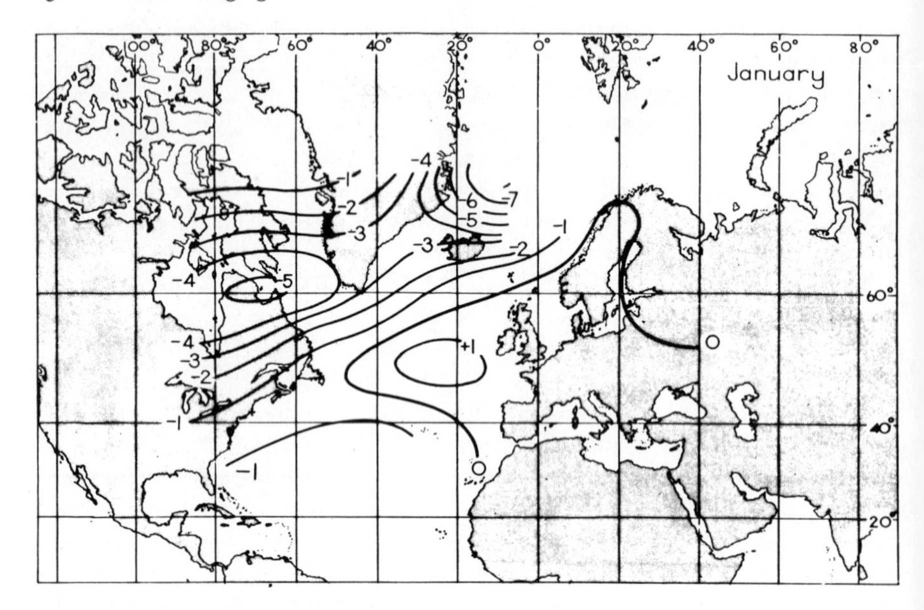

FIG. 10. Maps of systematic error (analyst's bias) in millibars:
(*a, above*) January.
(*b, below*) July.

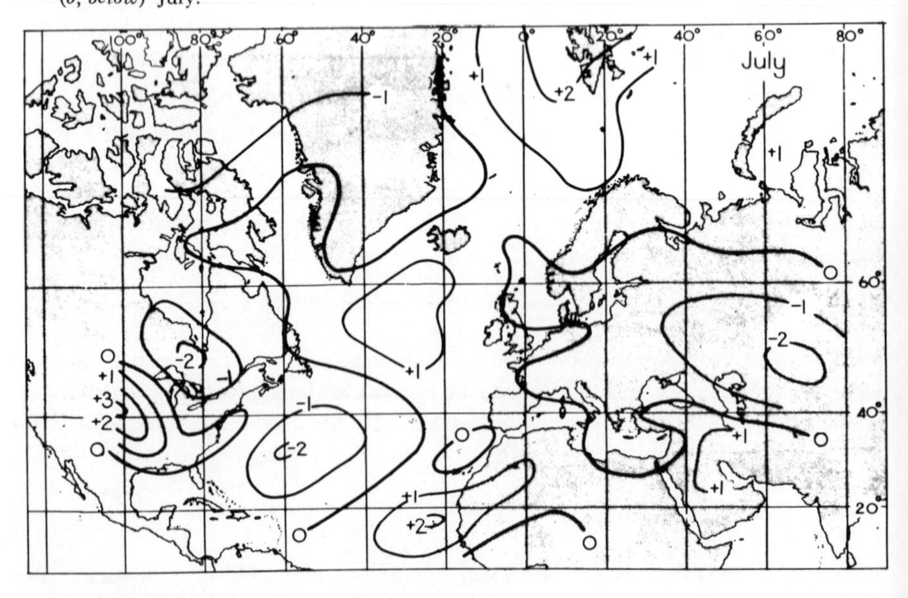

pressure gradients prevailing in summer in the northern hemisphere, and at all times in the tropics, however, a higher standard is required if the charts are to be reliable. For July in the northern hemisphere therefore the analysis was only considered acceptable over regions where the standard error did not appreciably exceed 1 mb., implying that errors of over 2 mb. would occur only about once in twenty maps.

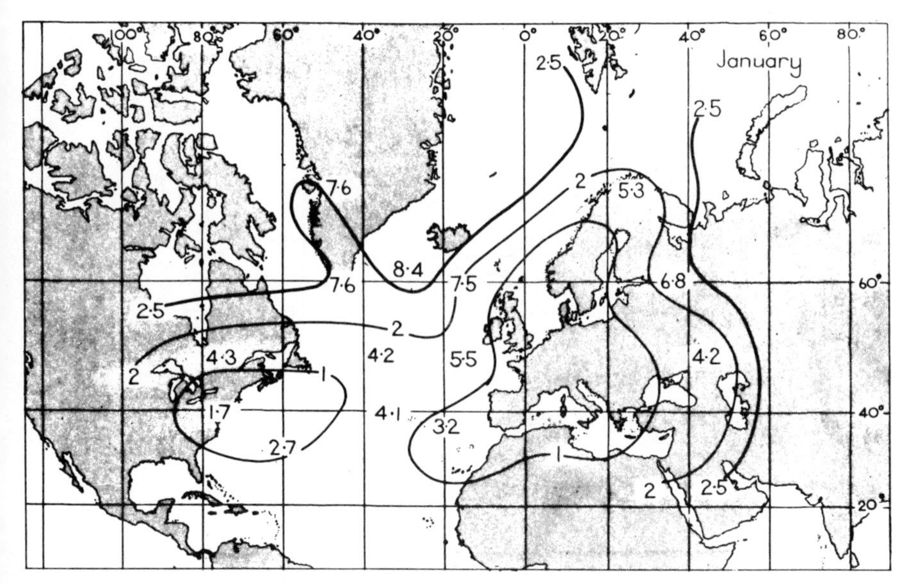

FIG. 11. Maps of random error (millibars). Plotted values: standard error of values on maps for individual years. Isopleths: standard error of values indicated by 10-year mean isobars.
(*a, above*) January.
(*b, below*) July.

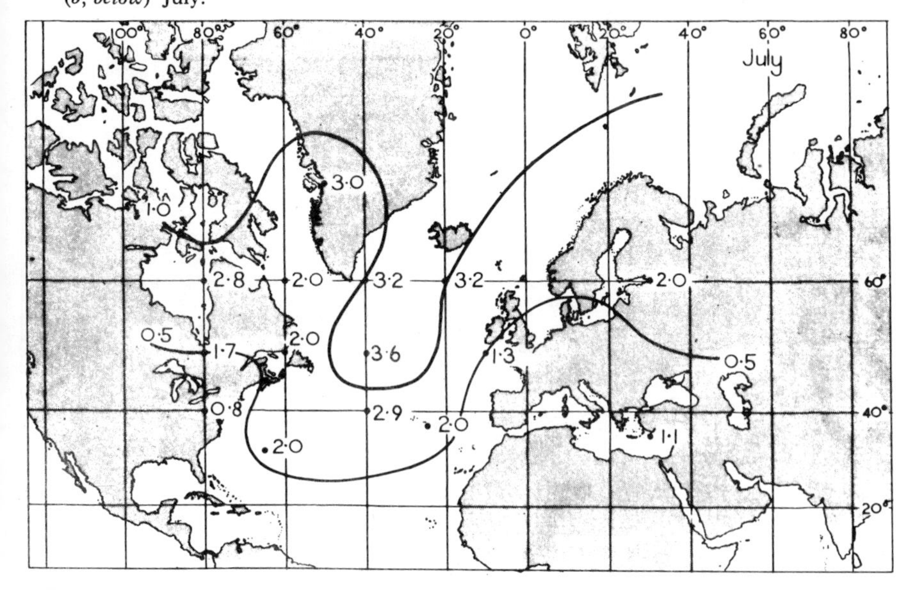

Error margins are, of course, reduced still further in the case of averages of more than 10 years, for instance, in the case of 40-year means to under a sixth ($1/\sqrt{40}$) of the random errors of the individual maps. This meant that the worst errors arising through bias and random errors combined, in cases when these happened to be additive, would be safely within the predetermined requirements across the whole width of the North Atlantic in the case of 40-year mean maps from the earliest years

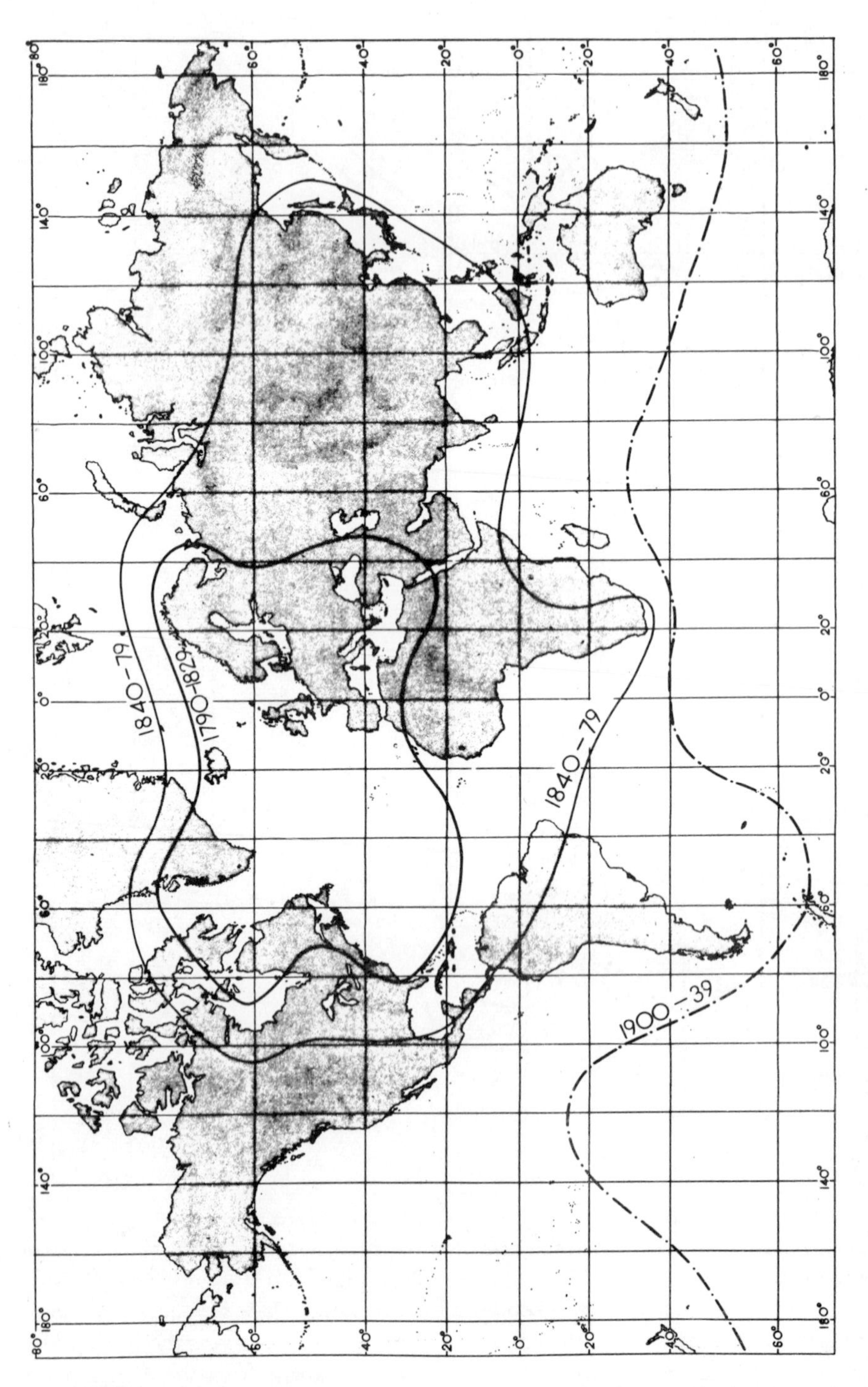

FIG. 12. Limits of reliable mapping (40-year mean isobars), defined by standard errors under 2·5 mb. in January, 1 mb. in July.

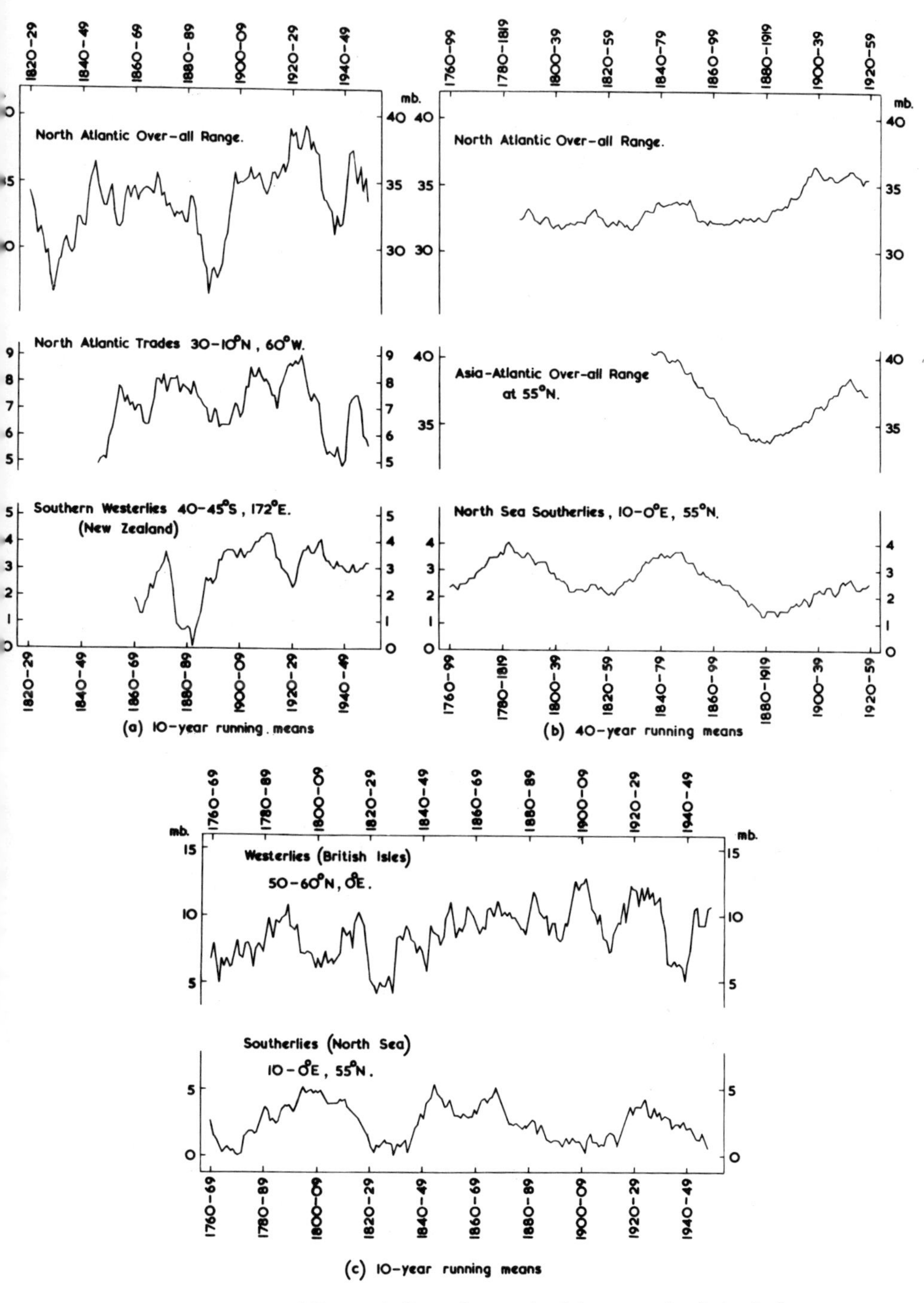

FIG. 13. Selected pressure difference indices of strength of the mean circulation in January.

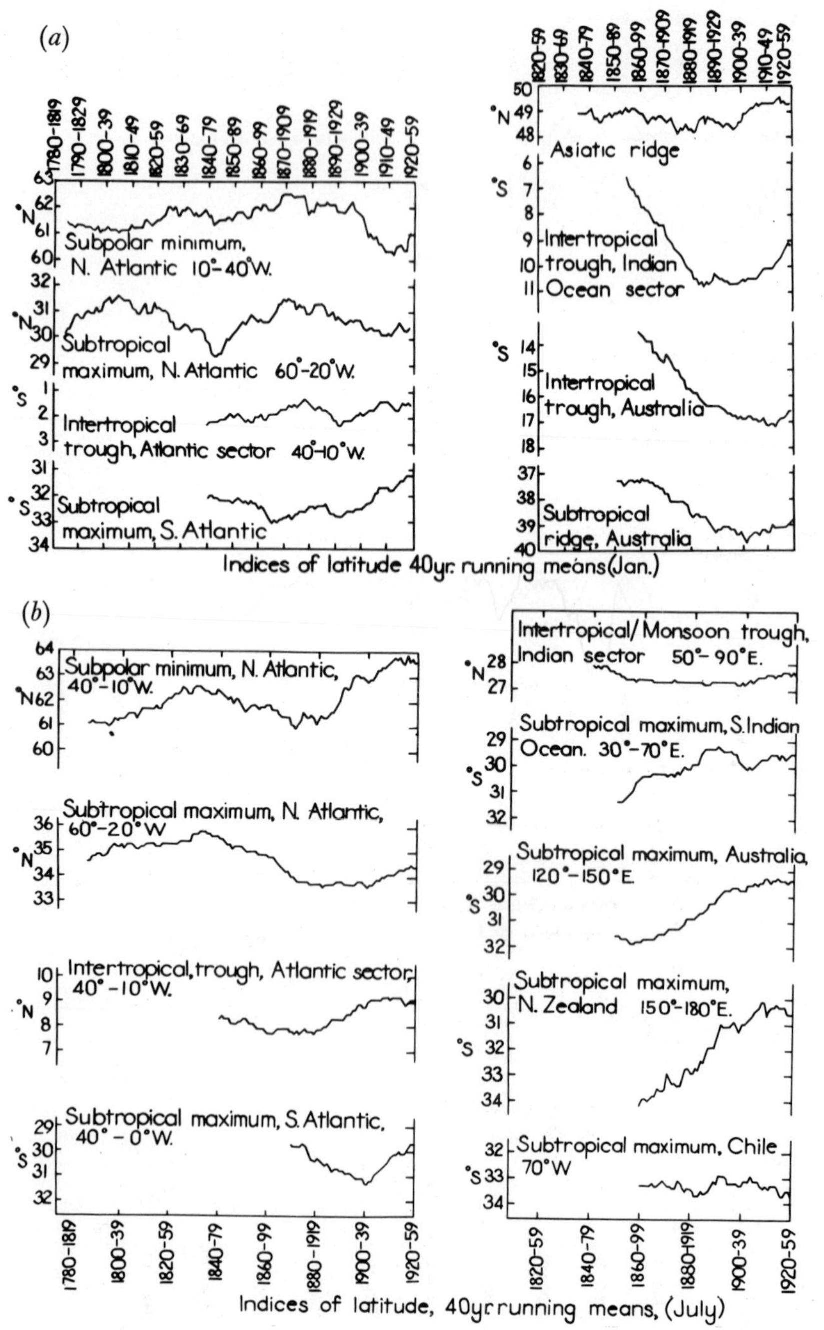

FIG. 14. Position indices for key features of the atmospheric circulation. Indices of latitude.
(*a*) January.
(*b*) July.

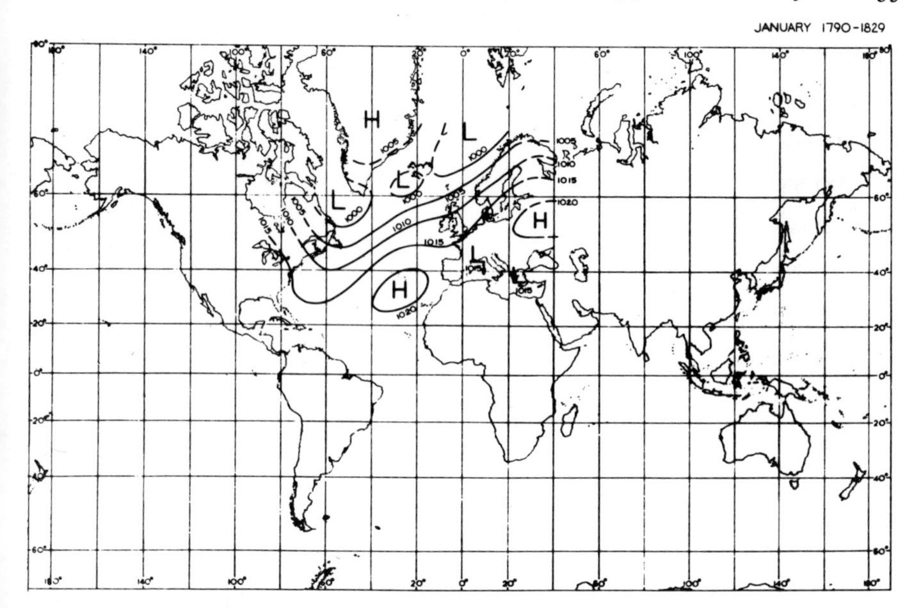

FIG. 15. Average atmospheric pressure at mean sea level in January (in millibars).
(*a*, *above*) 1790–1829.
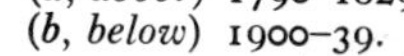
(*b*, *below*) 1900–39.

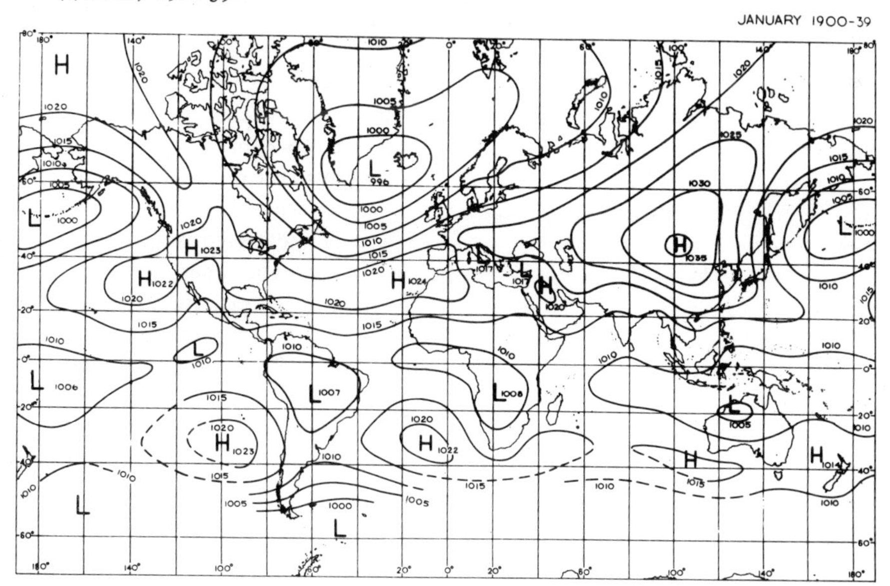

studied. The conservatively drawn limits of reliable analysis adopted for 40-year mean maps around different sample dates as a result of these tests are shown in Fig. 12. Measurements of the wind speeds implied by the pressure gradients on the test charts and final charts compared indicated that within the accepted region standard errors did not exceed about 3 per cent of the wind speed.

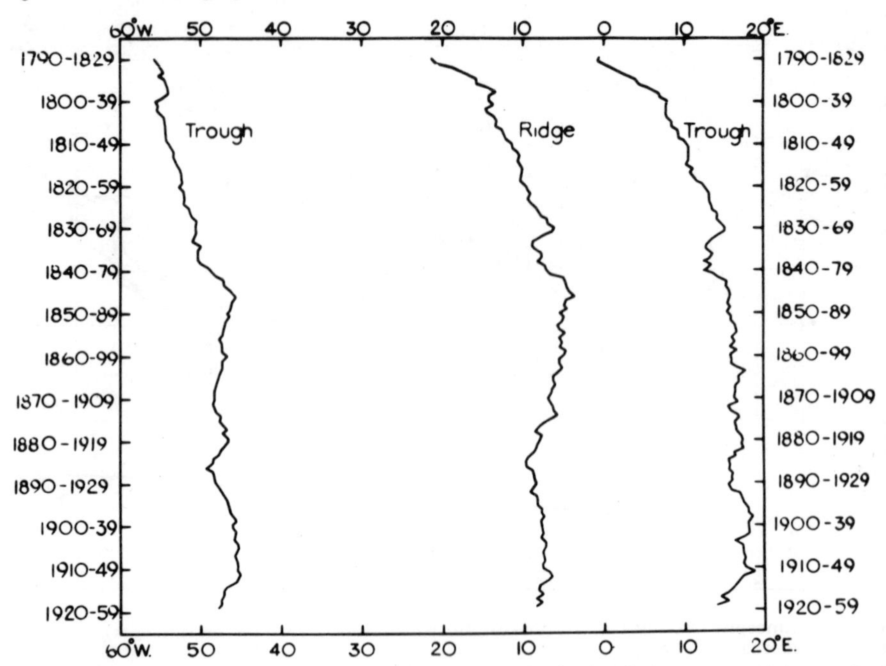

FIG. 16. Position indices for key features of the atmospheric circulation. 40-year averages for longitudes of lowest and highest M.S.L. pressure at 45° N in January.

The Probable Error which is expected to be exceeded in 50 per cent of any measurements made is about two-thirds (0·675) of the Standard Errors quoted, assuming that the normal curve of frequency distribution of errors applies.

The maps arrived at are thus related in a known way to the reliability of maps analysed over comparable regions and comparable periods with full data. The only bias which might have come through the testing system undetected would be toward minimizing differences from the normal patterns of recent times, since the tests actually measured the ability of the analyst to derive an average for 20 *recent* years from skeleton data. It might be desirable to repeat the tests on different groups of recent years. In fact, different 20-year periods were used for the tests of the January and July charts.

The actual results of measurements from the long series of January and July pressure maps from 1750 show progressive trends of strength and position of the main features of the atmospheric circulation, with patterns in the early years differing to an important extent from those of the present century. These are illustrated in Figs. 13–16. The progressive trends suggest that the possibility of any residual bias toward recent normals (or otherwise) can be discounted. Moreover, certain meteorological checks add credence by suggesting internal consistency in the changes observed, in particular reduced longitude spacing and slight westward displacement over the Atlantic and Europe (Fig. 16) of axes of high and low pressure in the early period when the pressure gradients for the main windstreams were weaker by several per cent and displaced equatorwards in the North Atlantic and

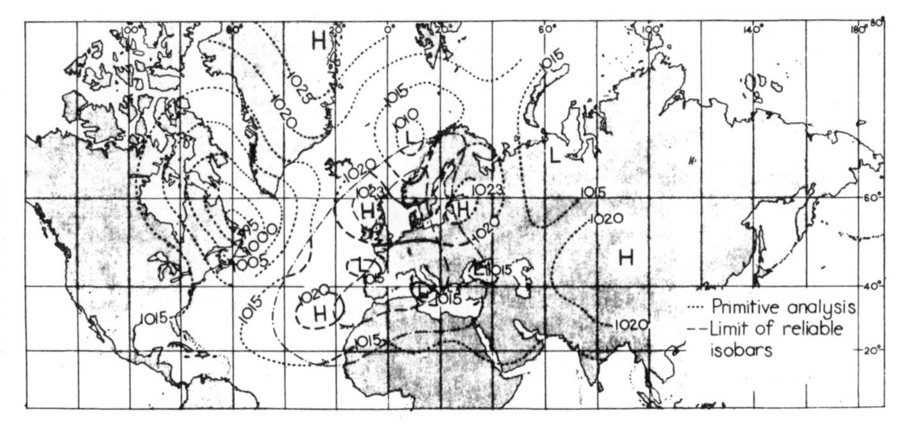

FIG. 17. (*a, above*) Monthly mean pressure at M.S.L. January 1795 (in millibars).
(*b, below*) Monthly mean pressure at M.S.L. January 1963 (in millibars).

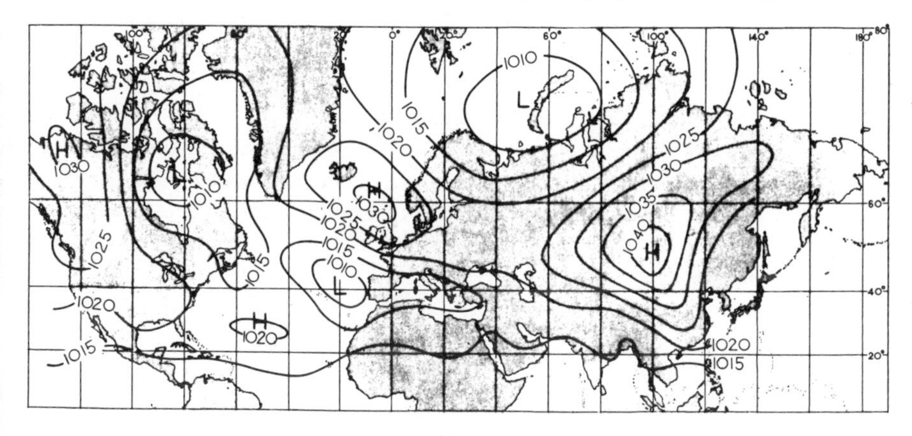

neighbouring sectors. This westward displacement of the pressure pattern over the Atlantic and Europe would be expected on theoretical grounds in the circumstances named.

What has been specified about the errors to which the early maps based on skeleton data are liable is not complete in an absolute sense, but amounts to a determination of the probable departures from the isobars on maps based on full data. Wherever the real pressure distribution is intricate and the isobars sinuous, the isobars on any small-scale map such as a hemisphere or world map are always too smooth. But the very localized details that are smoothed out are seldom of much interest for the dynamics of the large-scale circulation. The error distribution studied by the tests is the distribution of departures from the best set of smoothed isobars.

Doubtless other difficulties have been introduced by applying the results of tests of reliability in relation to the observation network over the North Atlantic to other parts of the world, though there is reason to believe these are not serious from experience with daily maps over the Southern Ocean (Lamb 1956). The extent of the region over which errors are not expected to exceed 5 mb. more than once in 20 maps has been conservatively estimated. It appears that the map of average pressure in January 1900–39 (Fig. 15(*b*)) drawn by this procedure covers a larger part of the world than has ever been covered before by data for strictly the same years everywhere and within largely known limits of error.

Broken lines have been used on the pressure maps (e.g. Figs. 15(*a*) and (*b*)) over regions where the general appearance of the pattern can be guaranteed though the positions of the lines are not reliable enough for any kind of measurements to be useful.

Fig. 17(*a*) illustrates the preliminary analysis of the circulation prevailing during a sample individual month of long ago, January 1795, and the portion of that analysis which can be accepted as reliable from the tests. This case has had some special interest, since the prevailing pattern of that month provided a closer parallel for the extremely severe January of 1963 (Fig. 17(*b*)) than that of any January since. The relationship appeared to have some forecasting value, since the course of the seasons in 1795 showed frequent resemblances to the months that followed in 1963.

Conclusion

The nature of the circulation changes revealed by the long series of maps, the decreased strength of the mean west-wind component over Britain in the eighteenth- and early nineteenth-century epoch of more frequent cold winters, and especially the accompanying westward shift of the axes of highest and lowest pressure over the eastern Atlantic and Europe, suggested the development of further techniques by which the abundant European weather data of still earlier years could be analysed to reveal circulation changes over a much longer period of time. These have been described elsewhere (Lamb and Johnson 1961). They indicate that the coldest climatic period was probably between 1550 and 1700, and was associated with less prevalent westerly winds over Britain and the Atlantic than in the present century and an abnormal frequency of northerly and north-easterly winds, particularly in the Norwegian Sea and over the Russian plain. Some independent verification of these points has already been obtained.

References

AHLMANN, H. W. 1949. 'The present climatic fluctuation.' *Geogr. J.*, **112**, 165–195. London.

BROOKS, C. E. P. 1950. 'Climate in everyday life' (Chapter 10: *Climatic Accidents*). London (Ernest Benn).

COURT, A. 1953. 'Wind extremes as design factors.' *Journal of the Franklin Institute*, **256**, 41–56, Lancaster, Pa.

DEFANT, A. 1924. 'Die Schwankungen der atmosphärischen Zirkulation.' *Geografiska Annaler*, **6**, 13–41. Stockholm.

DZERDZEEVSKY, B. L. 1961. 'The general circulation of the atmosphere as a necessary link in the sun-climatic chain.' *Annals of the New York Academy of Sciences*, **95**, Art. 1, 188–189. New York.

KRAUS, E. B. 1958. 'Recent climatic changes.' *Nature*, **181**, 666–668. London.

KRAUS, E. B. 1958. 'Recent changes of east-coast rainfall régimes.' *Quarterly Journal of the Royal Meteorological Society*, **89**, 145–146. London.

LAMB, H. H. 1956. 'Meteorological results of the *Balaena* expedition, 1946–47.' *Geophysical Memoir No.* **94**. London (Meteorological Office).

LAMB, H. H. and JOHNSON, A. I. 1959. 'Climatic variation and observed changes in the general circulation,' Parts I and II. *Geografiska Annaler*, **41,** 94–134 Stockholm.

LAMB, H. H. and JOHNSON, A. I. 1961. *Ibid.*, Part III. *Geogr. Ann.*, **43,** 363–400. Stockholm.

LISTER, H. 1959. 'Geophysical investigations of the Commonwealth Transantarctic Expedition.' *Geogr. J.*, **125,** 341–351. London.

MANLEY, G. 1958. 'Temperature trends in England.' *Archiv für Meteorologie, Geophysik und Bioklimatologie, Serie B*, **9,** 413–433. Vienna.

MANLEY, G. 1961. '. . . Early meteorological observations in the London region . . .' *Meteorological Magazine*, **90,** 303–310. London.

MITCHELL, J. M. jr. 1963. 'On the world-wide pattern of secular temperature change.' *Proceedings of the WMO/UNESCO Rome 1961 Symposium on Climatic Changes.* Paris (UNESCO – Arid Zone Research XX).

PETTERSSEN, SV. 1949. 'Changes in the general circulation associated with the recent climatic fluctuation.' *Geografiska Annaler*, **31,** 212–221. Stockholm.

SCHERHAG, R. 1950. 'Die Schwankungen der atmosphärischen Zirkulation in den letzten Jahrzehnten.' *Berichte des dt. Wetterdienst. U.S. Zone, Nr. 12*, 40–44. Bad Kissingen.

STEINHAUSER, F. 1961. 'Klimaschwankungen in Mitteleuropa', *Österreichische Akad. der Wiss., Sitzung der math. – naturw. Klasse* 27 April 1961, pp. 81–94. Vienna.

WAGNER, A. 1940. '*Klimaänderungen und Klimaschwankungen*'. Braunschweig (Vieweg).

FIVE

The role of atmosphere and oceans in relation to climatic changes and the growth of ice-sheets on land

Introduction

The growth of glaciers is a somewhat complex climatic problem. Table 1 lists the processes that cause growth and wastage.

Table 1. Processes affecting glaciers

Gain	Loss
Snow	Melting: (1) at surface, (2) internal, (3) at base[a]
Sleet	Run-off
Freezing rain	Evaporation
Drifting snow received	Drifting snow lost ("deflation" by wind)
Avalanches from surrounding rock	Calving of icebergs in the sea
Rime ice deposited by clouds and fog	
Refreezing of meltwater, mostly at some depth in the glacier	

[a] Heat is supplied by: (i) radiation from Sun and clouds, (ii) sensible heat brought by the winds, (iii) latent heat of condensation and sublimation of moisture brought by the winds, (iv) friction—internal and from motion over the bedrock.

At the present epoch four variables appear crucial in different places (Wallén, 1948)—that is, advance and retreat phases of the glaciers have been brought about primarily by changes of one of these parameters: (a) temperature and duration of the summer melting season, (b) precipitation, especially the amounts falling as snow, sleet or cold rain, (c) quantity of snow blown away by the wind, (d) loss by calving of icebergs into the sea.

Accumulation of ice fundamentally depends on latitude (i.e. radiation regime) and on the amounts of heat and moisture normally transported by wind and ocean, also on the geography, i.e. (1) general extent of land and sea, and (2) size, relief and slopes of the particular terrain. But it cannot be any local or regional factors that determine a general ice age, nor does the duration of the best-known ice ages in the past (i.e. Quaternary glaciations) appear to approach that of the existence of suitable geography.

The simplest theories are those that have sought to explain ice ages by the changes of just one variable: terrestrial geography or astronomical and other controls of the heat supply from the Sun. Let us consider these factors briefly, as a framework for our later discussion of the parts played by winds and ocean currents.

Suitable geography

Palaeomagnetism and other evidence suggest that the large-scale geography is a variable on the geological time-scale, specifically that continents and oceans have changed their positions relative to each other, and relative to the poles, during geological time (Runcorn, 1962), also that relief and positions of the principal mountain barriers have varied.

The present geography of the southern hemisphere, with continents just in the latitudes of strongest radiative heating and cooling, must heighten the latitudinal temperature difference there to a maximum, which might only be surpassed if there were rather more land in the main heating zone—though that would make the hemisphere warmer than it is. Simpson (1940) noted that annual mean air temperatures show continents warmer than oceans within 40° of the Equator, presumably because the greater cloudiness over the oceans reflects away and wastes much of the incoming radiation; in higher latitudes continents are colder than oceans. Thus the relative scarcity of land (under 25%) in the heating zone of the southern hemisphere 0–30° S, while there is abundant land south of 65° S, keeps the mean temperature of the southern hemisphere somewhat lower than that of the northern and accentuates the cold of the higher southern latitudes. The geography of the northern hemisphere, with a polar ocean remote but not quite isolated from the water currents of other latitudes and a land girdle in 60–70° N, may be a rather favourable arrangement for the development of a cold climate in latitudes about 50–70° N—though the northern hemisphere is at present somewhat warmer than the southern in all latitudes.

There is evidence (Lamb, 1955) that the establishment of a snow surface 1500 miles or more in W–E extent in moderate to high latitudes in winter affects the atmospheric circulation in ways that favour maintenance and further nourishment of the snow. This is traceable to the high albedo (reflectivity) of snow and ice surfaces, which reject most of the Sun's rays falling upon them, and the large amounts of latent heat demanded to get rid of the snow and ice. Thus northern hemisphere geography favours much winter snow north of 40–50° N, and anything which tended to hinder its melting in summer would favour an ice age.

Brooks (1949) stressed periods of mountain-building (orogenesis)—and the ensuing geological epochs while strong relief persisted—as liable to glaciation started by accumulation of snow and ice on the mountains in subpolar latitudes.

Long-term variations of the radiation supply

These might arise from: (a) possible variations of the Sun's output, (b) known long-periodic changes in the Earth's orbit, (c) screening of the Earth and lower atmosphere by veils of fine volcanic dust particles or by ordinary clouds.

Leading opinion has differed (Simpson, 1934, 1957; Kraus, 1960) as to whether the intake of heat from the Sun must have been reduced whenever an ice age began. Simpson suggests paradoxically that increased insolation might also produce this result by warming the oceans and, through increased moisture in the atmosphere, increasing snowfall on the mountains in high latitudes.

Geographical and radiative theories of ice ages are not mutually exclusive but operate on different time-scales. Some of the known or suggested astronomical variations (e.g. Earth's orbit) are periodic over intervals of 20,000–90,000 years and affect greatly the amount of solar radiation available at any place in summer or winter, though the total for the year as a whole remains constant. Of course, the total radiation actually absorbed in the course of a year must decrease when snow cover increases. Some of the very greatest climatic variations, ice ages and interglacial periods of greater warmth than today, have in fact occurred several times during the last 1 My,* while the main mountain ranges have stood where they now are. Doubtless the basic geographical pattern and the general level of the Sun's output must be suitable for ice ages to occur. But the last ice age, like postglacial times, yields evidence of climatic fluctuations down to periods of a few thousands of years, and even to centuries or less (Schwarzbach, 1961; Lamb, 1961).

There is a sense in which we are still living in the ice age with about 10% of the total land area covered with ice. (For the northern hemisphere the figure is 2% of the land area.) Glaciers in most parts of the world have undergone notable fluctuations during the last 500–1000 years and even during recent decades. Within the last 200 years or so the most advanced positions of land and probably of sea ice since the ice age were attained. Changes in the prevailing atmospheric and oceanic currents during the same period have been investigated. What can we learn from these very recent changes about the causes of growth of ice on land?

Observed variations of recent centuries

Figure 1 is a summary of observed variations in the length of glaciers averaged for different areas in the northern hemisphere since the year 1600, taken from Ahlmann, 1953. Common features are the advanced positions in the 1600s, 1700s and 1800s A.D. and notable retreat in the present century. There is no doubt that these features are general. Parallel variations have been reported from the Pamirs and central Asia. In the early 1600s travellers reported snow above 4300 m on the mountains of Ethiopia, where true snowfall is practically unknown today. Glacier advance was noted when Europeans were re-settled in south Greenland in the late 1700s (Weidick, 1959) and in Chile about the same time (Heusser, 1960); in both these areas there has been general retreat in the present century. The fullest historical documentation is from the Alps and Iceland, where it appears that glacial advance was considerable after the early Middle Ages, the most devastating advances being in the late 1500s and 1600s–early 1700s, respectively. The latter is also believed to have been the main period of glacier advance in Alaska. Maxima around 1750 and 1850 appear more or less contemporaneous in Alaska, Iceland and Europe. Variations of

* 1 My = 1 million years.

accumulation over long periods of years in northern Greenland and Antarctica may perhaps soon be deduced from the stratigraphy of annual ice layers in pits and boreholes in the ice-sheets—a much-hoped-for result of recent glaciological work. Preliminary impressions (see pp. 343–4) are that accumulation in the highest latitudes has followed a rather different course, tending to increase at

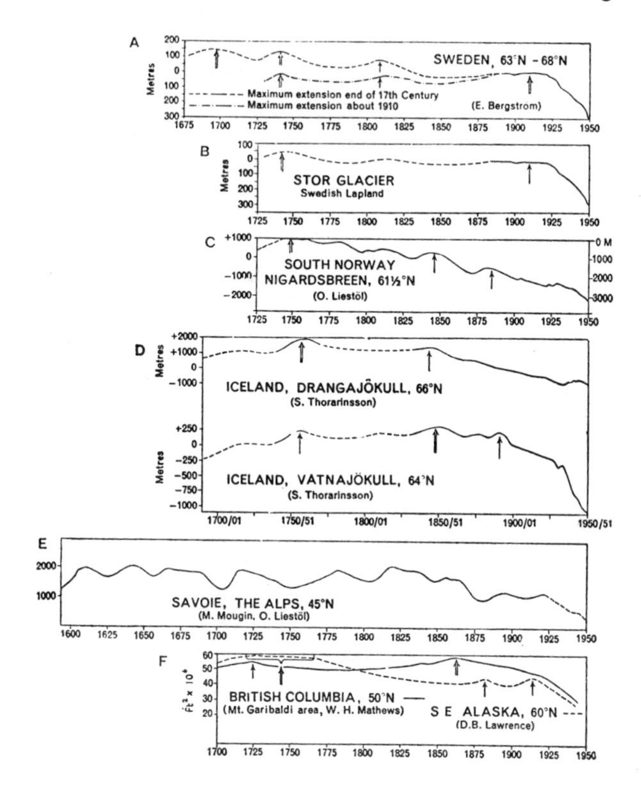

Fig. 1. Curves showing the variations of glacier termini (after H. W. Ahlmann).

times of modest rise of temperature and increased atmospheric moisture transport, as during much of the first half of the 20th century: with a slightly greater rise of temperature, as possibly around A.D. 1000–1200, melting might predominate.* (Melting certainly outweighed accumulation in all latitudes during the main postglacial warm epoch before 3000 B.C.)

* Langway (1962) has given figures for the rates of accumulation in different periods at 77° N 56° W on the ice-sheet in northern Greenland. From his Tables VII, VIII and IX, the following annual rates seem to have been typical:

	$g\ cm^{-2}\ year^{-1}$		$g\ cm^{-2}\ year^{-1}$
About A.D. 900	33·5	1884–1954	40·6
About A.D. 1200	33·3	1933–1955	40
About A.D. 1780	31·3	1952–1961	38

From 1550 to 1850 was a cold epoch, and the glacial recession since 1850 has been paralleled by a rise of average air temperature at sea level in most parts of the world by about 1° C, illustrated by the curves in Fig. 2. This may be compared with an estimated lowering of world temperature by 6° C in the last ice age, deduced from study of the remains of marine organisms in sea-bottom sediments by Emiliani (1955), and 12° C in temperate Europe and the Mediterranean. Similar figures are suggested by evidence of the ice-age lowering of snow line on the mountains (Wright, 1961; Flohn, 1952). The consequences of the more or less world-wide cold epoch 1550–1850 (sometimes called the Little Ice Age) were serious. Glaciers overran farms in Europe and Iceland and forests in North America. The Old Norse Greenland colony died out. Cultivation of

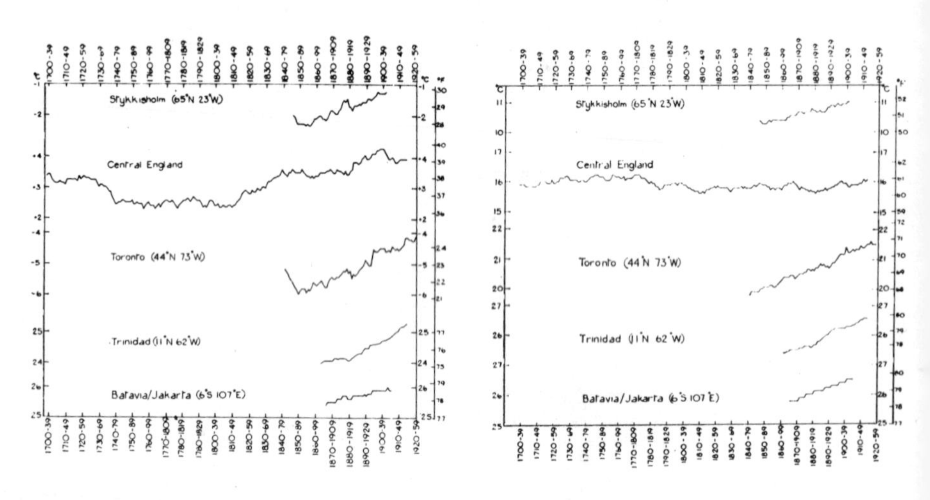

Fig. 2(a). Temperature trends in January at places in different latitude zones, 40-year running means.

Fig. 2(b). Temperature trends in July at places in different latitude zones, 40-year running means.

grain became impossible in Iceland and of certain fruits in districts where they had formerly grown in Europe and China. It was clearly a smaller-scale phenomenon than the major ice ages, but it has the virtue that at least some direct meteorological and oceanographic measurements exist for study.

It is possible to estimate rather roughly, but with sufficient accuracy for the present purpose, the changed extent of snow and ice from the changes in the positions of the mean isotherms in air and sea to correspond with the temperature-lowering already mentioned. The results indicated are given in Table 2. Estimates for the southern hemisphere are more difficult than for the northern, because of insufficient evidence of the limits of sea-ice in past ages. The Antarctic, unlike all regions north of 40–50° S, did not fully share the recent cold epoch; sea-ice seems to have been rather less extensive there around 1800 than since.

As in respect of the temperature change, the Little Ice Age appears as a minor episode. The change from 1900–1940 conditions represents about one-tenth to

Table 2. Estimated extent of ice (including sea-ice) and snow surfaces in different climatic epochs

	Winter maximum			Summer minimum		
	% of total area of the hemisphere	Difference from now	Equivalent latitude of the limit	% of total area of the hemisphere	Difference from now	Equivalent latitude of the limit
1900–1940 *approx.*						
Northern hemisphere	25		48·8	5·5		71·2
Southern hemisphere	13–14		60	7·7		68
About A.D. 1800						
Northern hemisphere	26–27	+1–2	47·3	6·1	+0·6	70·2
Southern hemisphere	13	0– –1	60–61	7·7	0	68
Maximum phase of Pleistocene ice ages						
Northern hemisphere	34–35	+9–10	41·0	16–17	+10–12	57·0
Southern hemisphere	24	+10–11	50	(21)	+13–14	(53)

Note. The equivalent latitude of the ice limit means the position it would occupy if the entire ice-covered area were circular and centred on the pole.

Notice that ice conditions in the northern hemisphere summers in the ice age were intermediate between those of present southern hemisphere summers and those of northern hemisphere winters. Both comparisons suggest that the general wind circulation in the ice-age summers would be much stronger than in northern hemisphere summers today. Turning to the ice-age winters, we see that the ice surface in the southern hemisphere then would be about as great as the snow and ice surface in the present northern hemisphere winters. The figures seem to imply a weaker winter circulation in the highest latitudes north and south in the ice age than now. In the lower latitudes it was probably much stormier in winter than now.

one-twentieth of the difference between now and the ice-age maximum. It was more serious in the North Atlantic and the land masses bordering it than elsewhere. Figures 3 and 4 show, respectively, the differences of prevailing sea temperatures (illustrated by January but similar in July) and sea-ice between 1800 and the present century. Prevailing water temperatures were apparently 3–4° C lower than around 1950 off Newfoundland and probably off south-east Iceland. The colder regime was pronounced everywhere north of 50° N. Some other areas had positive temperature departures, presumably attributable to displacement of ocean currents. Possibly there was stronger propulsion of the Gulf Stream on a more southern track than of late.

The northern Atlantic and surrounding land masses also appear to have been the regions which underwent the greatest cooling in the major ice ages. This recurring characteristic can be attributed to the fact that the Atlantic opening between Greenland and Europe was the only effective outlet for sea-ice from the Arctic Ocean; so that, when the amount of Arctic pack-ice changes, north and south shifts of the main thermal gradient which controls the atmospheric circulation are amplified in the Atlantic sector.

Figure 5 shows the supposed average positions of the snow and ice limit in January about A.D. 1800 and around the ice-age maximum compared with nowadays, based on the known changes of temperature. The ice-age picture in the North Atlantic follows Manley (1951). The position estimates are least

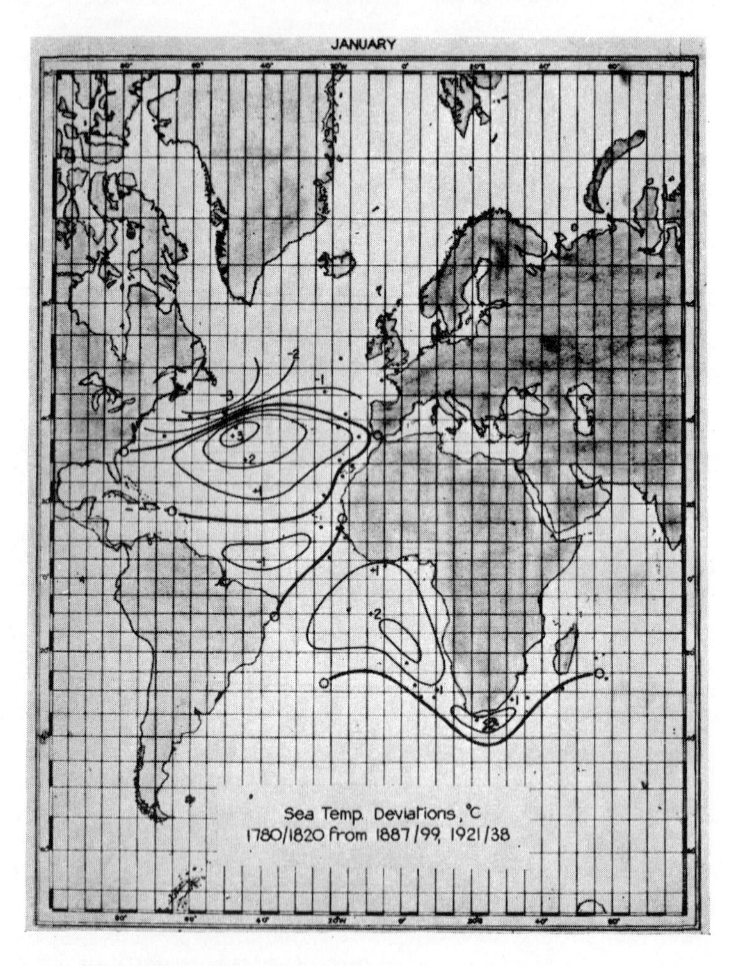

Fig. 3. Sea temperature differences (°C) in 1780–1820 from modern values (i.e. deviations from modern atlas values based on observations of the periods 1887–99, 1921–38).

reliable in the Pacific, but are certainly right in indicating much smaller displacement there. The greatest extensions of winter snow cover beyond present limits both in 1800 and in the ice age were probably in western Europe, the next biggest possibly in China.

Changes of area are not necessarily paralleled by proportionate changes of volume of ice on land. We may gauge the latter by examining world-wide

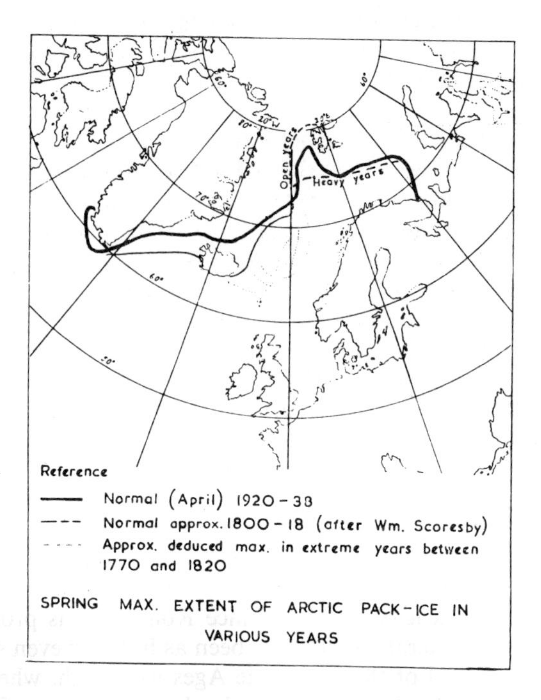

Fig. 4. Spring maximum extent of pack-ice on the Arctic seas in various years.

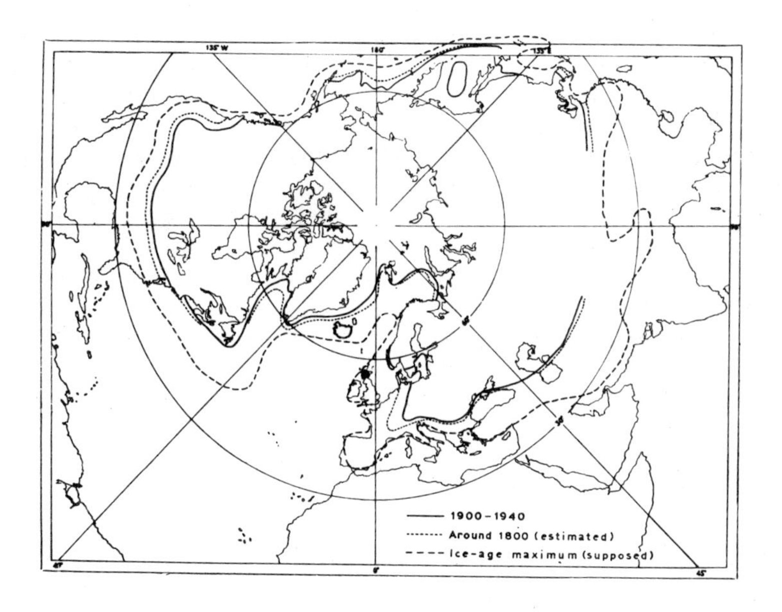

Fig. 5. Average positions of the snow and ice limit in January, various periods.

(eustatic) changes of sea level (Godwin, Suggate and Willis, 1958), since the substance of the ice must be drawn from the sea. Difficulty arises because the weight of ice on the formerly glaciated northern hemisphere lands was so great that they were depressed and have not even yet finished their recovery. This produces a continuing local (isostatic) fall of sea level relative to the land in formerly glaciated areas, especially the Baltic. Apparently southern Greenland again underwent a slight, but measurable, local isostatic depression with the added load of ice in the Little Ice Age after A.D. 1200. This has drowned some shoreside structures of the Old Norse colony. Sea-level changes must therefore be measured by averages of world-wide observations limited to the most tectonically stable areas, and except for very recent times they can hardly be trustworthy to within a few metres.

The tide gauge at Amsterdam indicates that sea level in 1682 (when the record begins) may have been 17 cm lower than in 1930 (Fairbridge, 1961), but this part of the world is affected by crustal warping (sinking accompanying the isostatic uplift of Scotland and Scandinavia) and the readings of the gauge may even have been raised slightly since 1680 by damming of the water in the soil and water channels following artificial reclamation of polders from the sea. There is a similar suggestion, however, from the Thames Estuary of slightly lower sea level in the recent cold epoch, but most of the local rise (2–4 m) of sea level in this area since Roman times is probably not due to climate. The general level may have been as high as, or even slightly higher than, now at the end of the early Middle Ages warm epoch, when the great sea floods came in East Anglia, the Netherlands and north-west Germany, and may have fallen about 1 ft (30 cm), at most, between then and the 1600s. But the striking thing is that, despite the serious consequences in places like Dunwich and the Zuyder Zee, these changes were so trivial by comparison with the 100-m lowering of world sea level at the ice-age maximum and the estimated further rise of 50–60 m (Bauer, 1955) if all the ice that still exists were to melt. Since the time about 1830, sea level in the region about the southern North Sea has been rising (relative to the land) at the rate of 10–15 cm a century, whereas from the last major ice age to the epoch of warmest postglacial climate about 4000 B.C. it appears to have risen at an average rate of 1 in. (2·5 cm) a year.

Whereas the lowering of air and sea temperature, and increase of area of snow and ice, during the so-called Little Ice Age of recent centuries in the northern hemisphere was of the order of a tenth part of the change between now and the Quaternary Ice Age maximum, the increase of mass of ice on land amounted to no more than a few thousandths (and possibly less than one-thousandth) of the major ice-age growth. Such growth as there was seems to have been mainly on those glaciers and ice-sheets which were nearest the open oceans—as in south Greenland, Iceland and Norway.

The smallness of the quantity of ice built up on land when the glaciers were advancing, probably from 1200 or 1300 to 1750, can only partly be put down to the brevity of the period—equivalent to 1–2% of the growth period of the Würm ice-sheets. Clearly there was no tendency to start forming the great northern hemisphere ice-sheets that had characterized the main ice ages.

Examination of the atmospheric circulation patterns back to 1750, and by indirect methods back to the beginnings of the cold epoch, suggests that the summer storm tracks across the North Atlantic were displaced well south of their 20th-century positions at the times of glacier advance in Iceland, Norway and the Alps. Figure 6 shows the changes in the mean latitude of the lowest pressure near Iceland in July since about 1800. Figures 7(a) and 7(b) show the mean barometric pressure and wind pattern in July in the 1940s, the time of quickest glacier withdrawal, compared with the estimated July depression tracks of the period 1550–1600, when the most rapid advance was starting, in Europe and Iceland. Figure 7(c) shows the estimated position of the prevailing depression tracks in the Julys of part of the early Middle Ages warm period, A.D. 1000–1200: the similarity with the 1940s needs no stressing.

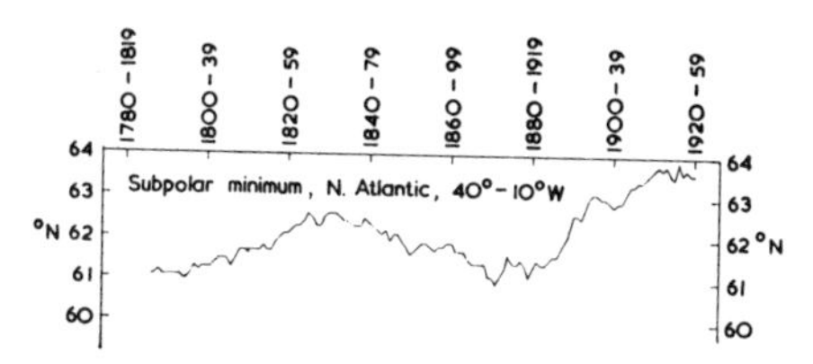

Fig. 6. Changes of latitude of the lowest pressure near Iceland in July, 40-year averages.

These displacements are in the same directions as those that have long been suggested as characterizing the differences between glacial and interglacial periods. Some parallelism between displacements of wind and ocean currents is not only to be expected in theory but is one of the most obvious aspects of the climatic changes since 1750–1800 (cf. Figs. 3 and 6)—a result which probably implies that in the major ice ages the colder Gulf Stream was strongly impelled almost due east towards southern Portugal or north-west Africa. There was an extraordinarily rapid spread of Arctic sea-ice, and evident cooling of the northern seas, between A.D. 1200 and 1800. About A.D. 880 Ottar, who later took service at the court of Alfred in England, explored the coast of Norway north from his home near Trondheim round the North Cape and into the White Sea: all this stretch of land remained in touch with the kingdom of Norway from that time on, the Finns paying tribute. Around 1050–1060 King Harald Hardråde of Norway (the same who died at Stamford Bridge in 1066 while attempting the conquest of England and who had seen campaigns in north Africa and in the Holy Land during a period of exile at Constantinople) explored the Arctic Ocean far to the north with a fleet of ships. Excerpts from his report as quoted by Nansen from Adam of Bremen (1070) read as if extensive ice was only encountered very far to the north and north-east, mostly beyond the limits of the last lands—presumably Spitsbergen or Novaya Zemlya. The ice was 8–10 ft thick, as in the warmest years in the present century but apparently even farther north. His expedition returned home after being overtaken by the winter darkness. Shortly before the year 1200, seals, walrus and whales were being hunted from Iceland and Norway as far as Spitsbergen and Novaya Zemlya. Very soon after 1200, however, the ice was increasing and the regular sailing

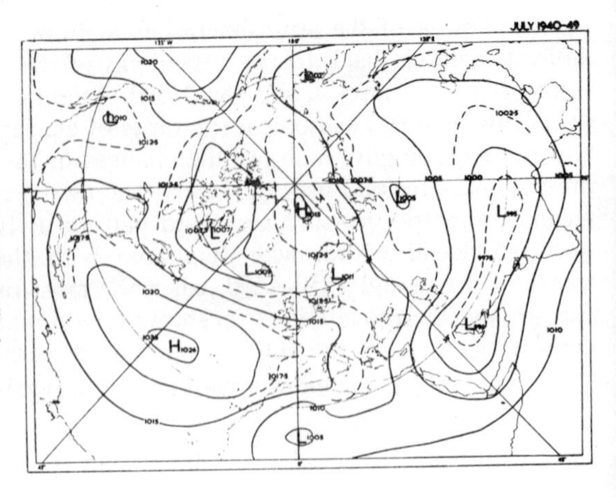

Fig. 7(a). Average barometric pressure in July 1940–49: the axis of lowest pressure in subpolar latitudes corresponds to the main depression tracks (indicated by arrows for the earlier epochs in Figs. 7(b) and 7(c).

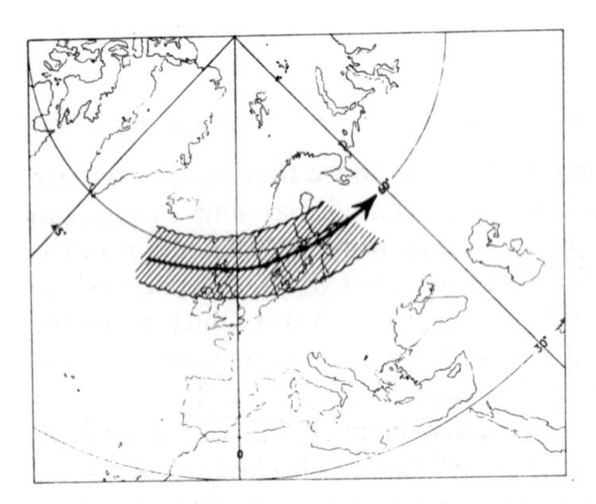

Fig. 7(b). Estimated zone of most frequent depression tracks (shaded) in July 1550–1600: this was a period of strong glacier advance.

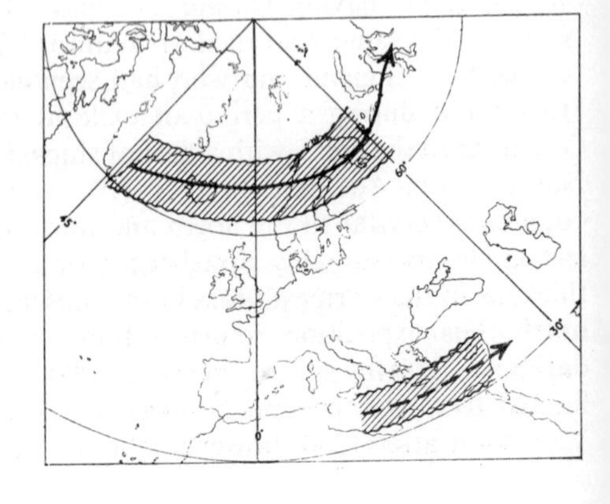

Fig. 7(c). Estimated zones of most frequent depression tracks (shaded) in July 1000–1100: part of the period of warmest climate in the last 2000 years.

routes of the period 1000–1200 between Iceland and Greenland near 67° N had to be abandoned. In the 18th century on at least one occasion a tongue of the polar pack-ice is believed to have reached the Faeroe Islands (62° N in the longitude of Britain): the occurrence is commemorated by a local place-name where a polar bear that came ashore was killed. Other similar tongues of the Arctic sea-ice may have been involved in the few recorded cases of Eskimoes in their kayaks turning up in Scotland and the northern isles between 1682 and 1843. The last occasion when extensive ice was met by vessels near the Faeroe Islands was in 1888. The appearance of a devastating spread of the sea-ice in our own sector between the year 1200 and the 1800s must, however, be viewed in the light of two facts:

(a) Since the only effective outlet from the central Arctic is in this sector, changes here are very much greater than in other sectors of the hemisphere.
(b) The main ice-bearing current from the Arctic moves down the east coast of Greenland, so that the edge of the polar ice normally lies SW–NE in this sector and variations measured at right angles to this line give a better idea of changes of quantity of ice than distances measured in the N–S direction. Moreover, in the cold epoch a branch of the cold current headed from East Greenland past eastern Iceland straight towards the Faeroes. The effect does, however, seem to have been a southward displacement of the sea-water isotherms in the broad Atlantic (cf. Fig. 3).

The southward shift of the depression tracks and precipitation accompanying them may have prevented any real start on the re-formation of the former continental ice-sheets in high latitudes. By the early 1800s the main streams of the atmospheric circulation, measured on average maps for January and July, had moreover become several per cent weaker than in the present century. This should imply a weakening of the transport of heat and moisture towards the polar regions.

Now it is time to notice that the glaciers whose variations in recent centuries we have chiefly considered (Fig. 1) are all either near or south of the commonest depression tracks in 60–70° N. Their increase and decrease were plainly related to temperature, just as the Asian and Chilean glaciers grew when the climate was cold. The few available studies of glaciers poleward of 70° N (and 70° S) suggest that accumulation there is greatest when precipitation is greatest and the atmospheric circulation most vigorous. Lister (1959) found from the ice stratigraphy that accumulation in Antarctica at the British Trans-Antarctic Expedition station Southice (82° S 29½° W) had risen to a maximum in the 1920s and declined since to about the level of the 1890s, a trend parallel with most measures of the strength of the general atmospheric circulation. Recent studies of the glaciers on Jan Mayen in 71° N 8° W (Lamb, Probert-Jones and Sheard, 1962) have shown a re-advance from about 1954 apparently associated with a doubling of the precipitation since 1920. The ice in Greenland and on Jan Mayen also appears to have advanced towards the end of the warmest postglacial climatic epoch around 2000 B.C. (Kinsman and Sheard, 1962). This was during the warm epoch itself but probably after its warmest phase was over. During the warmest phases before 3000 B.C. there was general recession of the ice. The north-western part of the Greenland ice-sheet in 77° N 56° W had its greatest accumulation recently (Langway, 1962; Bader, 1961) in about the same years as the Antarctic ice-sheet at Southice—when the atmospheric circulation was most vigorous (Fig. 8). Similar stratigraphic studies of the ice at the South Pole are provisionally considered by M. Giovinetto (unpublished) to indicate no major change since the 16th century or earlier apart from slightly greater accumulation during the warmer summers of the period 1900–1950. There may have been more snow (and more accumulation) from depressions affecting northern Greenland in the warmest recent decades just when the ice in southern

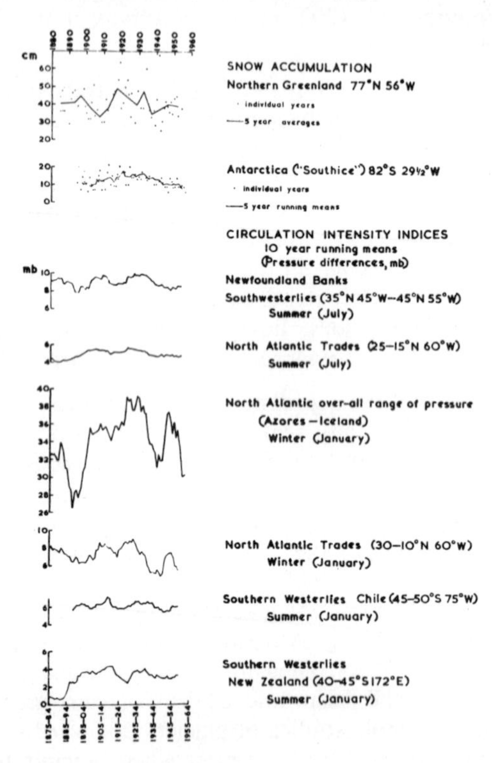

Fig. 8. Accumulation on the Greenland and Antarctic ice-sheets (5-year means and individual years since about 1890) compared with indices of atmospheric circulation strength in summer and winter (10-year means).

Greenland showed most signs of retreat. Figure 9 displays the pattern of accumulation on the ice-cap. The maxima on the west side of northern Greenland and on the east side of southern Greenland may indicate that the two ice-domes owe their origin to alternative depression tracks, the northern one to westerly wind components with lows in latitudes north of 75° and the southern one to easterly winds blowing on the north side of the Atlantic ("Iceland") depressions. The crests of the ice-domes might be expected to move slowly towards the accumulation maxima unless ice flow and iceberg calving corrected this, as they probably do.

The colder climate of the time around 1800, and especially the net deficit of temperature of the surface waters of the Atlantic Ocean between 50–60° N and 40° S are of the right magnitude to be explained by a deficiency of 1–2% in the radiation absorbed at the surface over a rather long period prior to that (Lamb, 1961). Calculations, based on the increased area of ice surface in each latitude zone corresponding to the total figures given in Table 2, indicate that increased wastage of solar radiation by reflection could not account for a reduction of more than about 0·5% of the total received. The equatorial rain-belt generally, though not the Indian monsoon, was apparently somewhat more

Fig. 9. Mean annual accumulation (cm) of snow on the Greenland ice-sheet (after H. Bader).

active in the 19th century than since, and it is possible that slightly greater world cloud cover contributed to lessening the intake of solar radiation, though it does not seem likely that this change was as great as that resulting from the greater extent of snow and ice. In addition to these two effects, therefore, reduction of the radiation supply itself by something of the order of 0·5–1% may have to be invoked to account for the coldness of the climate around 1800—whether this was due to a variation in the output of the sun or to frequent volcanic dust veils in the stratosphere or both.

Theories of ice-age development

Recognition of the cold climate of A.D. 1550–1850 as a brief cold episode with rapid spread of the Arctic sea-ice and increase in the area of ice and snow on land in latitudes below 70°, but no important waxing of the main polar ice-caps, seems to support those ice-age theories associated with the names of Simpson (1934) and Ewing and Donn (1956) that require an initial period with ice-free ocean to high latitudes supplying moisture for heavy snowfall on polar lands. It may be important to notice that the general wind circulation, and accompanying heat and moisture transport, was also weakened by comparison with nowadays. It is reasonable to expect that, just as the North Atlantic is affected by a cold tongue extending to lower latitudes than in the Pacific or in the southern hemisphere in cold climatic epochs, the warm tongue of Gulf Stream–North Atlantic Drift water will spread open water from the Atlantic far into the polar sea in warmer periods. The ice-sheets in the highest latitudes in Greenland and Antarctica show evidence of greater accumulation during recent rather warm decades. Contrary to Simpson's theory, however, Kraus (1960) appears to have demonstrated that no conceivable increase of precipitation could *start* the accumulation of an ice-sheet in the former regions of northern Canada and the Baltic unless summer temperatures first fell below present values. This would be still more out of the question if the open polar ocean implied world temperature 2–3° C above now, as in the interglacial periods and postglacial maximum.

Ewing and Donn also require an open ice-free Arctic Ocean whenever major ice-caps are formed on land. But if the Arctic Ocean had been completely ice-free, it seems certain that snow would have accumulated to form an ice-sheet over northern Alaska and low ground in north-east Asia as well as in Europe, Greenland and the eastern Canadian Arctic. Geological studies indicate that this did not happen (Karlstrom, 1961), and indeed the ice-free land in northern Alaska and north-east Siberia during the ice ages probably formed the land bridge by which the first peoples and animals of the Americas arrived from the Old World.

We may safely assume that in the great interglacial periods and in the post-glacial optimum (warmest) climate of about 5000–3000 B.C., there was no permanent pack-ice on the Arctic Ocean, and yet no ice formed on land. In fact, the ice-sheets left over from previous ice ages were melting with great rapidity, and world sea level rose correspondingly quickly. Let us consider the changes that would occur if the Earth began to cool, possibly through a decreased amount of radiation reaching the surface.

A permanent snow cover would be established first over East Antarctica, where the land is high and spreads over 180–200 degrees of longitude in the highest latitudes. It is reasonable to suppose, however, that in the Arctic at about the same stage, ice would form a permanent cover on those parts of the polar sea most remote from the warm water supply from the Atlantic—i.e. the sector off Alaska and north-east Asia—and that this might rather easily spread over the whole of the Arctic Ocean beyond the great submarine ridge (Lomonossov Ridge) which runs from the New Siberian Islands towards Ellesmere Land, roughly along the 140° E and 60–90° W meridians (Fig. 10). With this minor modification, which would explain the lack of growth of an ice-sheet in northern Alaska in the same way as the lack of such growth anywhere in the Arctic in the recent cold epoch, it seems possible to accept Ewing and Donn's suggestion. Conditions would then be ideal for growth of ice-caps in northern Greenland and the Canadian Archipelago, provided the radiation heating were somewhat feebler than now; the latter requirement is still more obviously needed in the case of Scandinavia. It seems necessary to disagree with Simpson and assert that the

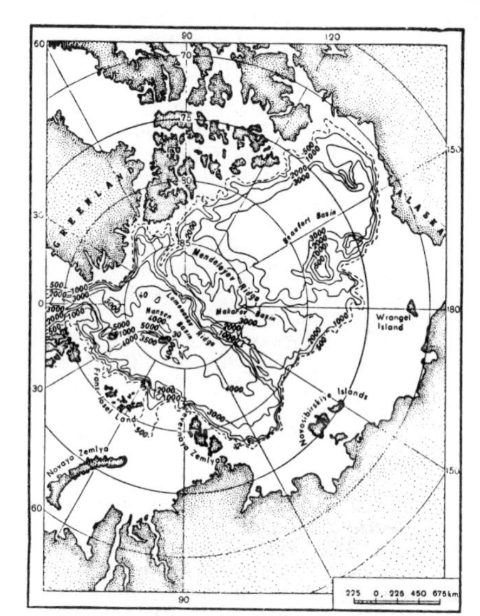

Fig. 10. Map of the Arctic Basin bottom relief (after N. A. Belov), depths in metres.

effective radiation supply was rather less than now, though possibly intermediate between present conditions and those in the Little Ice Age—a rather delicate balance. We are left with the awkward meteorological and oceanographic problem of why the waters remained open long enough, evidently for some thousands of years, past Spitsbergen and northern Greenland about as far as the Lomonossov Ridge, when they were closed by ice within 300–500 years from the onset of the Little Ice Age cooling and remain partly closed today. It seems necessary to assume a great prevalence of southerly winds and depressions moving north off East Greenland and in Davis Strait–Baffin Bay and across North Greenland while the Canadian and Greenland ice was growing. This may have been a straightforward consequence of the thermal pattern, especially if the Canadian ice grew rather before the Greenland ice while the seas were still warm. It seems necessary also to suppose a radiation supply persistently below, but only slightly below, that of today. The impression is gained that in the recent Little Ice Age epoch the temperature fell too fast, possibly because radiation was rather frequently reduced by volcanic dust. The Little Ice Age episode appears to bear a similarity to the epoch 900–450 B.C., at least in the northern hemisphere. Its time-scale is perhaps the same as that of some interstadials and some cold fluctuations in interglacial periods.

Acknowledgments. The author is indebted to the Director General of the Meteorological Office for permission to publish this article. He also wishes to acknowledge his thanks to Professor Reid A. Bryson of the University of Wisconsin for drawing his attention to the recorded exploits of Ottar and King Harald Hardråde in the northern seas.

References

AHLMANN, H. W. 1953. *Glacier variations and climatic fluctuations.* Bowman Memorial Lecture. American Geographical Society, New York.

BADER, H. 1961. *The Greenland ice sheet.* U.S. Army Cold Regions Research and Engineering Laboratory, Report 1–B2.

BAUER, A. 1955. 'Über die in der heutigen Vergletscherung der Erde als Eis-gebundene Wassermasse.' *Eiszeitalter Gegenwart*, **6**, 60.

BROOKS, C. E. P. 1949. *Climate through the ages* (2nd Ed.). Benn, London.

EMILIANI, C. 1955. 'Pleistocene temperatures.' *J. Geol.*, **63**, 538.

EWING, M. and DONN, W. L. 1956, 1958. 'A theory of ice ages.' *Science*, **123**, 1061; *ibid.* **127**, 1159.

FAIRBRIDGE, R. W. 1961. 'Eustatic changes in sea level.' In: *Physics and chemistry of the Earth.* Vol. 4, Ch. 3. Pergamon, New York.

FLOHN, H. 1952. 'Allgemeine atmosphärische Zirkulation und Paläoklimatologie.' *Geol. Rundschau*, **40**, 153.

GODWIN, H., SUGGATE, R. P. and WILLIS, E. H. 1958. 'Radiocarbon dating of the eustatic rise in ocean level.' *Nature*, **181**, 1518.

HEUSSER, C. J. 1960. 'Late Pleistocene environments of the Laguna de San Rafael area, Chile.' *Geograph. Rev.*, **50**, 555.

KARLSTROM, Th. N. V. 1961. 'The glacial history of Alaska.' *Ann. N.Y. Acad. Sci.*, **95**, Art. 1, 290.

KINSMAN, D. J. J. and SHEARD, J. W. 1962. Unpublished report on the glaciers of Jan Mayen.

KRAUS, E. B. 1960. 'Synoptic and dynamic aspects of climatic change.' *Quart. J. Roy. Meteorol. Soc.*, **86**, 1.

LAMB, H. H. 1955. 'Two-way relationships between the snow or ice limit and 1000–500 mb thicknesses in the overlying atmosphere.' *Quart. J. Roy. Meteorol. Soc.*, **81**, 172.

LAMB, H. H. 1961. 'On the nature of certain climatic epochs which differed from the modern (1900–39) normal.' *WMO/UNESCO Symposium on climatic changes and the arid zones*, Rome.

LAMB, H. H., PROBERT-JONES, J. R. and SHEARD, J. W. 1962. 'A new advance of the Jan Mayen glaciers and a remarkable increase of precipitation.' *J. Glaciol.* (in press).

Langway, C. C. 1962. 'Some physical and chemical investigations of a 411 meter deep Greenland ice core and their relationship to accumulation.' *Intern. Assoc. Sci. Hydrology Publ., No.* 58, Commission of Snow and Ice, pp. 101–118. Obergurgl 1961 Symposium.

Lister, H. 1959. 'Geophysical investigations of the Commonwealth Transantarctic Expedition, 1. Climate and ice mass balance.' *Geograph. J.*, **125**, 343.

Manley, G. 1951. 'The range of variation of the British climate.' *Geograph. J.*, **117**, 43.

Runcorn, S. K. 1962. 'Continental drift.' *Research* (London), **15**, 103.'

Schwarzbach, M. 1961. *Das Klima der Vorzeit* (2nd Ed.). Ch. XIX. Enke, Stuttgart.

SIMPSON, G. C. 1934. 'World climate during the Quaternary period.' *Quart. J. Roy. Meteorol. Soc.* **60**, 425.

SIMPSON, G. C. 1940. 'Possible causes of change in climate and their limitations.' *Proc. Linnean Soc. London*, 1939–40, Pt. 2, 190.

SIMPSON, G. C. 1957. 'Further studies in world climate.' *Quart. J. Roy. Meteorol. Soc.*, **83**, 459.

WALLÉN, C. C. 1948. 'Glacial-meterological investigations on the Kårsa Glacier in Swedish Lappland 1942–48.' *Geograf. Ann.*, **30**, 451.

WEIDICK, A. 1959. 'Glacier variations in west Greenland in historical time.' *Medd. Groenland*, **158**, No. 4.

WRIGHT, H. E. 1961. 'Late Pleistocene climate of Europe: a review.' *Bull. Geol. Soc. Am.*, **72** 933.

SIX

Trees and climatic history in Scotland; a radiocarbon dating test and other evidence

SUMMARY

Scotland constitutes a gap in our information about the Early Middle Ages warm epoch (*circa* 1000-1300 A.D.). Evidence has been sought from vegetational history as well as documentary records.

A sample tree found lying in a peat bog at an exposed part of the north-west coast where trees no longer grow was discussed in the *Quarterly Journal*, 1945, when it was thought to have grown there in the Middle Ages or later. The result of a radiocarbon dating test on this tree contradicts all the opinions then expressed about its age. The tree and other remains from the same bog are now shown to have belonged to the latter part of the post-glacial climatic optimum before 2000 B.C., and there is no tangible evidence that trees have grown at the point in question at any time since 1000 B.C. This compels a re-assessment of the other evidence, of what we may hope to learn from it and how much we know so far about the climatic history of Scotland in medieval and post-medieval times.

Documents of the times concerned, already used but not so far quoted in this connexion by various historians, have yielded the most promising indications to date. The isolated facts and impressions gained from these sources seem most simply explained by assuming that Scotland shared the general experience in northern lands of a warm epoch, accompanying the period of high culture, from 1070 A.D. or earlier, to around 1300 and that the subsequent deterioration had serious effects upon the economy. The evidence from Scotland, as opposed to that from neighbouring countries, of frequent bad seasons and deteriorating condition of the land, is so far, however, almost entirely indirect and in itself inconclusive. Only after 1550 are enough facts known to make the latter stages of the decline culminating in the dire years of the 1690's reasonably clear and unmistakable.

1. INTRODUCTION

Attention was directed in the *Quarterly Journal*, 1945 (**71**, pp. 154-6) to the possible implications as regards the climatic history of north-west Scotland of the finding of a log 17 ft long, the trunk of a well-grown pine tree, lying about 3 ft below the surface of a peat bog at an exposed point near the coast where it is reported that trees will not now grow. The purpose of this note is to provide a re-assessment of the matter in the light of new information, namely a radiocarbon test, and a brief review of other considerations that must be taken into account.

The problem was when did that tree and other relics near it grow. Opinion then inclined to the view that it grew in some proposed period of drier sunnier climate in north-west Scotland in the eighteenth century, though doubts arose because of its depth in the peat. The radiocarbon test, apparently conclusively, places the whole assemblage much earlier – before 2000 B.C.

In this, as in other connexions more familiar to meteorology, not too much in the way of general conclusions can be deduced from a single sample, but a review of the evidence and its limitations may nevertheless be instructive.

2. THE SITE OF THE SAMPLE TREE

The log was found near the gate of Badentarbet Lodge, Achiltibuie, Ross-shire, 50 ft above sea level, at 58° 02′ 10″N; 5° 21′ 15″W (National Grid reference 29/013101). The position is at the centre of the circle of 10 km radius, marked A, in Fig. 1. On this map the areas with woods today are marked in black, their extent somewhat exaggerated to ease recognition.

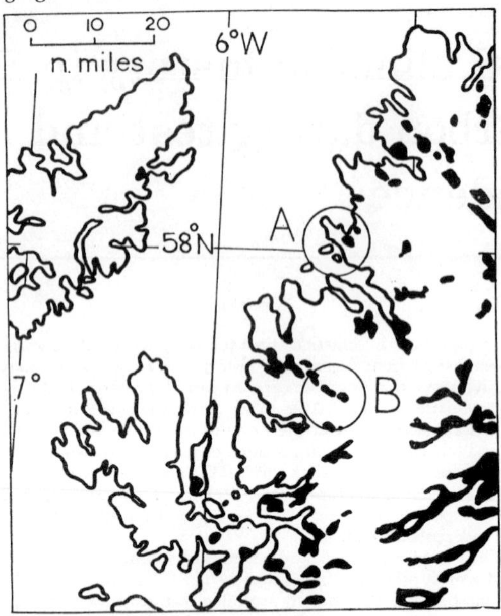

Figure 1. Map showing the part of the Scottish coast discussed. Present woodlands are shown, inland waters are not. The log was found in Badentarbet bog at the centre of the circle marked A, where the coast faces South. The Beinn Eighe Nature Reserve lies near the centre of the circle marked B.

The peat at the point in question is 4 ft thick and rests on glacial drift. Tree-trunks lying deep in the peat are actually very numerous in north-west Scotland, though this site is perhaps peculiarly near the windward coast. The tree-trunk, averaging 7½ inches thick, with no bark remaining, had about 80 yearly growth rings. It gave the appearance of having been " burnt and then blown over," but this burnt appearance is common because wood is slowly oxidized in the bogs.

There are many stumps of pine trees in this same small peat bed, some (presumably the youngest) of them indicating that the ground, when they grew, was no more than 2 ft below the present surface of the moor – i.e., the stumps nearest the surface are at two-foot depth in the peat.

The place is just south of the small Loch Vatachan (see Fig. 2 for place names), which occupies a bare low moorland valley ¾ mile wide that cuts through the peninsula where Achiltibuie lies and is open to north and south. The ground rises to over 500 ft (150 metres) on either side, east and west, of that valley and slopes gently downward to the south from the site of the find without interruption to the sea, barely 500 yards away, at the broad outer entrance to the firth known as Loch Broom. Winds from between S. and SW. have nothing to break their force, and gales are frequent. The topography probably funnels these winds to give added force at this locality. It may be noticed however that none of the woods shown in Fig. 1 reach any of the more open parts of the coast.

Dr. T. G. Longstaff of Badentarbet Lodge, finder of the specimen here discussed, added the following remarks (*Q.J.*, 1945) : " Scots pine will not grow now, and a plantation made 30 years ago, 8 miles to the north-east failed, ... the position chosen for the plantation was much more sheltered " and, further, that : " there are no natural pines left in Coigach, only struggling birch with rare rowan and about 20 acornless, scrubby oaks in the whole district."

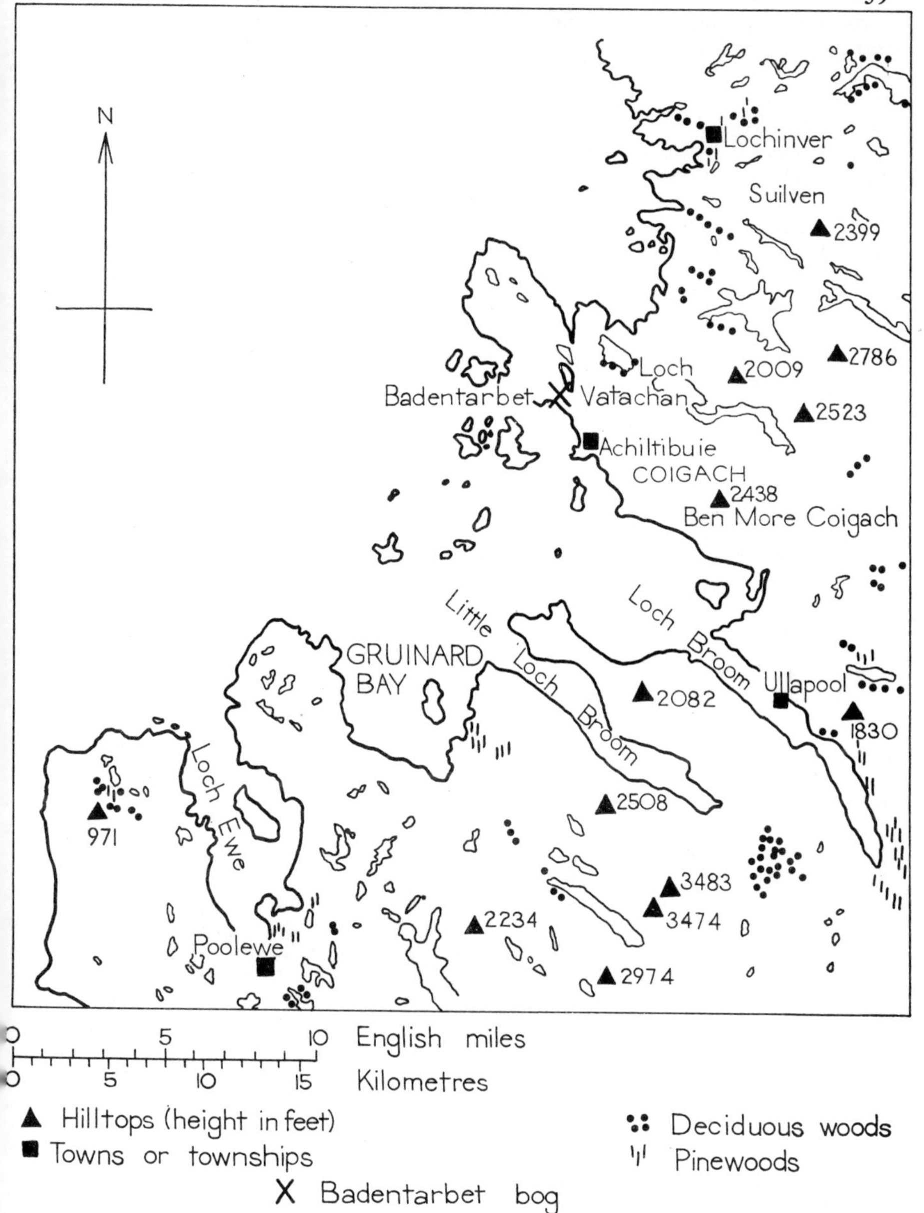

Figure 2. Place names and coast near Badentarbet.

Fig. 2 shows the location and type of present woods in the area, as indicated by the Ordnance Survey large-scale maps.

In so far as wind and wind-blown sea-salt might be suspected of being the most adverse climatic factors in this locality, the following view expressed by F. H. W. Green and D. N. McVean of the Nature Conservancy, Speyside Research Station, Aviemore (*personal communication* 1963) refers to the birches which occur within the same general area of north-west Scotland, though it has no obvious relevance to pine : " New birch seedlings fail to appear for a variety of reasons only one of which is directly climatic, namely, when and where dessicating winds are too strong during the fruiting period so that the catkins get blown off before maturing. This does not happen every year even in relatively exposed places, and must have happened even less before man's activity reduced the number of mature trees which gave local shelter . . . "

The generalized altitude zonation of vegetation for the Highlands of Scotland (trees → tall shrubs → dwarf shrubs → grasses and cryptogams) is described elsewhere by McVean and Ratcliffe (1962) as dipping towards the north-west due to increasing cloudiness, humidity, wind exposure and lack of summer warmth. Severity of exposure to wind and lack of summer warmth are stressed as the main factors limiting growth. Woodland seldom attains its natural limits in present-day Scotland, but the upper limits of sub-alpine scrub and the lower limits of montane vascular plants do show the natural sequence. Thus, the lowest good colonies of dwarf birch (*Betula nana*) are at 1,500 ft (about 450 m) in the east-central Highlands, but at 400 ft (120 m) in exposed districts in the north-west; for *Saxifraga oppositifolia* the corresponding heights are 800 ft (240 m) and sea level. " On the most exposed coasts of the north-west mainland, the Outer Isles, Orkney and Shetland, the forest and tall shrub zone vanishes altogether and the climax vegetation virtually at sea level is dwarf shrub heath." Introduction of the term ' climax vegetation ' indicates that it is not just a question of the climatic tolerance of individual species of trees etc. but of competition with other vegetation. These zones appear *a priori* likely to show some advances and retreats at their boundaries in response to climatic changes.

3. Cumulative climatic effects

There are other ways in which the climate of north-west Scotland, particularly through its effect upon the soils, may have made the situation prohibitive for the growth of trees. This depends upon the development of podsolization and blanket-bog.

Podsol is the name given to a type of impoverished soil developing in cool temperate and sub-polar climates where precipitation is considerable and evaporation limited, so that the upper layers of the soil have their organic material and soluble minerals leached out (washed into lower layers by the percolating water). These soils are usually greyish white in colour.

Bogs are formed by vegetation growing, and vegetation products collecting, in shallow lakes and pools and areas of ground that are habitually waterlogged. On the surface *Sphagnum* mosses and sometimes heather (*Calluna*) grow, and in time the substrata of the bog consist more and more of decayed moss together with such pollens, dust and other matter as gets blown or washed into the bog. Growth of the bog plants gradually raises the surface of the bog till sometimes in very wet periods the whole spongy mass becomes overladen with water, its strength gives way and the bog ' bursts,' i.e., masses of water and of the substance of the bog swill out over neighbouring, often better, land lower down the drainage basin. Many occurrences of bog-bursts in wet periods have been recorded, e.g., Solway Moss on 16 December 1772 (*Gentleman's Magazine*, June 1773) and near Charleville, Co. Cork on 7 June 1697 (New Style). Blanket-bog is the term used to describe a bog situation that stifles the growth of other forms of vegetation.

Professor H. Godwin, believes that podsolization and bog growth are the most important climatic control in rendering sites such as the one at Achiltibuie unfavourable for trees in recent times, though he stresses (*personal communication*, 1963) the desirability of the most thorough field study of the local stratigraphic conditions at any individual site considered, so that one may work out the process by which the trees came to be killed. I am indebted to him for the following paragraphs :

> " Blanket-bog develops as the end product of podsolization which leads first to a growth of *Sphagnum* peat over the mineral soil. This gives general water-logging,

beginning in the basins and flat areas and spreading gradually up the gentler slopes . . . . a moss peat, once established, is maintained in the given climate : the factor expressing its control most nearly being the rainfall/evaporation ratio or the rainfall/saturation deficit ratio. Once established, the access of oxygen to the mineral soil below is prevented and all trees rooted therein are killed. In time the dead trees rot at the water/air junction, fall over and are embedded. The stump, now waterlogged, is preserved, and the fallen trunk is preserved in so far as it has sunk into deoxygenated layers. The onset of blanket-bog formation is, in almost all cases save those of high elevation, marked by overwhelming of a basal tree layer growing on the mineral soil. What then is needed is to know the cause of the onset of blanket-bog formation.

Now there is a good deal of evidence suggesting that podsolization is a progressive process, going on at different rates on different soils, different slopes, different climates, and on different parent rocks. On acidic impervious rocks in the Highlands it has probably been in progress right through the post-glacial period. The process would ultimately lead to blanket-bog formation on all but strongly sloping and well-drained situations, but the onset would be at very various times. Naturally, if there was an oscillation of climate towards dryness the bogs would tend to dry out, cease to grow, and might become tree-covered. If there was an oscillation in the opposite sense, bogs would grow, extend and entomb forests that might have grown on their dried out bog surfaces.

In general, therefore the transition from dry to wet periods will be marked by layers of tree stumps in and below bogs, but one would need very many dated records before generalizations as to climate became reasonably valid. I have in fact been keeping for some time a card index of radiocarbon dates of such tree layers, but they are still too few to be conclusive. They are often associated with other evidence of climatic shift from dryness to wetness, particularly so-called recurrence surfaces, on which I have written at different times " (Godwin 1954).

In an interesting study of the forest history of the Beinn Eighe Nature Reserve, (at B in Fig. 1), which is in a rather more sheltered inland terrain some 25 mi (40 km) south of the Badentarbet site here discussed, Durno and McVean (1959) concluded that over much of the low ground of the Reserve, an open forest-bog complex appears to have been established at an early (i.e. early post-glacial) period with gradually diminishing tree cover since . . . . due to successive forest fires. Repeated moor fires, lack of seed parents and extreme degradation of the soil have effectively prevented recolonization by trees except locally on north-facing slopes where all the present woodland remnants lie. (These are, and have probably always been, the slopes most sheltered from strong winds). The authors think the present proportion of forest was probably reached by 1400-1500 A.D., although the more favourable habitats of the surrounding country would have remained forested until rather later.

Interference by man was certainly largely involved in the forest fires, both in the course of the old Highland warfare and to reduce the wolves which were finally exterminated about 1700 A.D.

4. The framework of world climatic history

Enough has been written to portray the complicated assortment of climatic, vegetational, soil and human influences to which tree growth in Scotland has been subject and on which it was hoped the Badentarbet specimen would throw some light. It is now necessary to outline what is actually known of the broad framework of climatic history, into which our specimen must fit somewhere.

Since the disappearance of the glaciers of the last (i.e., post-Alleröd) stage of the last ice age in Britain about 10,000 years ago, there has been one major period of warm climate, the ' Post-glacial optimum,' with estimated annual mean temperatures about 2°C higher than those of today (see Appendix). This is witnessed by manifold (especially botanical) evidence from all over the world, dated broadly around 7000 to 2000 B.C., with its peak about 5000 to 3000 B.C., a warm and, in much of Europe, rather moist period, the ' Atlantic period ' associated with an enlarged Baltic. Summer temperatures in Europe are estimated to have been 2 to 3°C higher than today's. Winter temperatures probably differed less from today's. Tree stumps in the peat bogs in many upland districts of Britain high above the present limit of trees, particularly in the Scottish Highlands, and a greater relative abundance than now of warmth-loving southern trees such as elm (*Ulmus*) and lime (*Tilia*) in the lowlands of England and Scotland, are amongst the testimonies to this warm, and presumably less windy climatic period (Godwin 1956; Steven and Carlisle 1959). Nevertheless the trees on the heights were small. Both in Britain and the Alps there is some evidence that the highest level of the forest limit was reached about the end of the warmest epoch around 3000 B.C. It would not be surprising if the greatest expansion of woodland to the exposed Atlantic coast and islands to the north and west was reached about the same time. After the optimum, climates became chillier and less favourable in most parts of the world, but continued to undergo somewhat lesser variations. In the Bronze Age there was a much shorter, but apparently also drier, warm period which dried out the bogs in many parts of Europe and raised the tree line in the Alps (Gams 1937) once more to about its previous maximum level; this lasted some centuries around 1200-1000 B.C. It is hardly identifiable as a separate phase in eastern Europe, but in the stratigraphy of the bogs in Scotland some tree layers of birch (*Betula*) and pine (*Pinus*) and heathers (*Calluna*) – Archibald Geikie's ' Upper Forestian ' – may belong to this period; bog growth ceased and bog surfaces became seasonally very dry in much of western and central Europe. At the same period the water level in many Alpine lakes became so low that bogs encroached upon or replaced the water surface. Brooks (1934, p. 379) referred to widespread tree remains of this date in the bogs of Ireland as well as Scotland and of juniper in the Shetlands and Faroes. This is the last ' optimum ' of which botanical evidence is known in Scotland.

There followed a rather rapid deterioration to a colder, and evidently wetter, climatic period, the onset of the so-called ' Sub-atlantic.' Water levels rose and human lakeside settlements in the Alpine region were swamped. Glaciers advanced in the Alps and Scandinavia : in parts of the Alps almost to the same limits as were attained around A.D. 1600-1800. Aario's study (1944) of the moraines produced in the Stubaier Alps in Tirol is quoted by Firbas and Losert (1949) : the dating by reference to corresponding features of the peat stratigraphy in the area is sufficient for present purposes. This glacier advance is certainly evidence of colder summers : whether the winters also became colder than before demands independent evidence – this is, however, suggested by the cessation of mining in the Alps and of traffic over the passes (Gams 1937) and apparently by folk memories of the deterioration enshrined in legend in the Alps, in central Asia (Altai) and in Scandinavia (Bergeron *et al.* 1956). This climatic phase is registered in the peat stratigraphy of the bogs from Ireland to Germany and south Sweden by a phase of re-growth (regeneration of the plant life of the bog) which produced by far the most marked recurrence surface in the stratigraphy (Godwin 1954). World-wide evidence agrees in indicating dates around 600-500 B.C. for the climax of this catastrophe; though Ireland and possibly western Scotland, where the climate would be always moister than in most of Europe, yield evidence of bog regeneration from 900 B.C. onwards and Gams gives the ninth century B.C. as the date of the disaster to the last of the lake settlements of the Hallstatt period. All glaciers now existing in the Rockies south of about 50°N are believed to have been first formed about this time, and the estimate by Gams that the area of ice in the Glockner region of the Alps in the Bronze Age was no more than 20-25 per cent of that in modern times (between 1600 and the 1930's) supports H. Kinzl's description of the present glaciers in the Alps as representing a new glaciation effectively produced since 1000 B.C. The moraines produced in the Stubaier Alps imply an extremely rapid growth of glaciers between about 1000 and 500 B.C.

There was a subsequent recovery, culminating (after further vicissitudes of which something is known in the 700's A.D.) in the period of warm climate around 1000-1300 A.D. (Professor R. A. Bryson (Aspen Conference 1962) has called it the 'Little optimum') with average summer temperatures in Europe 1°C or so higher than today's, and mean annual temperatures probably higher by 2 to 4°C in parts of the Arctic. Winter temperatures in Europe appear to have been quite similar to those of the present century. Evidence of this warm period is widely found in archaeology, glaciology, historical documents, cultivation patterns and (in places where human settlement was sparse or non-existent) in shifts of species limits in the natural fauna and flora in continental Europe, Iceland, Greenland and various parts of North America (Aspen Conference 1962). From Scotland no direct evidence of any kind for (or against) this warm climatic period of the early Middle Ages is known so far. For the proper meteorological interpretation of the period it is highly desirable that this gap should be filled.

The 'Little ice age' period of cold climate culminating between 1550 and 1700 (though well after 1700 in the case of the glaciers and sea ice) is by now established by copious evidence from almost all parts of the Northern Hemisphere. It generally produced the most advanced positions of the glaciers since the last (Würm) ice age. It is also believed to have produced a recession (lowering) of the upper forest limit by 70 to 200 m in various places from the heights to about its present altitude limits on the mountains of central Europe between 1300 and 1600 (Firbas and Losert 1949; Gams 1937). A net decline in extent of forest cover in the Beinn Eighe Nature Reserve about the period 1300 to 1500, obliquely referred to by Durno and McVean, mentioned above, may to some extent correspond with this.

5. Scottish detail

Interpretation of forest evidence in Scotland is obscured by the activities of man, particularly his forest fires, from the beginning of the Neolithic, about 3000 B.C., onwards. Nevertheless man's competence to interfere with nature was limited in scale, and some signs remaining of responses of the natural vegetation to climatic changes in Scotland much later than that may yet be found.

The writer has paid some attention to various other possible sources of evidence. It is not difficult to find hints of climatic deterioration after 1300 A.D. as part of the background to the increasing social privations and unrest in Scottish life (first in the Highlands and later on in a quite different form in the Lowlands in the east and south too) between at any rate the 1430's, if not earlier, and 1700 and more particularly from 1550 to 1590 onwards. (Historians might usefully investigate the causes of the rapid decline in fortunes of the old Celtic earldom of Mar in the east central Highlands about 1426, when it was resigned to the king and collapsed as a well-organized entity, and to the real nature of the troubles in the far north and north-west that led to the savage clan battle publicly staged at Perth in 1396). By contrast, the period that included the time of King Malcolm's court at Dunfermline making a home for Anglo-Saxon refugees from England about 1070 and the expansion of the Abbey and its activities till 1300 gives a quite trouble-free impression. The latter part of the thirteenth century has been described as "a Golden Age in Scottish history" (*The north-east of Scotland*, British Association, Aberdeen 1963, p. 81). This trend stands out from a straightforward analysis of the frequencies of difficult weather and dearths reported in *The Annals of Dunfermline*, though not specifically noticed by their compiler (Henderson 1879); equally clear is the evidence of a gradual, and at first halting, recovery after 1700.

Appropriate changes seem from fragmentary evidence to have occurred in Scotland both in the agricultural economy and in the extent of woodland about the time of sharpest climatic deterioration in Europe from 1550 or 1560 onwards. This phase was accompanied by lowering of the prevailing summer and winter temperatures in Europe (attested by evidence of glaciers, vine harvests and snow frequency), abnormal frequency of northerly and easterly winds in the winters and probably an increase of storminess as well as of wetness in the summers in the latitude of Scotland (Aspen Conference 1962; Lamb 1963).

Observational evidence of prevailing winds and weather at present being compiled on charts appears already sufficient to indicate that frequent depression tracks passed over or near Scotland between about 56 and 62°N in 80-85 per cent of the summers between 1586 and 1605 and between 1688 and 1700.

The port of Aberdeen used to export several varieties of grain, including 'cornes' thought to be some sort of wheat. How much was coastwise transport to other parts of Scotland, and how much went overseas, is not known: But in most of the years 1596 to 1612 (studied by Mrs. L. B. Turner (*personal communication* to Mr. L. P. Smith 1962)) the harvests either failed or were too poor to permit export in any quantity. This may indicate that the trade was a survival from better times. Wheat had certainly been grown and distributed by the abbey at Kelso in south Scotland and probably elsewhere in 1290, though the harvest reported was 84 per cent oats, 11 per cent bere or barley and only 5 per cent wheat (Dickinson 1961). Then we learn that in 1733 the growing of wheat was introduced "for the first time" in the lowlands of west Fife (in south-central Scotland) around Dunfermline (Henderson 1879): one suspects that this may have been *re*-introduction of wheat, though probably also a better variety than the medieval strains. Between 1693 and 1700, which were probably the coldest and wettest summers of all, every kind of grain harvest failed in all but the lowest and most favoured eastern parishes of Scotland in seven out of the eight years.

As might be expected, in England by contrast, only a minority of the summers seem to have fallen below the standard of weather required for a successful wheat harvest. Even wet summers often produced enough warm dry weather to save the corn and the drier sort of cool summers also turned out well: both these types sometimes produced bountiful years in England. Though there is apparently firm evidence of more frequent severe winters between 1550 and 1850 than in most earlier or later times, and the decline of the summers from 1300 onwards seems to have been sufficient to eliminate the earlier vineyards of southern England, failures of the wheat harvest sufficient to raise prices at Exeter (Hoskins 1964) over 25 per cent above the 31-year mean occurred on average only one year in 6½ between 1480 and 1549 and one year in 5 between 1550 and 1619. This is however a relative index which measures the variance rather than the absolute abundance of corn (let alone weather). Perhaps the frequency figure for 1550-1619 is about as high as such an index can go. The 31-year mean price level itself was rising steeply from about 1550 onwards. More significant presumably is the fact that even in England there were runs of bad summers producing widespread distress through harvest failure in the 1430's, 1550's and 1590's – the last group produced the Elizabethan poor laws.

In north-east Scotland it is reported in the *Laxdaela Saga*, to which Professor Manley has drawn my attention, that ships were built in Caithness around 950 A.D. This probably indicates availability of larger trees there than in any subsequent time, though the reasons for the change may not have been entirely climatic. There is in existence an eye-witness account from the 1600's of an experience, apparently familiar at that time near the north-west coast of Scotland, of woods dying, being blown over after standing dead for several decades, then soon overgrown by moss and absorbed into the peat. The report (Earl of Cromertie 1710) particularly concerns one wood that disappeared in this way between 1651 and the end of that century near the coast somewhere just south of Loch Broom, between there and Little Loch Broom (see Fig. 2). Geikie (1901) records that a wood in Dumfriesshire blown down as late as 1756 suffered a similar fate.

The previous discussion in *Quarterly Journal*, 1945, of the fallen tree found in the bog at Badentarbet, Achiltibuie, evidently within about twenty miles of the places referred to by the said Earl of Cromertie 200-300 years earlier, at first promised to throw further light on the matter but ended inconclusively. Verbal tradition in Coigach (the district around Achiltibuie) suggested that "scanty pines" might have existed in the 1700's, though Pennant in his 'Tour' in 1772 saw no pines, only "silver birch woodlets" near Ullapool. Another local tradition in Coigach was that a forest east of Badentarbet towards Ben More Coigach, 6 miles (10 km) south-east, burnt by the Danes presumably in the early Middle Ages, had apparently never grown again. Forests growing in places where such disasters are final are sometimes known as ' sub-fossil forests,' indicating that the environment no longer permits regeneration in the absence of the shelter provided by the older trees. More detailed knowledge of the history of the limits of forest and scrub in this part of north-west Scotland might therefore disclose an accelerated recession during the later Middle Ages which would be at least partly attributable to the climate changing.

Evidence of any tendency for forest and scrub to advance up the hills and towards the coast between 500 B.C. and 1000 A.D. should also be watched for, though conclusive evidence of that period may be almost impossible to find. Moreover, soil deterioration and the interference of man are likely to have acted against recovery of the forest after the cold wet period around 500 B.C.

6. Radiocarbon dating method

The technique of radiocarbon dating introduced by W. F. Libby about 1946 offers new possibilities of pursuing issues such as these. A useful article (Willis 1961) on the method and its validity appeared in a recent issue of *The Times Science Review* (see also Libby 1946; 1955). The present writer was encouraged by Professor P. A. Sheppard and the Meteorological Research Committee in 1960 to arrange for the method to be applied to the Badentarbet finds, since meteorology had so far been slow to take advantage of radiocarbon dating, though it was already much used by botanists and archeologists in related problems.

Dr. T. G. Longstaff kindly supplied a specimen from the principal pine tree referred to and some specimens of roots found a foot lower down at the base of the peat. Measurements were carried out at the National Physical Laboratory in 1962 (laboratory reference NPL 13 and 14).

When cosmic-ray primary particles, mostly protons, enter the Earth's atmosphere, they produce showers of secondary radiation which includes neutrons in the upper reaches of the atmosphere. Most of the neutrons collide with nitrogen atoms and are captured by the atomic nucleus; few survive to reach ground level. In the collisions the dominant reaction produces radiocarbon, C^{14}.

The radiocarbon, as $C^{14}O_2$, is assumed to mix uniformly, and sufficiently rapidly, throughout the atmosphere so that all living matter everywhere, being derived directly or indirectly from plant material, should have an identical C^{14} content. When an organism dies, its uptake of atmospheric $C^{14}O_2$ ceases, and the decay of the C^{14} atoms it already contains affords a measure of the time elapsed since death. This provides a method of age determination which can be applied universally to all organic material, provided that there is enough residual radiocarbon left in it to measure with accuracy.

The decay rate of the C^{14} is slow, the half-life being about 5,700 years. These considerations mean that the method is practicable for ages up to about 45,000 years, although this may be increased to about 70,000 years using the technique known as isotopic enrichment. The difficulties involved, however, make the routine application of this refinement hardly practical.

The assumptions of the method are, of course, sweeping, particularly as regards :

(1) constancy of C^{14} production (constancy of cosmic-ray bombardment) over very long periods of time;

(2) effective mixing of the whole atmosphere, since production of C^{14} is concentrated at high levels and high geomagnetic latitudes;

(3) no variations of the atmospheric C^{14} concentration arising, even over long periods of time, due to changes in the rate of exchange with the enormously bigger reservoir of CO_2 in the sea.

In principle, it is assumed that the concentration of C^{14} in the atmosphere and the ocean has been always and everywhere the same. These assumptions have been, and continue to be, the subject of a variety of tests, particularly by (a) 'dating' samples of organic matter of known age, (b) following the progress of enrichment of the atmosphere all over the world in radioactive carbon from nuclear bomb tests in recent years and (c) sampling the concentration of C^{14} in the water of different oceans and at different depths. It is found, for instance, that the concentration of C^{14} in the atmosphere underwent increasing dilution from the burning of fossil fuels in the modern industrial era, especially since 1890, though this has now been more than offset by the injection of 'bomb carbon.' It is also found that samples of organic matter of known date broadly around 1500 A.D. are systematically too rich in C^{14} by about 2 to 3 per cent. Samples from an earlier period, very broadly around 1000 A.D., show smaller concentrations of C^{14} than would have been expected, also by about 2 to 3 per cent. The oldest samples of known date before 500 B.C. again show positive deviations of C^{14} concentration above expectation by 3 per cent, increasing up to 5 per cent or so by 2000 B.C. (The 5 per cent is to some extent due to the hitherto adopted half-life of 5568 years being inaccurate : indeed it provided indication of the error in the assumed half-life.)

These test results open up a variety of questions of wide geophysical interest. They do not, however, appear to invalidate the principle of the method or the basic assumption of a sufficiently near approach to constancy of concentration of C^{14} in all living matter at all times. In practice, one attempts to make corrections for the known deviations and quotes margins of error accordingly. The final margin of uncertainty quoted by the National Physical Laboratory in the cases here reported allows for these sources of error.

It is important to choose samples which can be presumed immune from contamination by younger or older organic matter after death and to provide enough material, e.g., 5-10 ounces (150-300 grams) of wood to yield sufficient C^{14} for two or three tests. Pre-treatment techniques are however applied in the laboratories to avoid, and diminish, whenever possible the occurrence of errors due to this.

There are two stable isotopes that occur wherever carbon is found in nature, C^{12} and C^{13}, the former being the more abundant by a factor of about 100 to one. The actual value of the ratio may vary, depending on the physical and chemical processes to which the isotopes are submitted. For instance, such variations may be introduced during the process of photosynthesis by which plants extract carbon dioxide from the atmosphere. Variation may also be produced during the processing of the sample for the dating measurement itself. This variation in the C^{13}/C^{12} ratio may be measured very accurately on a mass spectrometer, and affords a means of calculating the similar variation produced in the C^{14}/C^{12} ratio. To a first approximation, the C^{14}/C^{12} fractionation is twice that of the C^{13}/C^{12} occurring in any given process : it is therefore possible to apply a correction to the observed C^{14} concentration to compensate for any fractionation that may have occurred.

7. Application of the radiocarbon dating test to the Badentarbet wood samples

(1) Wood of Scots pine (sample NPL 13), age 4,420 ± 102 years B.P.

(2) Roots, possibly of Scots pine (Sample NPL 14), age 4,220 ± 105 years B.P.

These results are reported in (Callow *et al.* 1963).

In these statements 'B.P.' stands for before present, meaning before 1950 A.D. The uncertainty or error margin quoted is compounded of the uncertainty of the experimental results, specifically one standard deviation of the physical measurement, plus an estimate of the variation of the atmospheric C^{14} concentration. The figures of radiocarbon age are based upon the so far generally adopted half-life of C^{14}, namely 5,568 years, as recommended by the Fifth Radiocarbon Dating Conference.

In view of the indications (see previous section) of long-period variations in the background concentration of C^{14} in the atmosphere, it may be prudent in interpreting these results to allow more particularly for the possibility that apparent ages around 2000-2500

B.C. represent a real age that may be 2 to 2½ per cent (80 to 100 years) greater. Furthermore, the best value for the half life of C^{14} from more recent fundamental work appears to be about 3 per cent longer than that which is still conventionally adopted pending a more reliable result. The Fifth Radiocarbon Dating Conference, meeting at Cambridge in July 1962, considered 5,730 ± 40 years as the best value, representing the mean of values given by three groups of research workers (Godwin 1962), though it was considered premature to adopt this as a final value.

The measurements indicate that the tree and roots found in the Badentarbet bog grew at sometime between 2270 and 2470 B.C. ± 100 years in each case, though for the reasons stated one may incline towards acceptance of the greatest ages that lie within this margin of uncertainty. Furthermore, the 5,730-year half-life would put the dates back to about 2400 to 2600 B.C. ± 100 years. The conclusion that concerns meteorology is that the tree-remains tested from this site belong to the latter part of the main post-glacial warm epoch. They grew between 2700 and at latest about 2200 B.C.

8. Conclusions

1 (a). Circumstantial evidence based chiefly on the annals of the medieval Court of Scotland and the abbeys etc. suggests that Scotland partook in the general experience of a warm epoch from 1070 (or earlier), to 1300 A.D.

(b) No supporting evidence has so far been found in the vegetation, though there are some indications that forest fires brought about a decline of forest extent from which there was no recovery between 1300 and 1700. Deterioration of crop yields in the course of these centuries is also suspected. Deficient summer warmth, windiness and wetness of the summers may have been the most important factors.

This decline appears to have pressed upon the life of the people in various ways, affecting husbandry and producing increasingly frequent dearths of food after 1550 even in the east and south of Scotland. An isolated case occurred as early as 1439. It probably affected first the north-west Highlands and districts of highest upland settlement in central Scotland, where the land was poorest, and may have been behind the country's troubles in the 1430's – an outstandingly severe decade all over Europe.

2. The tree found lying three feet down in the peat on the north-west coast at Badentarbet, as revealed by the radiocarbon test, did not belong to the medieval period. It grew before 2000 B.C. in the latter part of the post-glacial climatic optimum. There is no evidence, at least no remains have survived, of trees at that spot later than perhaps about 1000 B.C. – the stumps reported at two-foot depth in the peat.

3. Soil deterioration (podsolization and bog growth) probably inhibited recovery of the forest if indeed the climate improved there as in other northern lands from the cold period around and after 500 B.C. to the optimum around 1100 A.D.

4. Increasing human interference makes it hard to relate forest changes to climatic vicissitudes in Scotland from 3000 B.C. onwards. It is possible that reliable evidence of the sequence of climatic changes may yet be found in changes in the limits of scrub and of montane plants, which attracted less attention from primitive men and even today in Scotland reveal their natural limits, descending from south-east to north-west across the country.

5. Historical research, particularly an examination of any surviving records of abbeys and great estates, is most likely to yield further information about the climate and weather year by year in medieval Scotland.

Acknowledgments

The author is indebted to the Director-General of the Meteorological Office for permission to publish this article. He also acknowledges with thanks the help and encouragement of persons mentioned in the text as well as detailed information and advice received from Professor H. Godwin of the Cambridge University Botany Department, from Dr. E. H. Willis of the Radiocarbon Dating Laboratory in that Department and from Dr. W. J. Callow of the National Physical Laboratory. He also expresses thanks to Professor Gordon Manley, to Mr. E. M. Jope of the Department of Archaeology, Queens University, Belfast, Professors A. C. O'Dell and H. M. Steven of Aberdeen University for miscellaneous information, and last but not least to Mr. R. Cranna, Superintendent of the Meteorological Office, Edinburgh, for his continued interest in introducing further sources of data, particularly *The Annals of Dunfermline*.

Appendix

Temperatures in the warmest post-glacial epoch, around 5000-3000 B.C.

The prevailing temperature levels in the climatic optimum have been estimated from a variety of botanical and zoological phenomena in many parts of the world, and from the melting of glaciers, which subsequently re-advanced or even re-formed. Emiliani (1955), from examination of the abundance of different *foraminifera* species on the sea-bed and from $0^{18}/0^{16}$ ratio determinations upon them, puts the surface water temperatures of tropical oceans at 1 to 1·5°C above present values. Numerous authors have arrived at a figure of about 2°C above present levels for the annual mean air temperatures, particularly in Europe (see, for instance, Wright 1961, p. 960; Schwarzbach 1961, p. 178-9; Flohn 1952, p. 171 and Brooks 1934, p. 386). The highest figures quoted, 2 to 3°C above present, probably all stem from the Brooks (1934) estimate of the implications of the "great upward extension of the tree line to a level nearly 1,500 ft above the present." This should probably have been taken as referring mainly to the temperatures in the summer months, which are the critical climatic factor at the thermal limit of tree growth (see Sirén's (1961) conclusions for the northern tree limit in Finland in recent times). That the mean summer temperatures were 2 to 3°C above present normals has been independently concluded from pollen analysis in Denmark (Andersen *et al.* 1960) and in Austria (Gross 1958), as well as by Godwin for this country in the 'Atlantic' epoch, or 'pollen zone VIIa,' 5,000-3,000 B.C. (quoted by Steven and Carlisle 1959). The same estimate of the summer temperature anomaly has been arrived at for East Anglia by Shotton (1962) from the occurrence there of a warmth-loving European pond tortoise, which also reached Denmark.

References

Aario, L. 1944 'Einer nachwärmezeitlicher Gletscher-Vorstoss im Oberfernau in den Stubaier Alpen,' *Acta Geogr.*, **9**, pp. 2, 31.

Andersen, S. T., De Vries, H. and Zagwijn, W. H. 1960 'Climatic changes and radiocarbon dating in the Weichselian glacial of Denmark and the Netherlands,' *Geologie en Mijnbouw*, **39**, pp. 38-42.

Aspen Conference 1962 'The climate of the eleventh and sixteenth centuries,' *Tech. Notes 63-1*, Proceedings, Nat. Cent. Atmos. Res., Boulder, Colorado.

Bergeron, T., Fries, M., Moberg, C.-A. and Ström, F. 1956 'Fimbulvinter,' *Fornvännen*, Uppsala.

Brooks, C. E. P. 1934 'Post-glacial climates and the forest of Europe,' *Quart. J. R. Met. Soc.*, **60**, pp. 377-395.

Callow, W. J., Baker, M. J. and Pritchard, D. H. 1963 Nat. Phys. Lab. Radiocarbon Measurements I, *Radiocarbon*, **5**, pp. 34-38.

Cromertie, George, Earl of 1710 'An account of the mosses of Scotland,' *Phil. Trans. Roy. Soc.*, Vol. XXVII (for the years 1710-1712) London, pp. 296-301.

Dickinson, W. C. 1961 'Scotland from the earliest times to 1603.' Vol. 1 of '*A new history of Scotland*.' (Vol. 2 by G. S. Pryde: 'Scotland from 1603 to the present day,' publ. 1962 is also of interest.) Edinburgh, Nelson.

Durno, S. E. and McVean, D. N. 1959 'Forest history of the Beinn Eighe Nature Reserve,' *New Phytologist*, **58**, pp. 228-236.

Emiliani, C. 1955 'Pleistocene temperatures,' *J. Geology*, **63**, pp. 538-578.

Firbas, F. and Losert, H. 1949 'Untersuchungen über die heutigen Waldstufen in den Sudeten,' *Planta*, **36**, pp. 478-506, Berlin (Springer).

Flohn, H. 1952 'Allgemeine atmosphärische Zirkulation und Paläoklimatologie,' *Geologische Rundschau*, **40**, pp. 154-178, Stuttgart.

Gams, H. 1937 'Aus der Geschichte der Alpenwälder,' *Zeitschrift des deutschen und österreichischen Alpenvereins*, **68**, pp. 157-170, Stuttgart.

Geikie, A. 1901 *The scenery of Scotland* (3rd ed.), London (MacMillan).

Godwin, H. 1954 'Recurrence surfaces.' *Danmarks geologiske Undersøgelse*, II Raekke, No. 80, Copenhagen.

1956 *The history of the British flora*, Cambridge (University Press).

1962 'Radiocarbon dating.' *Nature*, **195**, 4845, pp. 943-945.

Gross, H. 1958 'Die bisherige Ergebnisse von C-14 Messungen und paläolithischen Untersuchungen für die Gliederung und Chronologie des Jungpleistozäns in Mitteleuropa und den Nachbargebieten,' *Eiszeitalter und Gegenwart*, **9**, pp. 155-187, Hanover.

Henderson, E. 1879 *The Annals of Dunfermline A.D. 1069-1878*, Glasgow (J. Tweed).

Hoskins, W. G. 1964 'Harvest fluctuations and English economic history,' *The Agricultural History Review*, **12**, Pt. I, pp. 28-46 London and Oxford.

Lamb, H. H. 1963 'What can we find out about the trend of our climate ?' *Weather*, **18**, pp. 194-216.

Libby, W. F. 1946 'Atmospheric helium three and radiocarbon from cosmic radiation,' *Phys. Rev.* **69**, pp. 671-2.

1955 *Radiocarbon dating*, (2nd edn.), Chicago (University Press).

McVean, D. N. and Ratcliffe, D. A. 1962 'Plant communities of the Scottish Highlands,' *Nature Conservancy Monograph No. 1*, London, H.M.S.O.

Schwarzbach, M. 1961 *Das Klima der Vorzeit*, Stuttgart (F. Enke Verlag).

Shotton, F. W. 1962 'The physical background of Britain in the Pleistocene.' *The Advancement of Science*, **19**, pp. 193-206, London.

Siren, G. 1961 'Skogsgränstallen som indikator för klimatfluktuationera i norra Fennoskandien under historisk tid,' *Communicationes Instituti Forestalis Fenniae 54·2*, Helsingfors.

Steven, H. M. and Carlisle, A. 1959 *The native pinewoods of Scotland*, Edinburgh (Oliver and Boyd).

Willis, E. H. 1961 'The validity of radiocarbon dating,' *Times Sci. Rev.*, Winter 1961.

Wright, H. E. 1961 'Late Pleistocene climate of Europe; a review,' *Bull. Geol. Soc. Amer.*, **72**, pp. 934-984.

SEVEN

Britain's climate in the past*

Summary

The paper surveys what is known of the main stages of Britain's climatic history over the 10,000–15,000 years since the ice age. Evidence is given of material changes during the last 1,000 years, which are believed to have included one of the warmest and one of the coldest epochs of post-glacial time, though neither lasted more than two to four centuries.

Numerical estimates of the magnitude of these climatic differences, and of the rapidity of change, are given so far as possible. These are important if such studies of Britain's experience in the past are to yield useful guidance for the future.

From about 1890 to the 1930s Britain, in common with most of the rest of the world, experienced a remarkable warming of the climate, which affected the length and dependability of the growing season and was accompanied by changes in the prevailing winds and amount and seasonal distribution of precipitation. These trends seem generally to have reversed since 1940 or somewhat earlier. Tables of climatic statistics based on observations made in certain recent decades should therefore be used with caution. No climatic table is of much value unless the years that it comprises are specified.

There is an obvious economic call for forecasts of the climatic tendency over the decades ahead. This need cannot be met until a scientific basis for such forecasts has been created. This depends on identification and fuller (quantitative) knowledge and understanding of the physical influences and atmospheric processes that determine climatic changes. Effects, whether accidental or intended, of man's activity have to be included here. These, as well as some natural events such as the erratic output of large quantities of volcanic dust into the high atmosphere, introduce unpredictable elements into the problem.

For a long while to come, therefore, the most relevant guidance to the future must be the fullest and most specific possible knowledge of past climatic behaviour.

Introduction

The title of this talk would not sound out of place in a meeting of academic historians. In what connexions should scientists be concerned with the history of our climate? We may define the aims as three:

1. To understand better the development of our environment with its flora and fauna, and to see whether agriculture or other aspects of the economy must have been affected. It happens that the history of the climate has been peculiarly neglected by historians, except in Iceland and Scandinavia where the effects could not be lightly dismissed.
2. To get numerical estimates of the variations which have occurred in the past and might occur again under analogous circumstances in the future.

* Lecture given to Section X of the British Association for the Advancement of Science at Southampton on 2 September 1964.

3. To identify at least some of the physical processes involved in climatic changes and the magnitudes of the effects attributable to various influences, such as volcanic dust veils in the upper atmosphere or excessive ice formation on the Arctic seas, affecting the terrestrial environment. This knowledge of the quantities involved is needed if we are to diagnose the symptoms of change now and some day, perhaps, be able to predict its course and amount.

We all know that one year differs from another. No two winters or summers are completely alike. Even one decade differs from another; though whether that is anything more than normal sampling variations about some long-term average requires careful examination. But when it comes to dealing with the figures representing the climatic experience of the last century or two, even expert opinion has been subject to sorry changes of fashion.

In 1686 Robert Hooke, F.R.S. of Freshwater, Isle of Wight, deduced from fossils discovered at Portland that in some previous age the climate of these parts had been tropical, and he suggested a shift of the equator and poles to account for it. It was around 1800 that the signs in Europe of former ice ages were first recognized for what they undoubtedly are. These extremes, involving very long periods of time, have long been accepted. Shorter-term changes also have from time to time thrust themselves on public notice. In 1492 the Pope (Alexander VI) was concerned about the freezing of the seas around Greenland, as a result of which no priest or bishop had been able to get there for 80 years. And it was alarm about the 'sudden variations in the behaviour of the seasons' to which the climate of Europe seemed 'more and more subject' about the end of the eighteenth century that prompted the organization of the first networks of weather observing stations, supplied with instruments for accurate measurement and charged with keeping records – at police stations in France in 1775 and by some similar arrangement in Prussia in 1817. An international network of observing points from Greenland to Moscow was arranged by the first meteorological society, in the Palatinate of the Rhine, with the active interest of the prince, in 1781.

By the end of the nineteenth century, however, we find the view increasingly held – and supported by the leading climatologists of the day – that the climate had long since become stabilized and had undergone no significant changes in at least the last 2,000 years. This view gained acceptance from the reading of ancient Latin texts which suggested that the climate of the Mediterranean in Classical times showed close, if not quite perfect, similarity with nowadays. Also it happened that the climate in the 1880s and '90s did revert to values similar to those of the years between 1760 and 1820, when many of the longer meteorological instrument records began. This view of climate as effectively constant, undergoing at most cyclical changes of no great importance, was taught to most of my generation in school. It was believed that you had only to average data over a long enough period of time to arrive at a figure to which the climate would always return.

But then, over the 30 to 50 years from 1900 on, most parts of the world underwent a progressive warming so marked that it could not be overlooked. The greatest changes were in the Arctic, where the total area of 'permanent' sea-ice shrank between 1918 and 1938 by about 20 per cent and the average open season for shipping at Spitsbergen lengthened from three to seven months of the year. Over the world as a whole, the average surface temperature rose by half a degree centigrade (just about 1° F) between 1882 and 1942 (Mitchell 1963). And so once more the fashion changed, the idea of climatic constancy was dropped and there was speculation about the prospect of an ice-free Arctic Ocean at the end of the century. But it turns out that the warming of the Arctic only became widely known (and I suspect it has quite lately been getting into the teaching in our schools) when it had ceased – at least for the time being.

So we really must take stock and seek firmer foundations for our understanding of this matter.

The main stages of climatic history since the ice age

Let us begin by stating what is known of the main stages – the biggest swings – of climate since the ice age. Knowledge of this sequence comes from many different branches of science. And the filling in of detail from historical times looks like engaging the humane studies as well. Indeed, the quest for knowledge of climatic history is bound to be a co-operative one in which we see that all learning is one.

The last glaciation, the *Würm ice age*, probably had two main *maxima*, the first one about 55,000 years ago and the last one (dated by radiocarbon tests of ocean bottom sediments (Emiliani 1961) and vegetation remains near the limits of the advancing ice-sheets (West 1960) only 15,000–20,000 years ago. Relics of the former low sea-level of the ice age persist in the form of old moraines on the bed of the Irish Sea (G. F. Mitchell 1960) and the Dogger Bank (Stride 1959).

The retreat of the ice was rapid and necessarily accompanied by a swift rise of world sea-level. Even before the seas filled up, however, there was a rapid spread of fauna and flora across the dry 'Northsealand'.

Sea-level appears to have risen 100 m. in 10,000 years, an average rate of a centimetre a year. There were, however, two major setbacks to this headlong rate of change. After the climate had become warm enough for a park landscape with some trees in England and Denmark around 11500–12000 B.C., the *Bølling interstadial*, the ice-sheets grew again to cover wide areas of Scotland and Scandinavia. And after another, even warmer phase, the *Allerød*, with birch forests here, and willow in Holland and Denmark (Flint 1957), cold climates returned once more for 600 years with local glaciers reappearing in the Lake District valleys (Manley 1959) and the Western and Central Highlands ice-covered, between about 8800 and 8200 B.C. This *post-Allerød recession* was apparently a climatic disaster of unparalleled severity, established within 50 to 80 years and killing the living forests wholesale. But this rapidity of disaster can probably be written off as a characteristic of what happens when there is a fairly small lateral shift of the zone of strong thermal gradient near the limit of an existing ice-sheet. The modern parallel is with the magnitude of the twentieth-century warming at Spitsbergen, mentioned earlier.

The break-up of the last of the main Scandinavian ice-sheet followed soon after this cold phase, about 8000 B.C. By 6000 B.C., or soon after, the warmest climatic period since the ice age, the *post-glacial climatic optimum*, was already beginning.

The European climates of that period seem at first to have been dry, the '*Boreal*' *period*, then moist after about 5000 B.C., the '*Atlantic*' *period*, when the sea had occupied the present North Sea and Baltic and Dover Strait had been cut. There may well have been an important change in the prevailing wind circulation about this time (*c.* 5000 B.C.) also, with the final disappearance of the bulk of the continental ice-sheet in North America. According to radiocarbon dating results, world sea-level continued to rise, presumably owing to continued melting of the expanded Antarctic ice-sheet and perhaps less important remnants of ice in North America, until about 3000 B.C., when the rise abruptly flattened out (Godwin, Suggate and Willis 1958). In that warmest epoch prevailing summer temperatures in Britain are estimated to have been 2 to 3° C above present normal values, chiefly on botanical evidence (Godwin 1956). Winter temperatures probably differed less from today's, and annual mean values may have been about 2° C above the present. Striking evidence of the nature of this period is given by the prominence among the natural forests of England at that time of warmth-loving trees like the lime and by the remains still existing of trees – albeit small trees – which grew on the heights of the hills in northern Britain 600 to 1,000 ft. (200–300 m.) above what appears to be the present natural tree limit. Trees also grew on the most exposed parts of the north-west coast of Scotland and in the now treeless northern isles, the Orkneys, Faeroes and Iceland. All this probably points to a less windy and more anticyclonic climate, with the prevailing storm tracks in much higher latitudes than now – consistent with suggestions from other evidence that the Arctic sea-ice had almost or wholly disappeared.

The beginnings of the climatic deterioration that followed may have been what set the peoples of Europe migrating and spread the more advanced, New Stone Age culture to these islands. Between about 3000 and 500 B.C. the climate underwent an erratic decline, with increased storminess, and finally the rapid advance of glaciers in the Alps and re-birth of many of them. But, in between, there were better periods, including probably for some centuries around 1200–1000 B.C. a *warm* '*sub-Boreal*' *dry-summer climate* which allowed the forests to regain something like their former altitude (Gams 1937) and coastward limits (Lamb 1964) even in Britain. But after about 900 B.C. the climate seems to have become increasingly wretched, the Atlantic fringe in the west being the first affected by wetness and cooler summers. This was the onset of the so-called *cool, moist* '*sub-Atlantic*' *climatic period*, which was once thought to have continued without significant change until today.

It is now known that former ways across the Somerset levels and other English lowlands then became first miry, and later flooded, so that water transport was used (Godwin and Willis 1959). The size of the Alpine glaciers in western Austria had increased by 500 B.C. from a small fraction of their present area around 1000 B.C. to something like the impressive maximum attained around A.D. 1650 (Gams 1937). By analogy with that comparatively recent period, annual mean temperatures in the early Iron Age would be 0·5 to 1° C lower than those of today; and the decline in 500 years from 1000 B.C. would amount to about 2° C. This would mean a great reduction of evaporation and wetter surfaces than before even in summer. The forests are known to have receded from the heights and the Atlantic coasts, but in

Britain the causation of this deforestation is hopelessly confused by the effects of human interference. Not much can be said therefore of how the climatic deterioration affected the patterns of settlement and cultivation in Britain, though it seems likely that in southern England the people and their agriculture would be driven to concentrate on the drier chalk uplands.

Some recovery followed, apparently reaching a climax in the early Middle Ages. It happened therefore that in Roman times here, as well as in the Mediterranean, the climate really was not far different from that of today. The coastline of the southern North Sea was, however, still somewhat different from today's. Over the centuries since, the sea has tended to gain at the expense of the land, no doubt gaining most in the warmer periods when sea-level would be relatively highest and in great storms, such as those between 1250 and 1570 which accompanied the climatic deterioration in the late Middle Ages. The combination of storminess with the end of a warm epoch accompanied by a maximum of world sea-level, whether or not these can be established as the facts of the situation in the period cited, must always threaten disaster to the low-lying lands about the southern North Sea. Brooks (1949 p. 372) states that the greatest damage from sea floods ('storm floods') occurred in this area in 1170–78, 1240–53, 1267–92, 1374–77, 1393–1404, 1421. To these must be added, however, some disastrous floods, admittedly at somewhat longer intervals, in the period of chillier climate that followed: in 1570, 1665, 1682 and 1775–76. The direct effects of weather and of changes of world sea-level are, however, complicated in this region, at least in the Netherlands, by progressive compaction of the peaty and sandy soils and slow warping of the earth's crust.

The sorts of evidence we have so far been consulting – glaciology, forest limits, archaeology and history – indicate then two more important climatic epochs, each lasting several centuries:

1. a *Little Optimum* or warm epoch culminating between about A.D. 1000 and 1300 and
2. a cold epoch, the coldest since the ice age, and often known as the *Little Ice Age*, culminating between about 1550 and 1700–1850.

In central Norway the limits of settlement, forest clearance and farming, were pressed rather quickly 100–200 m. farther up the hillsides and valleys in Viking times, between about A.D. 800 and 1000. And whether this is put down to the 'population explosion' or to increased technical power through greater output of iron and other metals, it assuredly points to improving climate – in the one case affecting human health and vigour, in the other making travel over the moors to the places where the ores were found easier. But later on, during the 1300s, climatic deterioration in Norway so reinforced the effects of the Black Death that a large percentage of the farms in exposed upland and coastal districts, and in the north, lay waste and unoccupied for 200 years. (The actual monetary value of the harvest in most parts of the country was well below the values of 1300–20 for more than a century – in the upland parts even of Oslo bishopric the value remained at least till 1500 under a fifth of what it had been about 1300. The disaster was complete and, so to speak, permanent (Holmsen 1961).) These changes can hardly have failed to affect our own country, especially Scotland, even though they are practically unmentioned by historians.

The writer is not in a position to assert that this factor should have been mentioned, for instance, by Beresford (1951) in his account of the many villages which disappeared in England between 1300 and 1600 and of the conversion from open field agriculture to sheep that was going on all the time: it may be significant however that he reports an apparent let-up in the process around 1500 and even some tendency to go back to the plough for a while around 1530 – these dates coincide with the only real period of temporary recovery of the climate (as regards both temperature and rainfall) between 1300 and 1600. That there has, however, also been a long history of attempts to record and interpret the facts may be seen from Camden's allusions to the old vineyards in his *Britannia* published in 1586, from the writings of gardeners who attempted vine-growing in England in the seventeenth century and from works such as J. Williams' book published in London (Baldwin & Co.) in 1800, entitled *The climate of Great Britain; remarks on the change it has undergone, particularly within the last* 50 *years, accounting for the increasing humidity and consequent cloudiness and coldness of the springs and summers.*

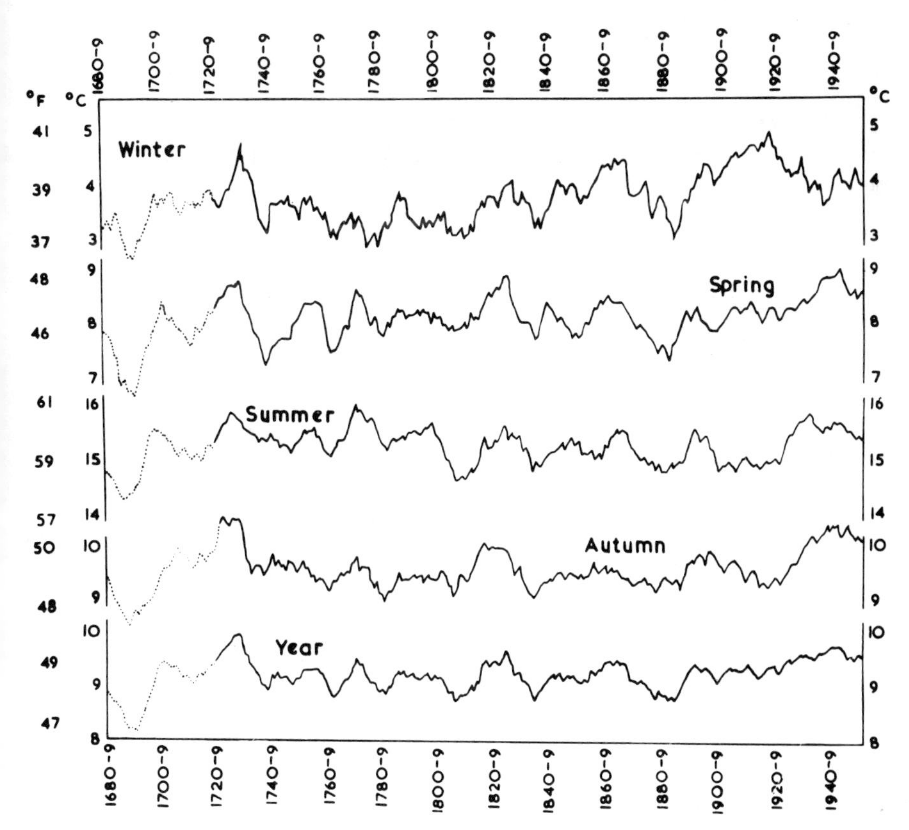

Fig. 1. Average temperatures in central England 1680–1960 (after Manley), for each season and for the year, shown by 10-year running means.

To get a more dependable view of the situation, however, we can now turn to meteorological analysis.

Meteorological investigations of recent observed climatic changes

In this country we possess the longest usable climatic record of observations made with scientific instruments, thanks to our pioneer observers encouraged by the Royal Society from 1666 onwards and to the patience of my friend Professor Gordon Manley (1958, 1961) in rendering the values comparable with those to be obtained by modern standard techniques of exposure. The series of monthly mean temperatures for the lowlands of central England appears trustworthy from about 1700 on-

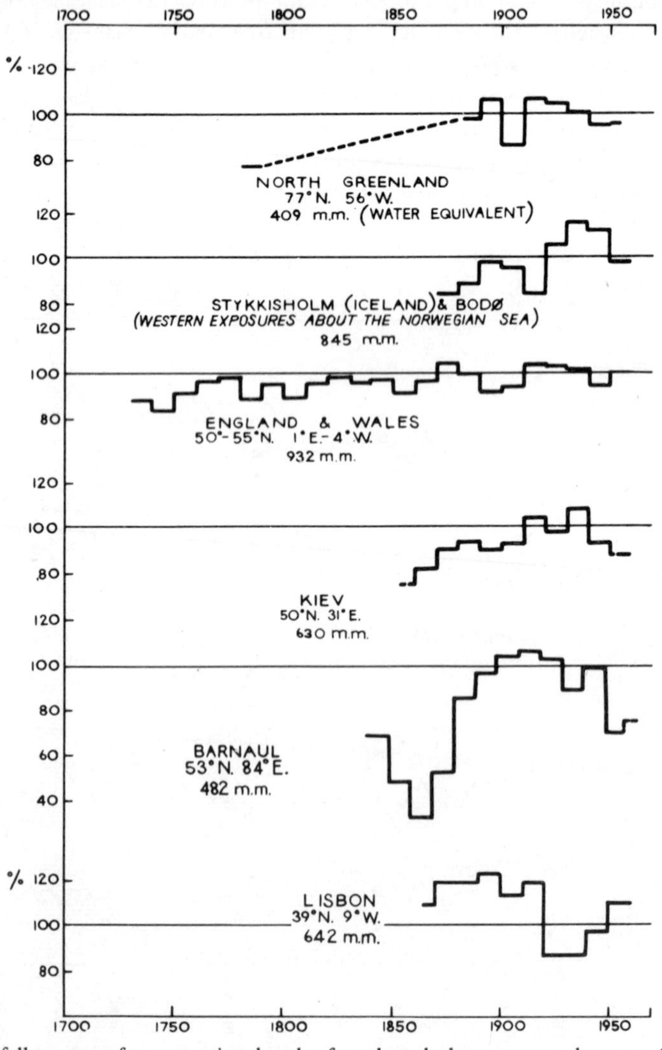

FIG. 2. Rainfall averages for successive decades for selected places or areas between Greenland and western Asia, plotted as percentages of the over-all means for 1900–39, these means being quoted in millimetres (figures for the whole year).

wards, and probably within a few tenths of a degree from 1680. We also have a series of monthly rainfall figures from 1727 averaged over England and Wales (Nicholas and Glasspoole 1931): this series may give slightly too low values in the earliest years because of over-exposure of the rain-gauges, but is also broadly trustworthy. These temperature and rainfall series show that climatic changes have taken place within the instrumental period. In conformity with many other indications, prevailing temperatures and rainfall here as elsewhere in temperate Europe appear to have been on the whole increasing over the last 200 years or more. These results are illustrated in Figs. 1 and 2. The differences may not appear large, but in terms of average temperature the winters in central England changed character from the long-term average for the Dutch coast to that of Dublin when the coldest and mildest decades are compared.

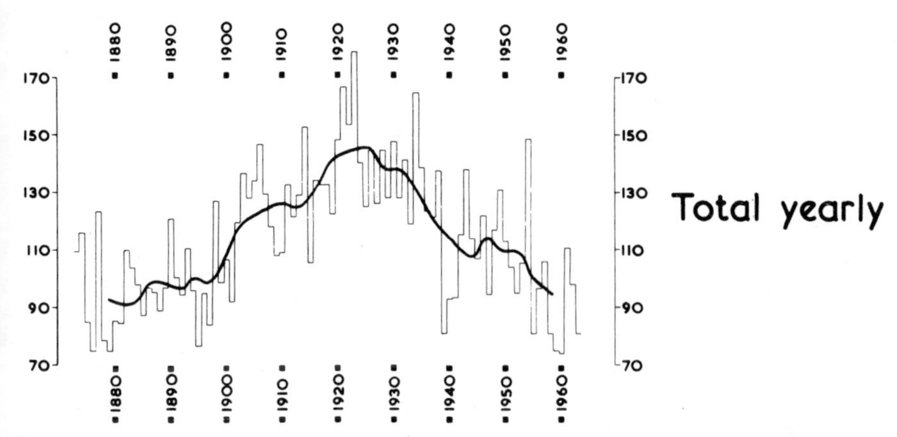

Fig. 3. Number of days classified as Westerly type over the British Isles each year 1873–1963. (The superimposed curve shows the course of the 10-year running mean, when plotted at the middle of each 10-year period.)

There is some suggestion of reversal of these trends since about 1940; and, although there have been fluctuations before which interrupted the prolonged improvement of the climate, the corresponding changes in the prevailing wind circulation over the northern hemisphere have been striking. The (10-year) frequency of weather types in the British Isles associated with westerly winds has decreased since 1940 by about 30 per cent as compared with a period of probably exceptional dominance of westerly winds in the first four decades of this century. Fig. 3 shows the frequency of days classified as westerly type in the British Isles each year since 1873 with remarkably high values in the years of culminating frequency between 1916 and 1935. The recent decline of the westerlies has been accompanied by rising frequency of other winds, particularly those with northerly components. The average temperatures for the peak summer months of July and August in central England in the 1930s and '40s were rather above 16·2° C compared with 15·5 to 15·6° C at the beginning of the century and again in the last 10 years; for those best 20 years the July + August rainfall in England and Wales was only 91 per cent of the 1916–50 average, compared with 106 per cent over the last

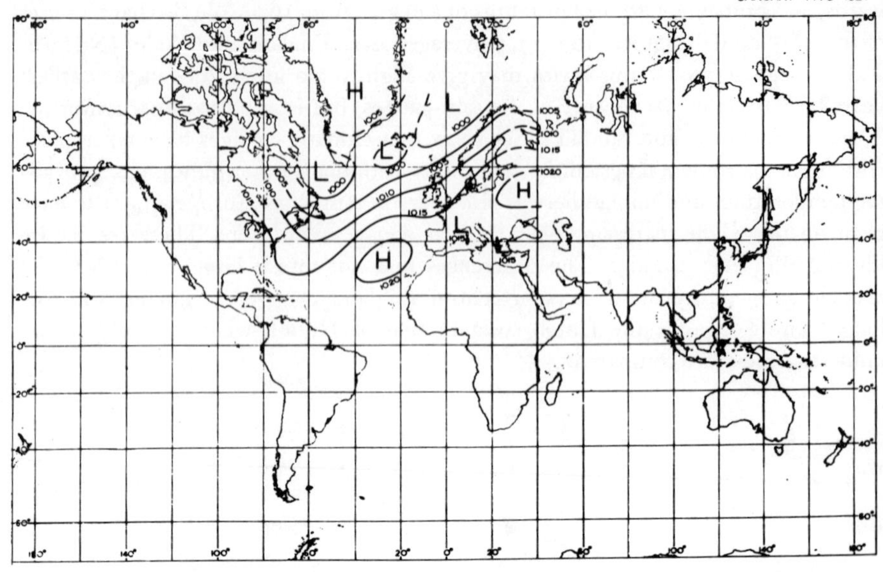

FIG. 4. Average pressure distribution in January (in millibars)
(*a, above*) 1790–1829.
(*b, below*) 1900–39.

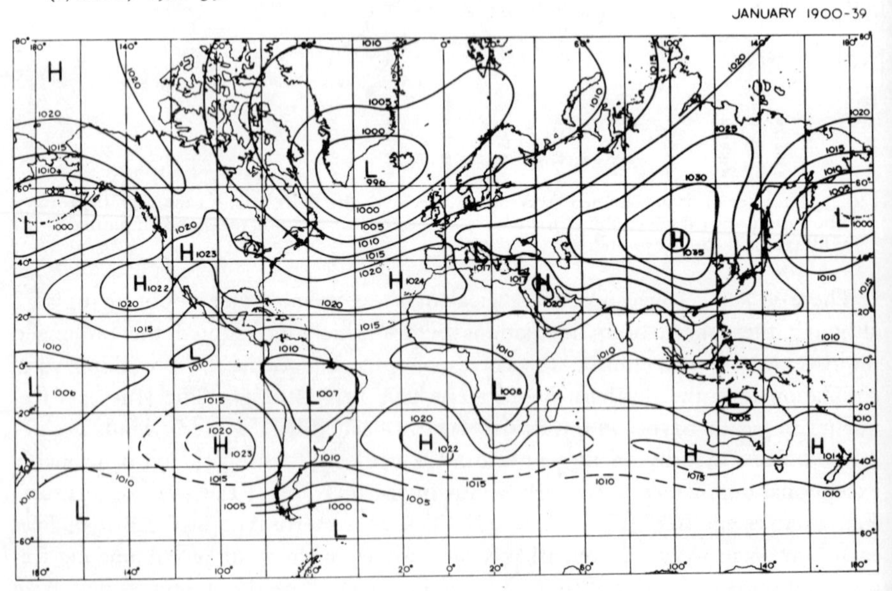

14 years. The mildest winters were in the decades between 1910 and 1939, giving December–January–February average temperatures of 4·5° C compared with under 3·7° C for the last ten winters.

The artificial climates in which most of us spend our time, indoors and in the cities, largely insulate us from these changes. Probably most people have some

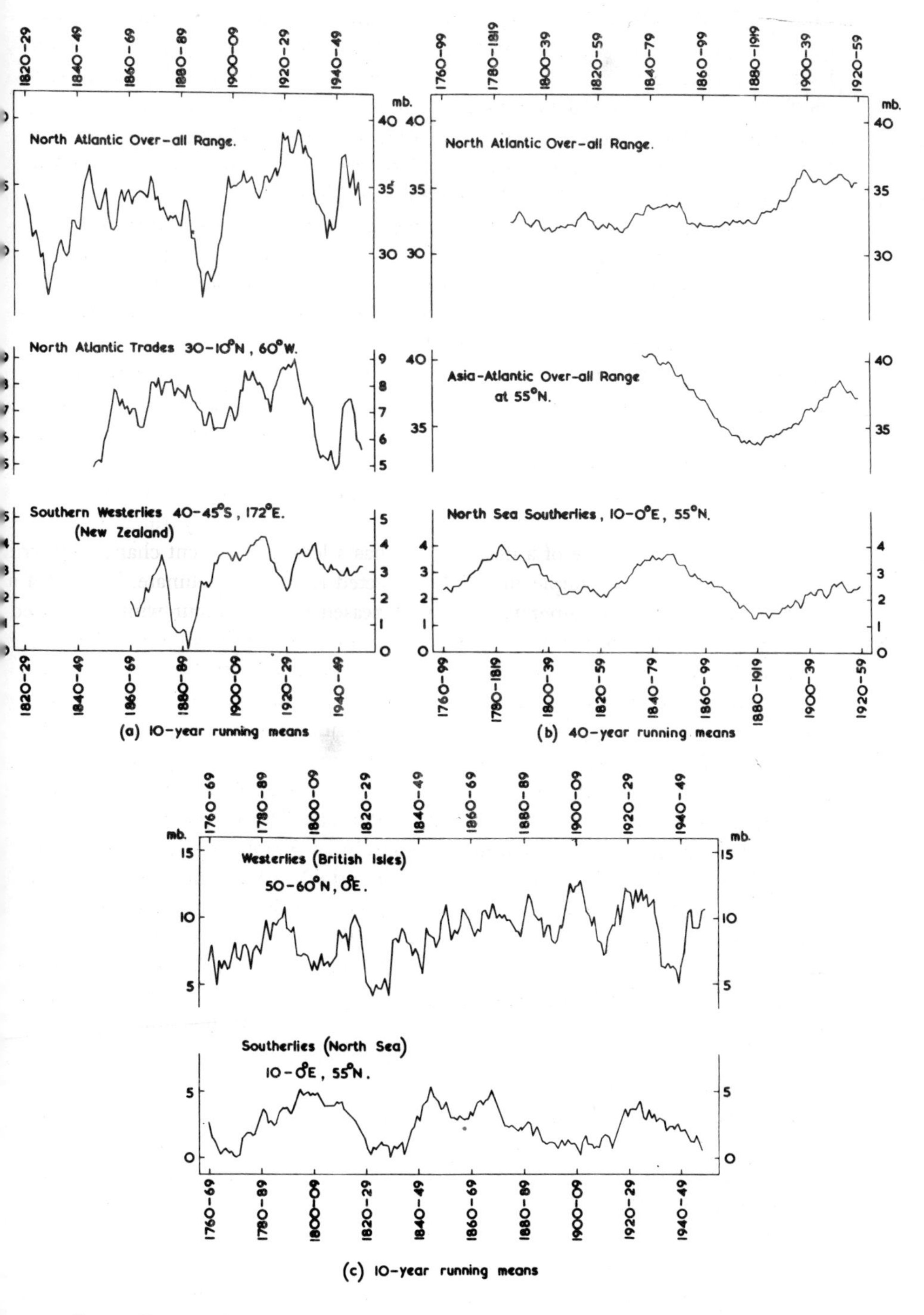

FIG. 5. Pressure difference indices of prevailing wind circulation strength in January.

impression of poorer summers since 1950, but only noticed the one 'big' winter in 1962–63. Nevertheless, the change of temperature level almost doubled the frequency of snow-covered ground in the lower lying districts of England and Scotland in the 1950s compared with 1920–39. (At Ross-on-Wye, Cambridge and Perth the figures were 11, 11 and 15 days a year in the 1950s compared with 6, 7 and 9 before the war.) The average length of the growing season (daily mean temperatures 6° C or above) at Oxford in the 1930s and '40s was 2 to 3 weeks longer than in the last century; but since 1950 it has fallen back 1 to 2 weeks.

When the figures are submitted to the standard statistical tests, it turns out that the changes in the prevailing character of our summers since 1950, though noticeable and affecting the frequency of success with exotic crops such as the apricot or the vine, have not yet reached a statistically significant level – neither as regards the somewhat lower average temperature nor the increased average rainfall. This means that the variability of our summers has all along been so great that the poorer record since 1950 could still be regarded as just one of the accidents of sampling a different batch of years from the same climate. On the other hand, the increased frequency of snow-covered ground and the decreased frequency of westerly weather types (over the year as a whole), when the years since about 1940 are compared with the previous 30 or 40 years, appear both to be statistically significant (t test): the differences are of a magnitude that has a less than 1 per cent chance of occurring in different sample runs of years selected from the same climate. The drop of average winter temperature and the increased variability of our winters (increased frequency of severe winters) since 1938 (F test) appear significant at about the 3 per cent level.

From the prevailing wind circulation patterns, revealed by the average distribution of barometric pressure reduced to sea-level, the climatic experience in Britain over the last 200 years appears as part of a world-wide phenomenon. The strengths or prevalence of all the world's main windstreams, as shown by the pressure gradients on the mean charts, have been increasing and reached a maximum around 1920–30, followed by some decline. This is illustrated by the January maps for 1790–1829 and 1900–39 compared in Fig. 4 and by the graphs in Fig. 5 of the pressure differences, also in January, corresponding to the North Atlantic westerlies, the Trade Winds and the southern hemisphere westerlies. Winters in this country were most consistently mild in those decades when the flow of west winds from the Atlantic was most marked. The summers tended to be driest and warmest in those decades when the depressions and low pressure belt of the North Atlantic were farthest away to the north. There was a northward shift of the low pressure belt in summer from 1800 to the best decades of the present century, apparently accompanying the retreat of the Arctic sea-ice.

While the general wind circulation was becoming stronger, the pressure systems that control our weather were becoming larger in scale, and therefore more widely spaced eastwards from the fixed disturbance of the major wind-flow at the Rocky Mountains barrier. This showed itself by a progressive eastward displacement of the prevailing positions of high and low pressure over the Atlantic and Europe, illustrated for January in Fig. 6.

These aspects have been described here, partly because they illustrate the world-wide nature of the phenomenon and partly because they open the way to a technique which has been used to analyse the purely descriptive accounts available to us of weather and climatic vicissitudes from the early Middle Ages.

Meteorological investigation extended to the medieval period

Europe between about 45 and 55° N and between Ireland and Russia is a region for which abundant manuscript information exists about the character of particular months and seasons, especially those of any sort of dramatic character, from quite early historical times. Allusions occur in state, local, monastic, manorial and family accounts and chronicles and in personal diaries. The region is continually under

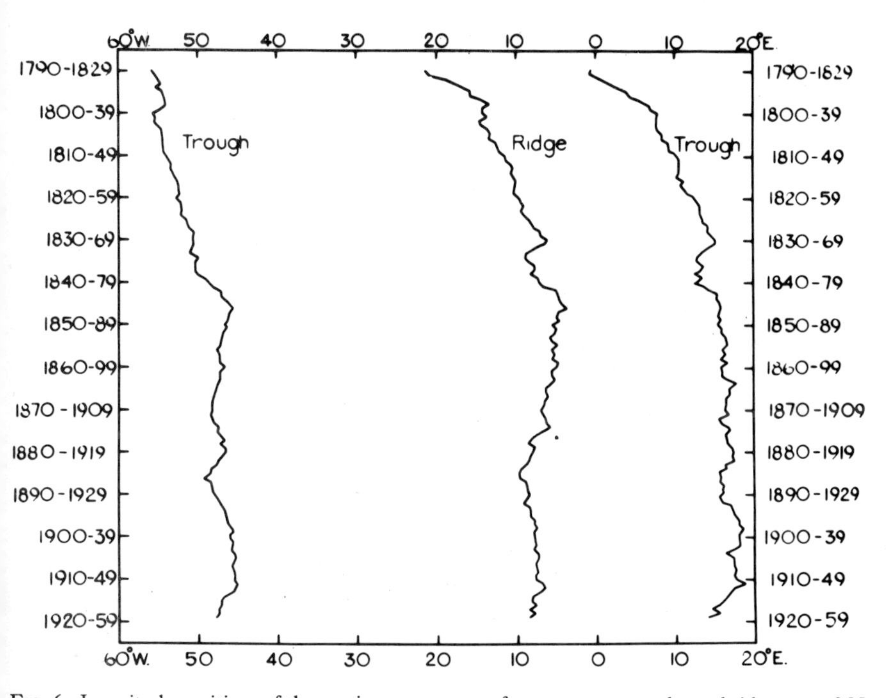

FIG. 6. Longitude positions of the semi-permanent surface pressure troughs and ridges at 45° N in the Atlantic sector in January; 40-year running averages of the longitudes of minimum and maximum average pressure for the month.

the play of the depressions and anticyclones associated with the troughs and ridges in the main flow of the atmosphere, the great circumpolar westerly flow aloft in the zone of main thermal gradient between the tropical and polar air masses. The waves (ridge-trough pattern) in this upper westerly flow should lengthen and be displaced eastwards, together with the average positions of surface low and high pressure (as in Fig. 6) and corresponding surface weather anomalies, when the gradients strengthen or the régime of warm air spreads toward higher latitudes. Analysis of the incidence of good and bad weather anomalies in different longitudes across Europe may therefore tell us something about the general wind circulation. The relative frequencies per decade of reported dry and wet summer months, mild and cold winter months, have been used to define indices for such an analysis (Lamb and Johnson 1961, Lamb 1963).

The results are depicted in Fig. 7.

These results do show eastward and westward movements across Europe of concentrations of wet and dry, warm and cold months, similar to the movements of the troughs and ridge in Fig. 6 and agreeing with those movements since 1800. The

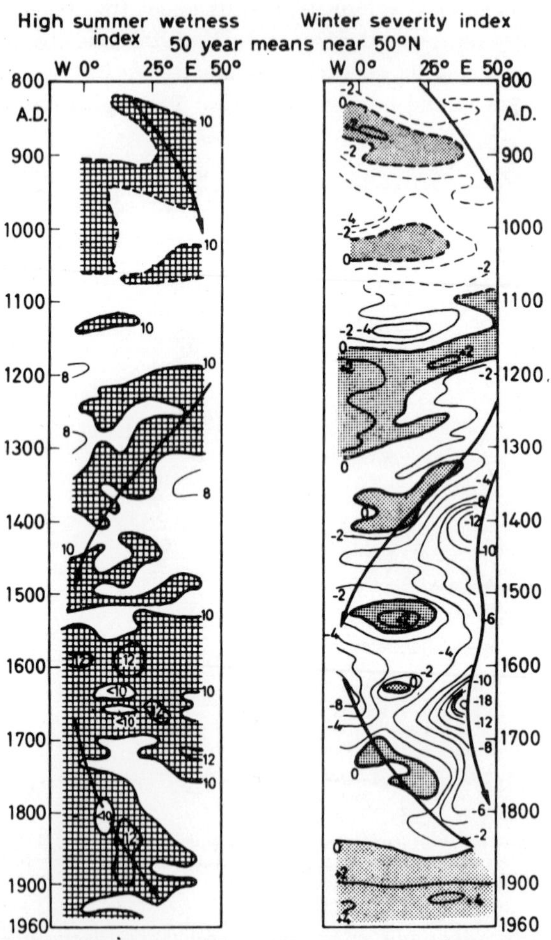

Fig. 7. Summer Dryness/Wetness and Winter Mildness/Severity Indices in different European longitudes near 50° N from 800 to 1959, overlapping half-century means.

Cross hatching indicates excess of wet Julys and Augusts. Dots indicate excess of mild Decembers, Januarys and Februarys.

The definitions of the indices are as follows:

Winter Mildness/Severity Index – the excess number of unmistakably mild or cold winter months (D, J, F only) over months of unmistakably opposite character per decade – excess of cold months counted negative. (Unremarkable decades score about 0. Extreme decade values of the index in Europe range from about +10 to −20.)

Summer Dryness/Wetness Index – each month (July and August only) with material evidence of drought counted 0, unremarkable months ½, months with material evidence of frequent rains and wetness counted 1. (Unremarkable decades score about 10. Extreme decade values of the index in Europe range from about 4 to 17.)

movements in summer and winter are broadly parallel. Measurement reveals that the longitude displacements are so large that, to explain them in terms of the dynamics of the prevailing upper west-wind flow, we have to suppose that the flow both weakened and became displaced progressively south from 1300 to 1550, recovering again from 1700 onwards to the present century. A prevailing warm epoch, with dry anticyclonic character in summer, in Britain between about A.D. 1000 and 1300 appears to be confirmed. A cold epoch, with the depressions passing on much more southern tracks near Scotland in summer and quite frequently south of the British Isles in winter, is indicated between about 1550 and 1700. It appears possible to verify these characteristics by actual observed wind charts for Britain and much of Europe in the individual summers and winters of the seventeenth century.

The deduced main zones of frequency of travelling depressions in the summers of the 1000s and 1550–1600 are shown in Fig. 8 compared with the average pressure in the Julys of the 1940s, the warmest and driest group of summers in the twentieth century.

Fig. 9 displays the course of the indices in England each decade since 1100. These graphs tell the same story; but for many purposes it would be useful to discover what average values of temperature and rainfall these frequency indices imply. This has now been attempted on the basis of correlations between the indices and decade values of temperature and rainfall since 1680–1740; but one must be careful to state, where possible, the margins of error. In cases where these cannot be given, or are too wide, one must avoid final commitment to an opinion before our knowledge warrants it.

The results are given in Figs. 10, 11 and 12. Error margins shown are three times the standard error of the estimates, i.e. 99 per cent confidence limits. It is at once clear from these error margins that only the bigger changes within the centuries studied can be regarded as firmly established: this, however, appears to apply down to the half century of milder winters between 1500 and 1550 whose probable average temperature comes out just outside this limit of difference from the previous 50-year period (Fig. 10(*c*)) and well outside that from the succeeding half century. The lowest (thin broken) line for winter temperature is derived directly from the regression equation on Winter Severity Index values; the bold (broken) line represents an adjustment for probable under-reporting of mild winter months in early times to make the average winter temperatures in the warmest epoch, and in periods when westerly winds are known to have prevailed, not lower than those of today. It was found possible to estimate the average annual rainfall from apparently statistically significant correlations with decade averages of annual temperature and winter temperature. The summer temperature estimates are less securely based, but depend on study of their behaviour in relation to the Summer Wetness Index *and* anticyclonic or cyclonic character of the circulation: this gives the lowest (thin broken) line for the early period on Fig. 10. The bold (broken) line represents the figures apparently required to meet various botanical indications. And finally the thin (continuous) curves are what in regard to all the evidence and indications at present available are the provisional values recommended by the analyst.

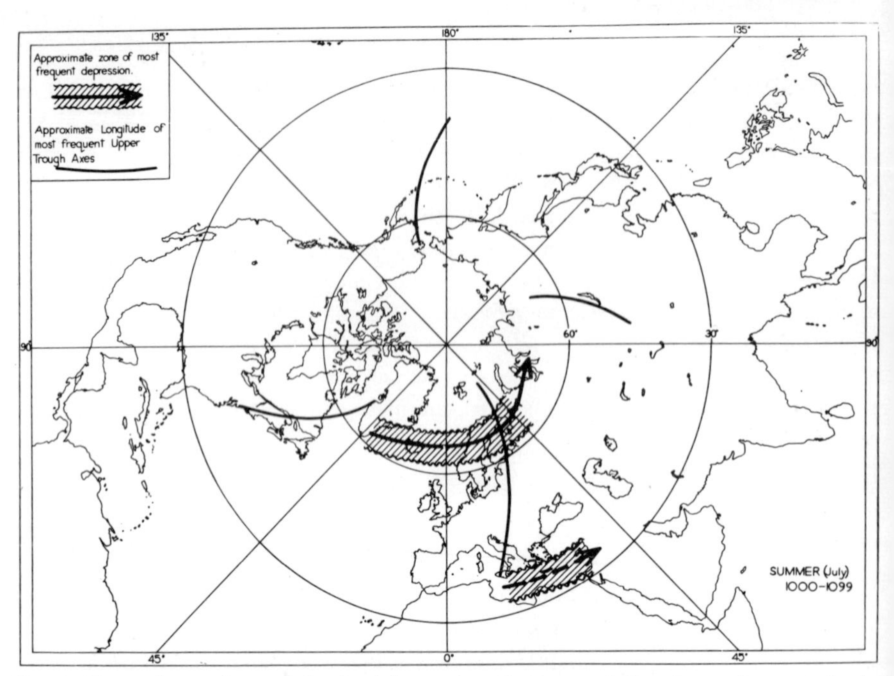

Fig. 8. Zones of most frequent (surface) depressions ('storm tracks') and axes of troughs in the flow of the (upper level) circumpolar westerlies, deduced for

(*a*, *above*) Julys of the eleventh century A.D.

(*b*, *below*) Julys 1550–1600.

and (*c*, *opposite*) Average surface pressure in millibars for the Julys 1940–49. (For comparison of the axis of lowest pressure between Iceland and northern Europe with cases (*a*) and (*b*).)

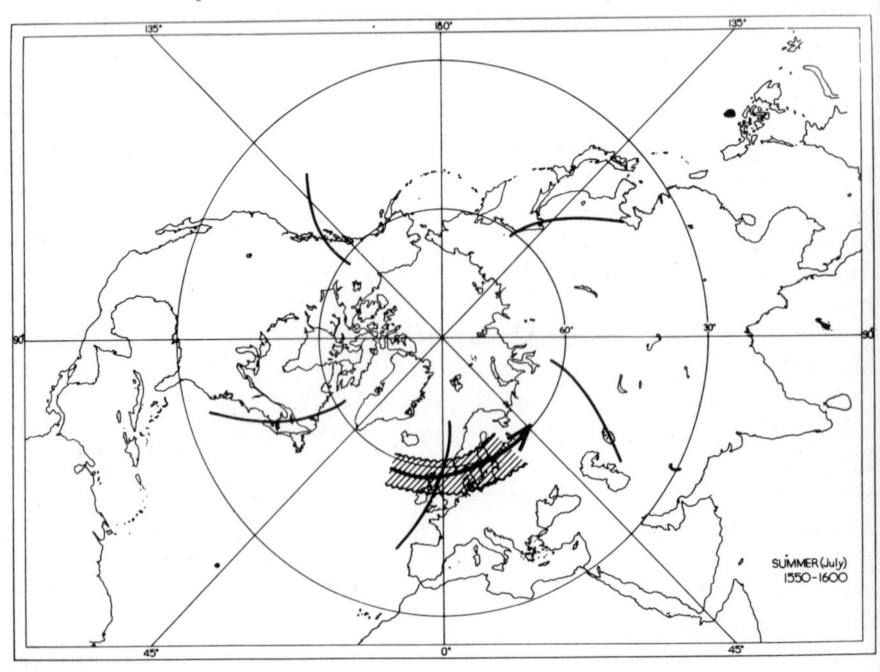

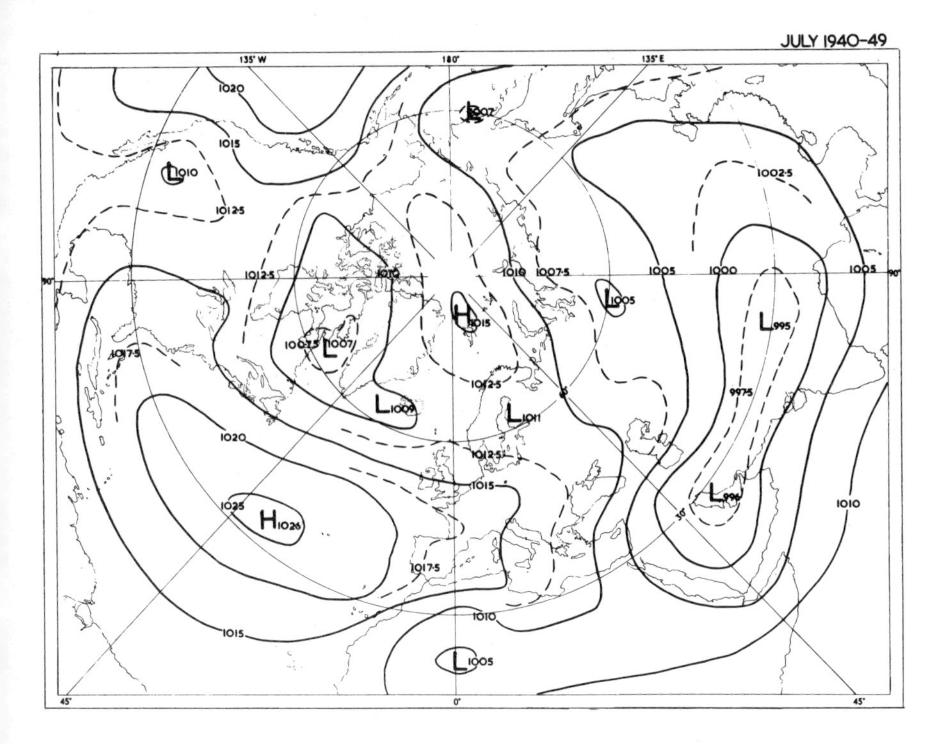

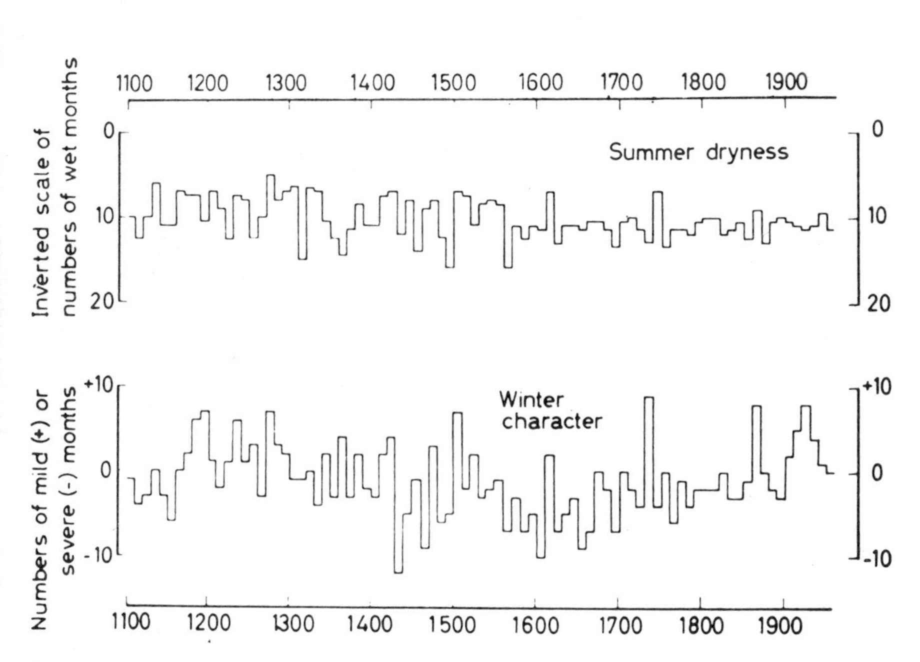

FIG. 9. Values of the indices of Summer Dryness/Wetness and Winter Mildness/Severity in England for each decade 1100–1959.

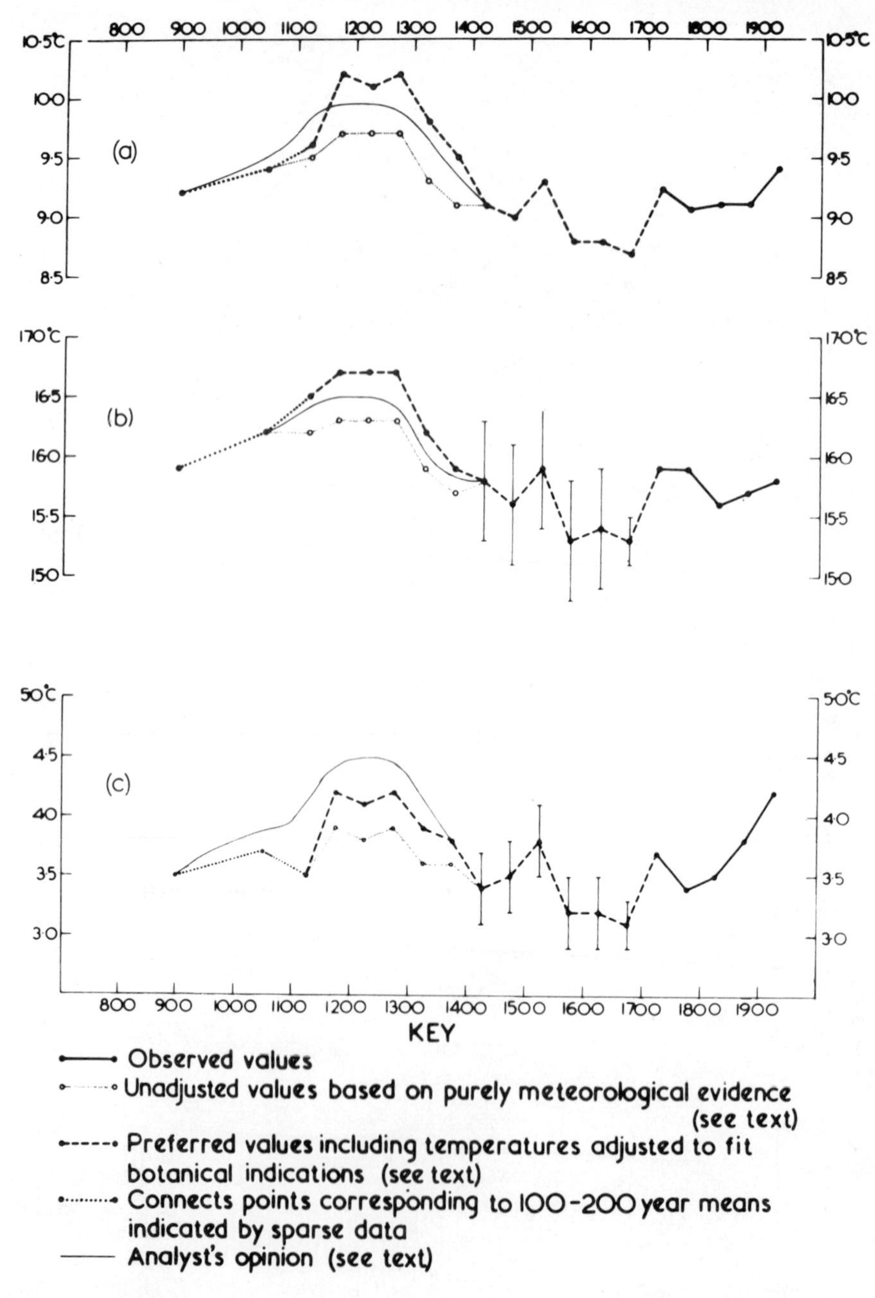

FIG. 10. Temperatures (° C) prevailing in central England, 50-year averages.
(*a*) Year.
(*b*) High summer (July and August).
(*c*) Winter (December, January and February).
Observed values (as standardized by MANLEY) from 1680. Values for earlier periods derived as described in the text. The ranges indicated by vertical bars are three times the standard error of the estimates.

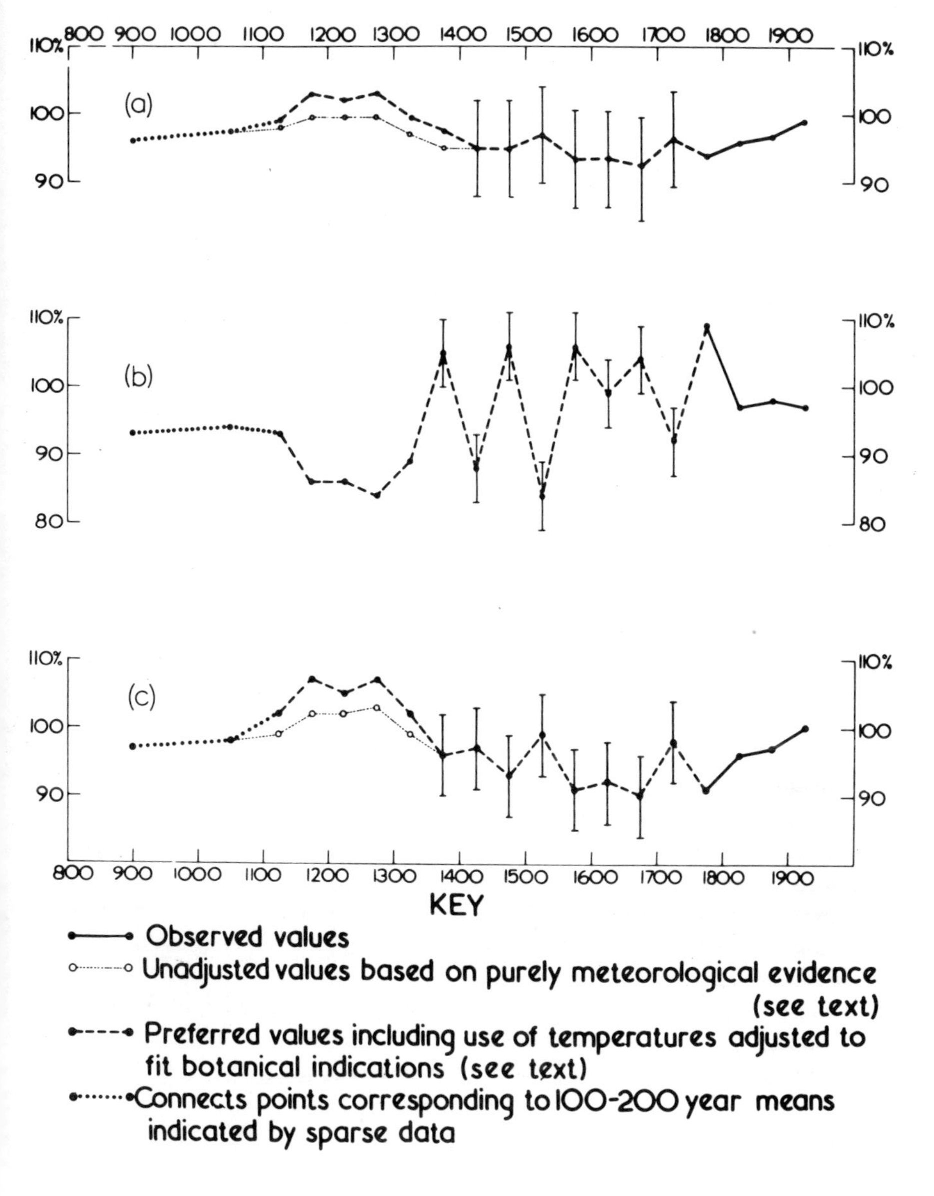

FIG. 11. Rainfall amounts (as percentage of the 1916–50 averages) over England and Wales, 50-year averages.

(*a*) Year.

(*b*) High summer (July and August).

(*c*) Cooler 10 months of the year (September to June).

Observed values (as presented by NICHOLAS and GLASSPOOLE) from 1740. Values for earlier periods derived as described in the text. The ranges indicated by vertical bars are three times the standard error of the estimates.

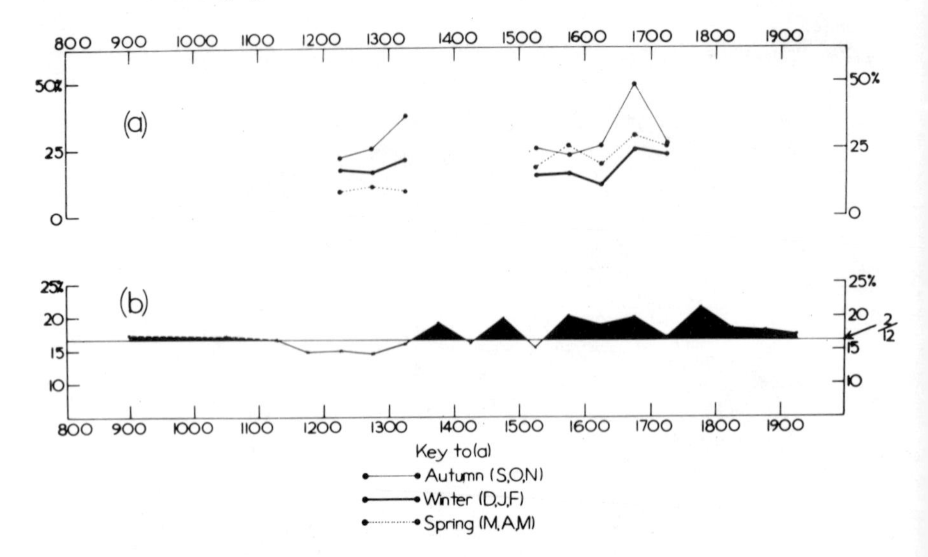

FIG. 12. Seasonal rainfall characteristics deduced for England and Wales.
(*a*) Frequency (percentage) of months described as wet in autumn, winter and spring. (Snowy months have not been included in the counts, because the equivalent rainfall is nearly always below normal. Data insufficient before A.D. 1200 and between 1350 and 1500.)
(*b*) Percentage of the year's total rainfall falling in July and August. (Shaded area indicates excess over the proportion due for 2/12 of the year.)

Botanical indicators from neighbouring continental areas are listed in Table 1. They suggest a pretty general lowering of the temperatures of the warmest month of the year since 1300 by about 1° C. Moreover, the highest levels reached by the plough on the hills in northern England were in the twelfth and thirteenth centuries beyond the limits of the wartime emergency ploughing campaign of 1940–44 (Beresford *loc. cit.*). About the 1230s medieval village settlements and their strip cultivation were spreading so far on to the higher ground as to cause anxiety for the preservation of enough pasture.

Viking burial-grounds of the period 1000–1300 in south-west Greenland, in which graves were dug deep and trees rooted in earth now permanently frozen, seem to imply a subsequent fall of annual mean temperatures there by 2 to 4° C. Anomalies should, however, be expected to be greatest in places closely affected by shifts of the limit of persistent snow and ice surface, as in the present century at Spitsbergen and along much of the Greenland coast.

All this suggests that the evidence of the English medieval vineyards should be given such weight as it plainly suggests. The distribution of those vineyards, with their size and continuity of cultivation as indicators of success, may be seen in Fig. 13 and compared with the modern limits of vine growing shown in Fig. 14. There had been vineyards which were well thought of in England from earlier Saxon times – of the status of the few Roman vineyards after A.D. 280 we have no knowledge. Their success in the period 1100–1300 was such that the French trade sought to have them abolished by an early treaty of peace with England (Ellis 1833).

TABLE 1. *Anomalies c. 1150–1300 by reference to the average values about 1900 of mean temperature of the warmest month indicated by botanical and viticultural evidence.*

Displacement noticed	*Corresponding (previous) temperature anomaly*
Lowering of the upper tree limit (or upper limits of particular species of trees) in the Vosges, Black Forest and Sudetenland by 100–200 m., between A.D. 1300 and 1500 (Firbas and Losert 1949)	+0·7 to 1·4° C
Lowering of the upper tree limit on Monte Rosa and in the Swiss Alps (Valais) after 1300 (Gams 1937) by 70 m.	+0·5° C
Lowering of the upper limit of cultivation of fruit and grain crops in the mountain districts of central Europe after 1300 (Gams 1937)	No figure given
Lowering of the upper limit of vineyards in S.W. Germany (Baden) by 220 m. after 1300–1430 (Müller 1953)	+1·5 to 1·6° C
Retardation by 20 days to mid-October of the average date of grape picking in the Vivarais district (45·7° N 4·8° E) near Lyon between about 1550 and 1800 (Arago 1858) – Calculated to give the same number of degree days above the 6° C threshold marking the beginning of the growing season in early March	+1·0° C*

* Probable that some additional lowering of summer temperature had taken place before 1550, though this might be offset by the recovery since 1800.

For success with the grape-harvest the vine makes the following climatic demands:

1. Freedom from late spring frosts, especially at and after flowering
2. Sufficient sunshine and warmth in summer
3. Not too much rain
4. Enough autumn sunshine and warmth in regions where the summer is only just warm enough, to raise the sugar content
5. A dormant winter season, in which frosts are seldom serious.

Severe frosts have affected the northern limit of vineyards in France and Germany in a few of the most historic winters – cultivation was never resumed in some parts of France after 1709, and the winters of the 1430s may have had a similar outcome both in France and Germany. Probably a prolonged period of frost and extreme temperatures below −20 to −25° C are required for this to happen. Such temperatures have occurred in some of the former English vine districts, but it seems likely that (with the possible exception of Ely in the 1430s) such frosts only occurred after cultivation had already ceased: severe frosts are less likely to have been a limitation in England than on the continent. The figures which follow suggest that, first and foremost, the coolness of spring and the incidence of frosts in

May, and to a lesser extent insufficient summer warmth, are likely to have been most serious in England.

Table 2 gives relevant climatic values near the modern northern limit of commercial vineyards, and Table 3 indicates how far twentieth-century temperatures in the best of the former English vine districts appear to fall short of the lowest values required. (It is true that individual enthusiasm has succeeded in operating isolated vineyards – not always open unwalled vineyards – in specially favourable sites in the south of England at one time or another in most centuries since the Middle Ages, but these have never continued long after the retirement or death of the enthusiast.)

TABLE 2. *Temperatures (° C) representing the modern northern limit of commercial vineyards.*

	Average lowest in May	*Extreme lowest in May*	*Average temperature of July*	*Average temperature of October*
Reims (1891–1956)	+0·5	−2·2	18·9	10·3
Luxemburg (1854–1956)	+1·7	−3·3	18·1	9·7
Köln (1851–1930)	+3·3	−0·5	18·6	10·5
Frankfurt/Main (1851–1936	+2·8	−1·0	18·6	9·7
Apparent lowest acceptable values (approx.)	+1·0	−2·0	18·0	10·0

TABLE 3. *Shortfall of prevailing temperatures (° C) in 1921–50, below the values in the bottom line of Table 2, in what were in 1150–1300 by report the best English wine districts.*

District and Station used	*Average lowest in May*	*Extreme lowest in May*	*Average for July*	*Average for October*
Fenland (Cambridge)	1·5	2·5	1·0	0
Hereford–Gloucester border (Ross)	0·5	0·8	1·3	0
Middle-lower Severn and Thames valleys (Oxford)	0·5	0	1·0	0
London (Greenwich*)	0	0·2	0·2	0
Mid Essex valleys (Halstead)	1·5	1·9	0·7	0
Kent (Canterbury†)	0·1	1·9	0·6	0

* Greenwich temperatures may be raised slightly by the artificial climate of the built up area of London.

† Canterbury data 1921–44 only.

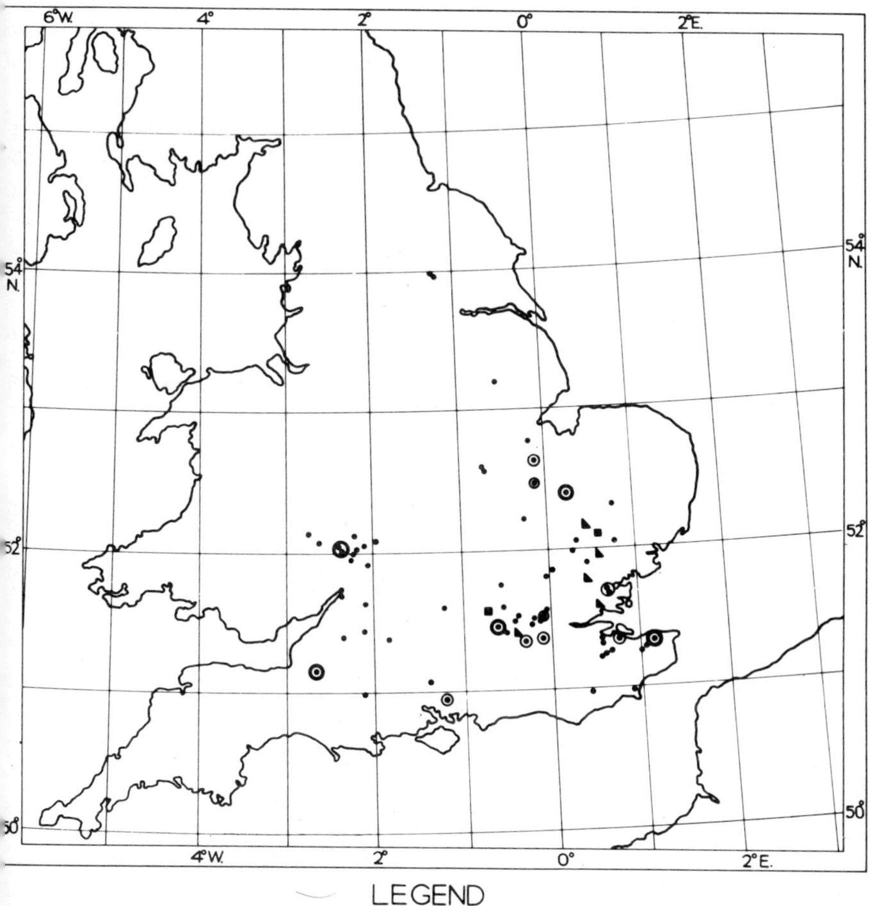

LEGEND

- Vineyard, usually 1–2 acres or size not known.
- ◣ Vineyard, 5–10 acres.
- ■ Vineyard, over 10 acres.
- ○ Denotes evidence of continuous operation for 30–100 years.
- **○** Denotes evidence of continuous operation for over 100 years.

FIG. 13. English vineyards recorded between A.D. 1000 and 1300.
Sources: W. Camden, *Britannia – or a chorographical description of Great Britain and Ireland* (first edition 1586) translated into English, revised and digested by E. Gibson, London 1722; H. C. Darby *et al.*, *The Domesday geography of England* (in several vols.), Cambridge 1952 ff.; H. K. Ellis, *A general introduction to Domesday Book*, London (Commissioners of Public Records) 1833; E. Hyams, *Vineyards in England*, London 1953; G. Ordish, *Wine growing in England*, London 1953; A. L. Simon, *English wines and cordials*, London 1946; *Ordnance Survey* large-scale maps; and various local works.

The summer temperatures, only 0·7° C above the 1900–50 averages, indicated by the recommended (thin) curve in Fig. 10 do imply that climatic conditions in the medieval English vineyards were not fully equivalent to those of the northernmost commercial vineyards on the continent today, though the difference would be only a few tenths of a degree. It is noticeable in Fig. 13 that the longest continued, and presumably most successful, English vineyards were not the biggest ones; probably careful management and choice of ground was always a factor in the successful ones.

Conclusions

1. The differences during the last 1,000 years in the long-period temperature averages in England are small enough – only 1 to 1·5° C – to account for impressions in some quarters that there have been no significant changes of climate in Britain since the beginning of the '*sub-Atlantic*' *period* around 500 B.C.

2. Nevertheless this small difference of average temperature implies that the summer climate of southern England has ranged between the modern values for northern France (Normandy–Marne) and south Yorks. The change in the average length of the growing season between the opposite extreme climates of the thirteenth and seventeenth centuries over most of England probably amounted to 15–20 per cent on ground between sea-level and 200 m. elevation.

3. The range of variation of 50-year *average* summer temperature has apparently been about as great as that of *average* winter temperature, but the range of temperatures characterizing the individual extreme winters exceeds that between the extreme summers. Probably of wider importance, however, are the variations implied in the length of the growing season and in the incidence of frosts that are prolonged and severe.

4. Rainfall variations have been at least as notable as those of temperature. Although annual rainfall was apparently lowest in the cold-climate period between 1550 and 1700, the difference as regards wetness of the ground was probably offset by less evaporation and wetter summers. Nevertheless, sites chosen for building in the English valley-bottoms in that epoch suggest the ground may have been on the whole drier than in recent times. In Scotland, the effects of summer wetness and reduced evaporation are believed to have made that an epoch of wetter ground.

5. The seasonal distribution of rainfall shows some marked variations. The autumns have been always more prone to wetness than the springs, but the extra high frequency of wet autumns around 1300–50 and 1650–1700 probably affected many things. Shortening of the season for work on the farms in Scotland in the late 1600s played a part in the famine years of the 1690s. The contributions of the summers and winters to the year's rainfall have undergone the biggest changes. The medieval warm epoch is seen as one of dry summers – an oceanic, summer-anticyclonic type of régime. In the subsequent cold epoch, and to some extent ever since, the summers have contributed a more than proportionate share of the year's rain, especially in the latter half of each century, whereas the winters became relatively dry. The dryness of the winters in the sixteenth century is particularly often stressed in the records. That was the time of onset of most 'continental' climate and sharpest lowering of temperature levels. (The same could be said of the years since 1960.)

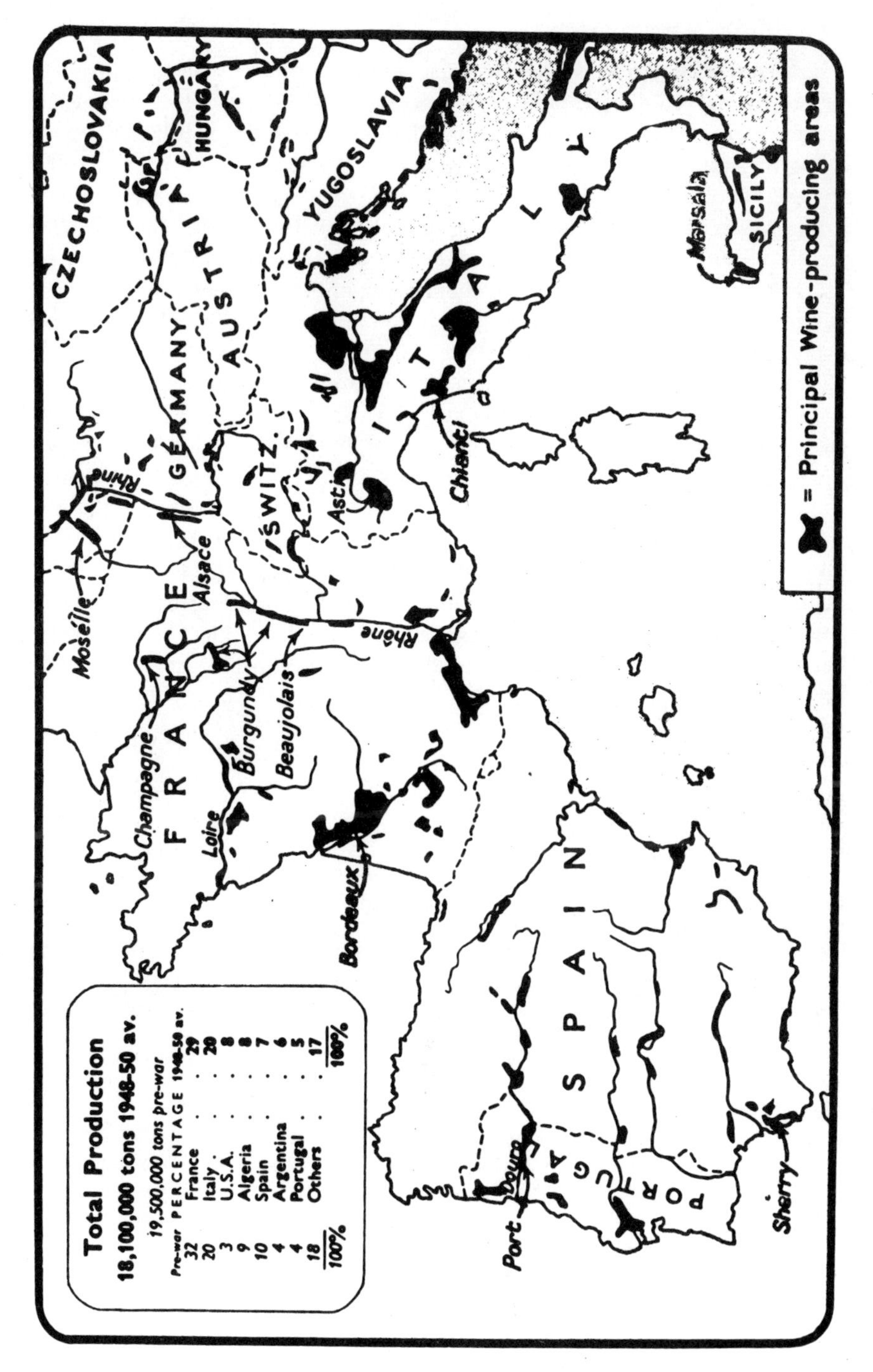

Fig. 14. Distribution of modern commercial vineyards in Europe, from *The Oxford Economic Atlas*, 1954 edition (reproduced here by courtesy of the Clarendon Press).

Finally, there is a practical conclusion about the judicious use of climatic tables at the present day. A climatic table summarizes the weather conditions that occurred in some period of past years, which should always be specified. It is not much use unless the years are specified and are broadly the same for all elements of the climate. Yet most users are concerned only with the future. To use a climatic table in this way is tantamount to assuming (usually unwittingly) that the climate will remain constant. A table of statistics of the past can never be a substitute for a forecast. But forecasting the climatic trend must wait until the proper scientific basis for it exists – knowledge of all the atmospheric processes and possible external agencies involved as well as the magnitudes of their effects.

In the meantime, practical decisions for the future involving climate have to be made by many people. The climatic statistics of the past have to be used for as much as they are worth. Meteorological services and the users have to choose what period of years is most relevant to incorporate in the table. This is not necessarily the most recent 30 to 50 years. Indeed, the best choice may vary according to the purpose the user has in mind. Probably the last 10 years should always be included, and beyond that such additional decades as appear on grounds of similarity of the environment, as regards ocean temperatures and extent of ice, as well as similarity of the prevailing wind-circulation patterns and strength, to offer the best analogy. When concerned with *long* periods ahead, at least an equally long period of past years should (if possible) be surveyed.

References

ARAGO, F. 1858. 'Sur l'état thermométrique du globe terrestre.' *Œuvres de François Arago* (Barral), Tome V, Paris and Leipzig.

BERESFORD, M. W. 1951. 'The lost villages of medieval England.' *Geogr. J.*, **117**, 129–149. London.

BROOKS, C. E. P. 1949. *Climate through the ages.* London (Ernest Benn), 2nd edition.

ELLIS, H. K. 1833. 'A general introduction to Domesday Book', in 2 vols. London (Commissioners of Public Records).

EMILIANI, C. 1961. 'Cenozoic climatic changes as indicated by . . . deep-sea cores . . .' *Annals of the New York Academy of Sciences*, **95,** Art. 1, 521–541. New York.

FIRBAS, F. and LOSERT, H. 1949. 'Untersuchungen über die Entstehung der heutigen Waldstufen in den Sudeten.' *Planta*, **36,** 478–506. Berlin.

FLINT, R. F. 1957. *Glacial and Pleistocene Geology* (e.g. pp. 394, 397), New York (John Wiley).

GAMS, H. 1937. 'Aus der Geschichte der Alpenwälder.' *Zeitschrift des deutschen und österreichischen Alpenvereins*, **68,** 157–170, Stuttgart.

GODWIN, H. 1956. '*The history of the British flora.*' Cambridge (Cambridge University Press).

GODWIN, H., SUGGATE, R. P. and WILLIS, E. H. 1958. 'Radiocarbon dating of the eustatic rise in ocean level.' *Nature*, **181,** 1518–1519. London.

GODWIN, H. and WILLIS, E. H. 1959. 'Radiocarbon dating of prehistoric wooden trackways.' *Nature*, **184,** 490–491. London.

HOLMSEN, A. 1961. *Norges historie.* Oslo and Bergen (Universitetsforlaget).

LAMB, H. H. 1963. 'On the nature of certain climatic epochs which differed from the modern (1900–39) normal.' *Proceedings of the WMO/UNESCO Rome 1961 Symposium on Changes of Climate*, (*Arid Zone Research XX*). UNESCO, Paris.

LAMB, H. H. (1964). 'Trees and climatic history in Scotland'. *Quarterly Journal of the Royal Meteorological Society*, **90,** 382–394. London.

LAMB, H. H. and JOHNSON, A. I. 1961. 'Climatic variation and observed changes in the general circulation', Part III, 391–397. *Geografiska Annaler*, **43,** 363–400. Stockholm.

MANLEY, G. 1958. 'Temperature trends in England, 1698–1957.' *Archiv für Meteorologie, Geophysik und Bioklimatologie, Serie B*, **9,** 413–433. Vienna.

MANLEY, G. 1959. 'The late-glacial climate of north-west England.' *Liverpool and Manchester Geological Journal*, **2,** Part 2, 188–215.

MANLEY, G. 1961. 'A preliminary note on early meteorological observations in the London region . . . with . . . estimates of monthly mean temperatures 1680–1706.' *Meteorological Magazine*, **90,** 303–310. London.

MITCHELL, G. F. 1960. 'The Pleistocene history of the Irish Sea.' *Advancement of Science*, **XVII**, 313–325. London.

MITCHELL, J. M. 1963. 'On the world-wide pattern of secular temperature change.' *Proceedings of the WMO/UNESCO Rome 1961 Symposium on Climatic Changes* (*Arid Zone Research XX*), 161–181, Paris (UNESCO).

MÜLLER, K. 1953. *Geschichte des Badischen Weinbaus.* Laar in Baden (von Moritz Schauenburg).

NICHOLAS, F. J. and GLASSPOOLE, J. 1931. 'General monthly rainfall over England and Wales, 1727 to 1931.' *British Rainfall 1931*, 299–306. London (Meteorological Office).

STRIDE, A. H. 1959. 'On the origin of the Dogger Bank in the North Sea.' *Geological Magazine*, **XCVI,** 33–64. London and Hertford.

WEST, R. G. 1960. 'The ice age.' *The Advancement of Science*, **XVI,** 428–440. London, British Association.

EIGHT

What can we find out about the trend of our climate?

THE winter 1962–3, with average temperature 0°C for the 3-months period December–February in the English lowlands, has been the coldest since 1740. Such temperatures are normal about Oslofjord, Danzig and Breslau. The weather patterns producing the cold weather by a repetition of northerly and easterly winds have been similar to those which occurred more often in the 18th and early 19th centuries, but rarely since. The winter development appears to have been notably similar to that of 1795. The region of anomalous cold embraced Europe, the European sector of the Arctic and beyond. January 1963, with a monthly mean temperature of −3·5°C at Bedford (Cardington) and −2 to −3·5°C widely over central and southern England (6 to 7° below 'normal'), was the coldest month since the Januarys of 1814 or 1795 and probably in some places the coldest since 1684, a case which it also resembled—the great snowy winter on Exmoor, Somerset described by R. D. Blackmore in *Lorna Doone*. (A quarter of a century ago public controversy arose over this feature of Blackmore's book and some opinion, now seen to be mistaken, held that such winter conditions were impossible in south-west England.) Comparative temperature figures are now available thanks to the work of Professor Gordon Manley (1959, 1961) on old instrument observations from about 1680 onwards in or near London and a little later in other parts of England including Plymouth and Lancashire. 1962–3 has also been remarkable for the frequent snowfalls and depth and persistence of snow cover—50 to 60 days by the end of February in many areas—probably in this respect also unmatched since 1814 or earlier.

Whenever abnormal spells of weather occur, the question is raised: 'Is the climate changing?' The truth is that climate is never quite static. Every year, every decade, differs from another. One has to be careful to see both 'the wood' and 'the trees'. Problems of planning for the future are, however, inescapable—sometimes for months, sometimes for many years ahead. Studies of climatic variations clearly answer to a practical need. The enormous quantities of observational data from all parts of the world must be sifted to establish the salient facts, to set them in perspective and to probe for understanding of the physical causes. Such understanding is a prerequisite for worth-while advice about the future.

Taking a long view of the climate over many years or decades, the variations from one year to another can be regarded as a matter of chance—random fluctuations—though they may be superimposed upon a trend. But the meteorologist considering any one particular season, and the individual days within it, can usually 'explain' the anomalous wind-circulation and weather in terms of the particular thermal pattern and associated steering of depressions and anticyclones. Sometimes the main anomalies of the thermal pattern of the lower atmosphere appear to be linked with anomalous aspects of the thermal condition of the Earth's surface itself, of a nature that cannot be quickly changed owing to the large heat capacity involved. Sea temperatures and the depth of water involved, ice and snow cover, may be important in this connection.

Thus the 1962–3 winter began with several features that probably favoured weaker than normal circulation over the Atlantic and steering of depressions on to southern tracks in the European sector. In particular, the cold season was earlier established in autumn 1962 over Siberia than over Canada, making for vigorous cyclonic activity over the Pacific, which transported mild air across Canada, hindering the normal winter development there until mid-December and reducing the thermal contrast between Canada and the Atlantic. Over the eastern part of the Arctic and in the Greenland–Barents Seas a heavy ice situation had been developing, and a cold summer had left the North-Sea–Scandinavian region colder than at the start of any cooling season for long since. A large-amplitude cold trough was established over Europe in November–December 1962, before the one over Canada, and maintained itself against onslaughts from the west in February 1963 when the Atlantic storms became more vigorous after eastern Canada had at last become very cold.

Turning to the long-term climatic trends, the general use of climatic tables —i.e. of statistics of climatic behaviour over *past* years—as a guide to the future begs the important question: 'Will the same pattern of behaviour be repeated over the years with which the reader is concerned?' It is essential (though as yet rare) that climatic tables should specify which past years the figures relate to—and that the figures for all elements of the climate should relate, as far as possible, to the same period of years. Table 1 shows how much, even in recent times, the question of period can affect the figures in a climatic table.

TABLE 1. Sample differences between recent periods of years

Period	Average number of weeks in the year with sea ice at the coasts of Iceland	Av. daily max. temp. in London (Kew) in January (°C)	Av. daily min. temp. in London (Kew) in January (°C)	Av. daily max. temp. in London (Kew) in July (°C)	Av. daily max. temp. at Toronto in July (°C)
1871–1900	9	6·0	1·2	21·7	20·3
1901–1930	4	7·4	1·8	22·4	20·9
1921–1950	1·5	6·9	2·1	22·7	21·5
1950–1959	4	6·5	2·1	21·7	21·9

These figures reflect the warming of the Arctic and temperate zones from the last century to this. Summer temperatures at Toronto and autumns in England have continued this warming, at least until very recent years, though most other figures which we might sample would show some falling off since about 1940. Mitchell (1961) has shown from computations of surface temperature changes all over the globe that the world-wide average temperature rose by about 0·5°C from 1880 to 1940 and has fallen by 0·1 to 0·2°C since then.

The continued high level of winter night temperatures in London (Kew) can probably be put down to the artificial effects of the growth of the city and the ever more artificial temperatures of the water of the nearby River Thames, attributable to warm effluent waters from the factories, etc., along the banks in the London reaches. At the end of January 1963, when the frost had already exceeded in length and severity the frosts of 1895 and 1929 and others when there was much ice on the river in central London, no speck of floating ice was seen in London: instead when the air temperature was low, the river was often seen to be steaming to a height of 1–2 metres (3 to 6 feet) or more. The water temperature thermogram* (Fig. 1) of the Royal Research Ship *Discovery III*

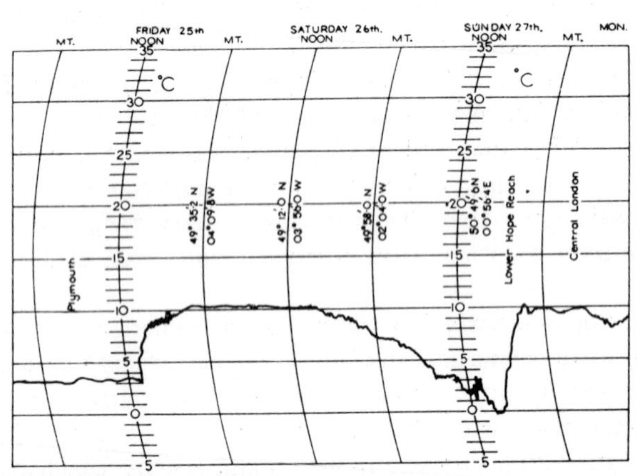

Fig. 1. Why there was no frost fair at Westminster in 1963. Water temperatures measured at 10 foot (3 metres) depth by R.R.S. *Discovery III* on voyage from Plymouth to London on 25–27 January 1963, and moored near London Bridge on 27th. The voyage began on a SSW heading to the South-West Approaches 49°N, 4–5°W, where water temperatures 9·8 to 10·3°C were observed. The value fell to −0·2°C in the mouth of the Thames, where ice belts along the shores were up to a mile or more in width. Water temperatures were again between 8·0 and 10·3°C in the inner Thames all the way from East Tilbury (Lower Hope Reach) to where the vessel moored slightly on the Surrey side of mid-stream opposite Custom House Quay (between London Bridge and Tower Bridge). There was no sign of ice as far up river as the electric power station at Kingston, but ice began half a mile farther up and at Hampton Court, only 2 miles farther up, it was possible to cross the river on the ice. (The Thames-side observatories at Kew and Greenwich, both in the reaches showing great artificial warmth, are therefore now suspect as points for sampling the atmosphere, as they became long-since for some magnetic work)

sailing into London on 27 January 1963, at the end of the severest phase of the frost revealed a rise of water temperature of 10°C from the mouth of the Thames, where ports were obstructed by ice, to the clear waters (with temperatures varying between 8 and 10·3°C) in central London. About the same date, at

* This thermogram is reproduced by courtesy of Dr. G. E. R. Deacon, F.R.S., Director of the National Institute of Oceanography, because of its great interest as a record of how artificial London's climate has become.

one East Anglian port explosives had to be used to release ships, and even on the Bristol Channel ice floes restricted the use of the port of Cardiff.

Callendar (1961) has given figures of 0·05 to 0·15°C for the rise of mean annual surface air temperatures in big cities since about 1900 due to urban growth. The effect is, however, much stronger in the coldest winter weather when the artificial heating is concentrated beneath a low-level inversion: winter night temperatures generally in the country districts of Surrey 10–20 km. farther out of London often fall 3 to 6°C, on some nights 7°C or more lower than at Kew, and the days are commonly 1 to 3°C colder in the country than in central London.

In January 1963, when the light east winds prevailing would have carried the effects of the warmth of the city towards Kew and away from Greenwich, the night temperatures observed at various places in London and in the country just to the south were as follows:

	Mean Minimum (°C)	*Lowest Minimum* (°C)
St. James's Park, Westminster	−2·7	−9·4
Kew	−2·7	−9·7
Kensington Palace	−3·6	−9·4
Greenwich	−3·7	−12·2
Regent's Park	−3·8	−11·1
Hampton, Middlesex	−4·1	−12·2
Addington Hill, Surrey	−4·5	−10·0
Croydon	−4·7	−13·9
Wisley	−4·7	−13·9
Gatwick Airport	−5·1	−16·7

On four nights the difference between Kew and Gatwick was 8 or 9°C.

Kew and Greenwich are close to the river Thames in the artificially warmed reaches. Hampton is near Hampton Court where the river ice was crossable on foot in January 1963.

False impressions about the trend of winter conditions are therefore likely to have gained currency (and influenced the provisions made for keeping essential services going—heat, light and transport) for at least two reasons:

(1) the abnormally easy years experienced in the first four decades of this century. (Because meteorological observations were then more abundant than ever before, those very decades have provided most of the figures available in published climatic tables.)

(2) the increasing effectiveness of the artificial heat sources in London and other big towns.

Tables 2 and 3 give a different perspective. In particular, the 42-year period between 1896 and 1937 stands out as one of abnormal immunity from winter difficulties. This was when many easy-going customs grew up, ranging from injudicious plumbing and the abandonment of laying in food stocks for winter in isolated districts to modern fashions of wearing brief underwear!

The sharp change in the frequency of severe winters since about 1940 has also affected central Europe; their frequency in Breslau (Wroclaw) in the 1940s and 50s was greater than at any time since 1810.

It is important to consider whether the greater frequency of severe winter weather in the latest decades is

(i) Only a temporary lapse from the warm climate attained in the early 20th century, possibly to be followed by a renewed trend to still greater warmth.

TABLE 2. The incidence of cold winters in England since 1680

Winters with mean temperature below +3°C (December, January and February) in central England. (Normal +4°C : those here listed make up the coldest quartile. Winter 1681 means winter 1680–81, etc.)	Number per decade	Winters with at least one freezing month (mean temperature ⩽ 0°C)
1681, 1684, possibly also 1685, 1687 and 1689 ..	2 to 5	1684
1691, 1692, 1694, 1695, 1697, 1698	6	1692, 1695, possibly also 1694 and 1698
1709	1	1709
1716, 1718	2	1716
1729	1	
1731	1	
1740, 1741, 1746	3	1740
1755, 1757	2	
1760, 1763, 1765, 1766, 1767	5	1763
1771, 1772, 1774, 1776, 1777, 1778	6	1776
1780, 1784, 1785, 1786, 1789	5	1780, 1784, December 1788
1792, 1795, 1797, 1799	4	1795, December 1796
1800, 1802, 1803, 1805, 1808	5	
1814, 1816	2	1814
1820, 1823, 1827	3	1820, 1823
1830, 1831, 1838	3	1830, 1838
1841, 1845, 1847	3	
1855	1	1855
1860, 1861, 1864, 1865	4	
1871, 1875, 1879	3	December 1874; 1879
1880, 1881, 1886, 1887, 1888	5	1881
1891, 1893, 1895	3	December 1890 ; 1895
	0	
1917	1	
1929	1	
	0	
1940, 1941, 1942, 1947	4	1940, 1947
1951, 1956	2	1956
1963		1963

(ii) A return to conditions normal in the past century or two.

(iii) The beginning of a climatic decline to still harsher conditions.

The fall of average winter temperatures—now (since 1940) perhaps 1°C below the average for the four mildest decades has been fairly small, but at a level that makes it very significant for frequency of frost and of snow lying in English lowlands and, probably, in neighbouring countries between 50° and 60°N.

It is not possible to answer these questions firmly yet, though (i) appears more and more unlikely as the turning points of many climatic trends recede into the past, and (iii) may have become more likely since the great increase of the Arctic sea ice since about 1958 (see later Fig. 3). To make any headway with the problem, we need to study the mechanism by which the changes have been brought about and seek to identify any external influences at work.

THE ATMOSPHERIC CIRCULATION: THE MECHANISM OF CLIMATIC CHANGES

Not many years ago climatic variations were almost only investigated in terms of the temperature or rainfall records at this or that place. The welter of seemingly unrelated facts was bewildering, until the recent warming trend appeared as a common feature.

TABLE 2A. Cold winters in England, provisional list, 1400–1679.

Winters with descriptions similar to those in Table 2. Bold face indicates Thames frozen in London (probably always required a monthly mean temperature ≤ −1°C over much of southern England)	Number per decade
1403, 1404, **1408**	3
	0
1423, possibly also 1429	1–2
1432, 1433, 1434, **1435**, 1436, 1439, possibly also 1431 and 1437	6–8
1443, possibly also 1440 and 1441	1–3
1458	1
1460, 1464, 1465, 1469	4
1470, possibly also 1477	1–2
1481, possibly also 1487	1–2
1491, 1492, 1496	3
1506, possibly also 1508	1–2
1511 or 1512, **1514**, possibly also 1517	2–3
	0
1534, **1537**, possibly also 1536	2–3
1546, possibly also 1541 and 1548 or 1549	1–3
1554	1
1561, **1565**, 1569, probably also 1564	3–4
1571, 1573, possibly also 1570 and 1578	2–4
1584, 1586, 1587, possibly also 1580	3–4
1595, probably also 1590 and 1599	1–3
1600, **1608**, possibly also 1601, 1603, 1605	2–5
1615, possibly also 1612 and 1618	1–3
1621, possibly also 1623, 1624, 1625 and 1628	(1–5)
1635, 1637, possibly also 1631	1–3
1649, possibly also 1644, 1645 and 1646	1–4
1655, 1658, possibly also 1656 and 1659	2–4
1663, **1666**, 1667	3
1670, **1677**, 1679, possibly also 1672	3–4

The first attempts to gain a synoptic view of how this warming trend was brought about were the studies of changes in the general atmospheric circulation between about 1889–1900 and the 1920s–30s by Defant, Wagner and Scherhag. The work of Defant, Wagner and Ångström (1935) further introduced the question of responses of the atmospheric circulation to possible changes in the radiation supply, for instance with variations of atmospheric opacity due to greater or less prevalence of volcanic dust or other things. The principal findings of these and the more recent studies by the present author (Lamb and Johnson 1959, 1961, Lamb 1963), to be described below, were that the global wind-circulation was increasing in vigour during the period of climatic warming, and the main depression tracks, at least in the North Atlantic, were spreading more and more into the highest latitudes as the warming proceeded. There was evidence that the ocean currents, specifically the Gulf Stream–North Atlantic Drift, underwent parallel changes to those of the prevailing winds. It also appears from studies of the cold climate around 1800 and of the warm climate of the early 1900s that the shifts north and south of isotherms and depression tracks in the Atlantic sector, and neighbouring longitudes over N. America and Europe, have been greater than in other sectors. This amplification of climatic variations in the Atlantic sector must be due to the geography, which favours meridional movements of winds and water: it was also operative in the ice age–interglacial sequence of the Pleistocene.

TABLE 3. The incidence of snow-cover on low ground in Britain

Place	Before and including 1937–8 in 15 to 22 years of record	Since 1937–8 (25 winters)
	No snow-cover	
Kew	7 winters in 22	3 winters in 25
Ross-on-Wye	5 ,, 22	2 ,, 25
Cambridge	2 ,, 22	2 ,, 25
Stonyhurst, Lancashire	2 ,, 17	0 ,, 25
Perth	3 ,, 18	2 ,, 25
	5 days or less with snow-cover	
York	4 winters in 21	4 winters in 25
Lerwick, Shetland	4 ,, 15	0 ,, 25
	15 days or more with snow-cover	
Kew	0 winters in 22	3 winters in 25
Ross-on-Wye	2 ,, 22	6 ,, 25
Cambridge	3 ,, 22	8 ,, 25
Stonyhurst, Lancashire	1 ,, 17	14 ,, 25
York	5 ,, 21	12 ,, 25
Perth	2 ,, 18	11 ,, 25
Lerwick, Shetland	2 ,, 15	21 ,, 25

Precipitation changes significantly affecting the average annual rainfalls in the equatorial zone, within the arid zones of both hemispheres, in eastern U.S.A. and Argentina and Australia (Kraus 1955, 1958) and in the polar regions, where the accumulation of ice on the Greenland and Antarctic ice caps was also affected (Lamb *et al.* 1962), have accompanied the circulation changes in an entirely logical manner.

Increased vigour of the wind circulation should itself cause a rise of temperature in the higher latitudes, owing to increased heat transport. But increased exchange of air between different latitudes should also cool the tropical zone. In reality, the tropical zone shared in the general warming. Circulation changes alone could not readily explain significant changes of world temperature. It is easier to picture a general strengthening or weakening of the winds as produced by changes in the energy effectively available from the sun or from the heat stored in the oceans. Possible effects of changes in the amounts of ozone (produced by solar ultra-violet radiation), or of carbon dioxide, in intercepting solar and terrestrial radiation at different levels in the atmosphere (Kraus 1960) must be considered—also changes of the response (albedo and heat capacity) of the Earth's surface to radiation received, owing to man-made vegetation changes, irrigation, etc. (Flohn 1963).

Satellite observations are the best hope of improving our knowledge of possible slight variations in the incoming radiation and of the transmission of energy through the atmosphere to and from the Earth's surface (Wexler 1962). In the meantime, studies of the circulation patterns of the past may enable us to gain further insight into the distribution—the 'anatomy' as Dr. Sutcliffe has called it—of past climates and the nature of various climatic changes.

INVESTIGATION OF CIRCULATION CHANGES

The writer set out to reconstruct monthly mean-pressure maps over as much of the world as possible, from the earliest years for which reliable observations could be found. The intimate relation between winds and pressure distribution, expressed by the geostrophic wind equation, means that maps of average pressure reveal the pattern of prevailing, or at least of resultant, winds. January, the month of strongest winter circulation in the northern hemisphere, and July, the month of peak (maximum) development of the northern summer circulation including the Asian monsoon, have been studied first. There is reason to believe that the most important results from these two months apply to most of the other months as well.

Reliable barometers have been in use in many places since the 18th century. Problems of satisfactory exposure of this instrument are not as great as with thermometers and raingauges and were solved correspondingly earlier. Correction for the temperature of the unheated room, and reduction to sea level and standard gravity (45°N) remained to be done. The network of observations over parts of Europe was so close from the late 1700s that it was possible to identify the most reliable observing stations. Uncertainties about the heights of one or two observing stations above sea level were resolved from the pressure distribution itself. The errors to which the earliest pressure maps were liable were estimated in the following way. The first analysis of recent years was made with the same skeleton network of observations as existed for the early years. These charts were then analysed again with full data, and the distribution of errors of the first analysis was studied. Geographical limits could then be laid down beyond which the isobars would be unreliable. The greatest standard error* allowed was ±2·5 mb. This was the limit of tolerance generally adopted, but was reduced to ±1 mb for the northern hemisphere in July, when greater errors than this might radically alter the pattern and pressure-gradients of the rather weak summer circulation. Areas of the map with greater errors were not accepted.

The final charts cover most of the world, excluding the wide Pacific and the two polar regions, from 1850. Random errors are reduced when one considers averages of groups of years. Happily this means that 40-year average maps (within the above-mentioned limits of tolerable error) can be presented from eastern North America across the Atlantic to eastern Europe from 1790.

The maps have been published elsewhere (Lamb and Johnson *loc. cit.*). Fig. 2 illustrates the changes of pressure-gradient, and by implication of wind, measured off the maps. The progressive increase of the main zonal winds up to about the 1920s is found to be a world-wide phenomenon; it is shown alike by the North Atlantic westerlies (various other indices were used besides the one

* The expression used was Standard Error $= \sqrt{\frac{\Sigma x^2}{n-1}}$ where x stands for the errors on the individual maps and n for the number of values of x available for test (n was 20 or 21). Any systematic errors (bias of the analyst towards too high or too low pressure) appeared so small as to be negligible over the North Atlantic between 30 and 60° N.

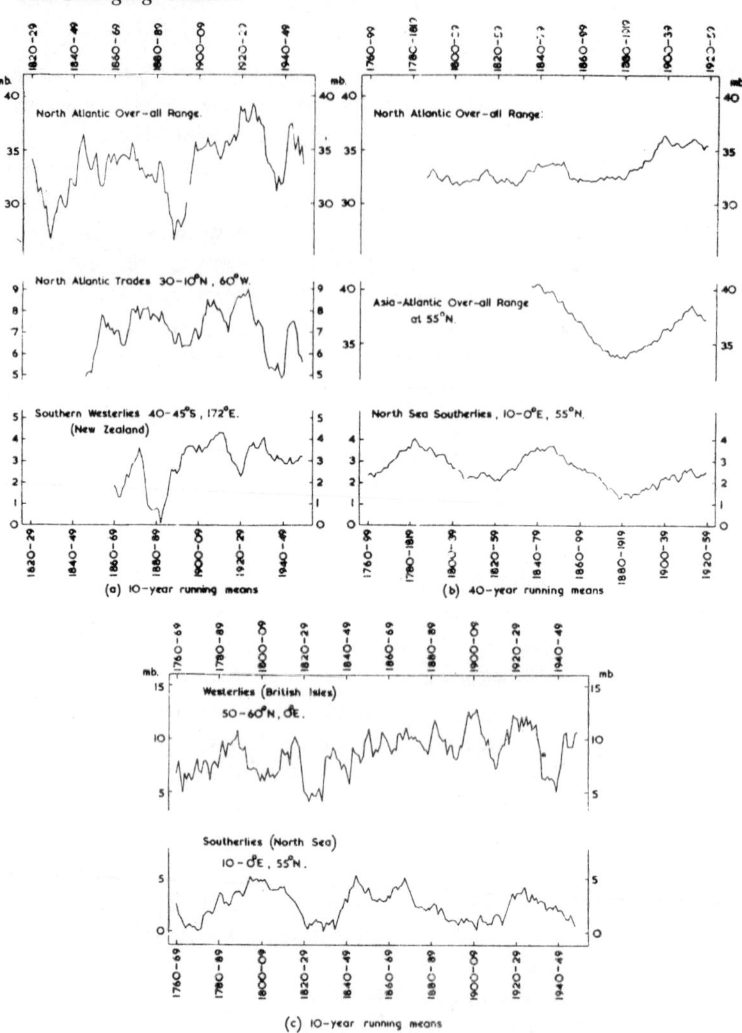

Fig. 2. Pressure difference indices of circulation intensity in January

illustrated, which is the simple over-all pressure difference between the regions of the Azores anticyclones and of the Iceland depressions), the North-East Trade Winds, the summer monsoon windstreams of south and east Asia (not in Fig. 2) and the southern hemisphere westerlies (the 'Roaring Forties') whether measured, as here, over New Zealand or over southern Chile. In January, and probably in most other months, this increasing strength of the westerlies has been under way over Europe (lower section of Fig. 2) from 1760, or earlier. All the curves agree in suggesting that the vigour of the circulation has begun to decline again over the last 30–40 years; both the short-term peaks and troughs on the curves have tended to become successively lower.

The meridional components of the circulation, illustrated in Fig. 2 by the curves for pressure-differences in winter between Siberia and the Atlantic, and across the North Sea (pressure-gradients for northerly or southerly winds), do not show any trend but only fluctuations, which may have a fairly regular recurrence period of 50–70 years.

Trends in various indices measuring the average latitudes and longitudes of prominent features of the general circulation are also interesting. As has been mentioned, the main depression paths, indicated by the latitude of lowest average pressure in January and July, were moving generally farther north during the period of strengthening of the main zonal wind systems. That was during the general climatic warming period from 1800 (or probably earlier) to about 1930. The slackening of the general zonal circulation, which seems to have set in over the last 30 years or rather more, has been accompanied by a marked tendency for Atlantic depressions to revert to more southerly tracks. The 10-year mean latitude of lowest pressure between 10° and 40°W, which was 65–67°N in July and 62–63°N in January in the optimum years around 1930 has been 2 to 5° farther south in the most disturbed runs of years since.

This southward shift of the depression tracks, and therewith of the zone of maximum windiness (gale frequencies) over the ocean to the regions south of Iceland, preceded any renewed increase of the Arctic pack-ice. (By 1938 the sea ice had retreated farther north than ever before in modern times, and those who reasoned from extrapolation alone began to speak of the possibility of an open Arctic Ocean by the end of the century.) The cause of the new southward trend of the depression tracks, which is most marked in the eastern North Atlantic sector, is therefore not simply a matter of ice. It may be connected with the shortening of wave length between troughs in the upper westerlies (discussed below), which has favoured an increased (and apparently still increasing) frequency of surface northerly outbreaks of cold air moving south in the Norwegian Sea. Not surprisingly, with decreased windiness in high northern latitudes and increased frequency of N and NE winds in the Norwegian and Barents Sea since about 1940, an increase of the sea ice is now reported. By 1962 its extent in this sector was apparently greater than at any time since the 1880s, and in mid-February 1963 (Fig. 3) appears unmatched since the worst years before 1815.

The best available index of extent of the Arctic sea ice over a long period of time is its incidence on the coasts of Iceland, which lies within the sector where the biggest variations have occurred. Indices published by Koch ('The East Greenland Ice', *Medd. om Grønland*, **130**, Nr. 3, Copenhagen 1945) and Thorarinsson (Fig. 3 in 'The thousand years struggle against ice and fire', Reykjavik 1956) are tolerably consistent from 1780 onwards. Figures for weeks per year with ice on the coasts of Iceland are as follows: 1780s *13*, 1790–1819 *9*, 1820s–1830s *8½*, 1840s–1850s *5*, 1860s *13*, 1870s *8*, 1880s *12*, 1890s *7*, 1900–19 *5*, 1920s–1940s *1½*, 1950s *4* (1950s estimated from various current sources). The worst individual year recorded was 1695, and it seems probable that the average extent in the 1690s was even greater than that in the 1780s.

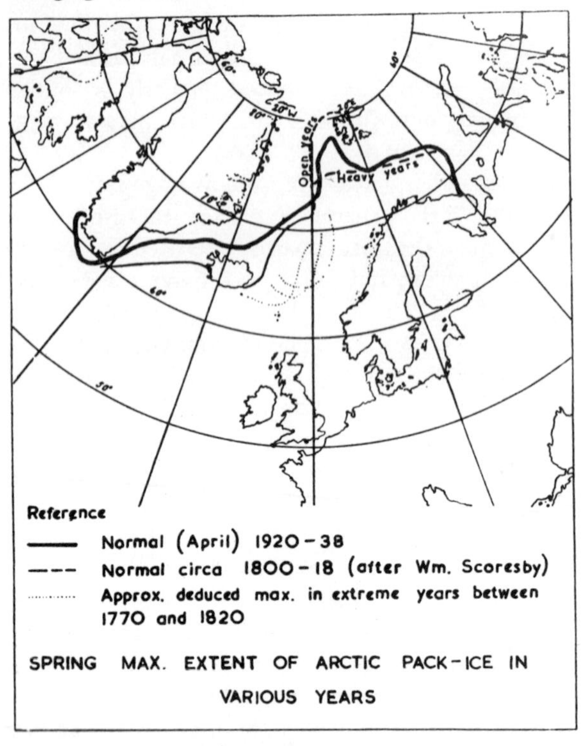

Fig. 3. (*a*) Normal position of the limit of sea ice at the end of the winter production season: *bold line* present century, *narrow line* 1800–1818. Dotted lines indicate approximate positions reasonably supposed to have been reached by ice tongues in the most extreme individual years about 1770–1820

One element in the present situation remains different from the cold epoch as existing about 1800. Water temperatures in the broad North Atlantic are still close to the values usual in the 1920s. There has been some fall since about 1955 and some suggestion of lateral (southward) displacement of the warmest North Atlantic Drift water—no doubt associated with the corresponding shift in the latitude of the greatest prevalence of W and SW winds. Between 45°N and Iceland water temperatures now seem most similar to those of the 1880s and 90s, and 1 to 3°C higher than in 1780–1820. (The situation may also be more similar to the 1500s, or earlier, before the seas had reached their coldest, than to the 1700s.)

The southern position of the main depression tracks in recent years has given some disappointing summers in Britain and neighbouring parts of northern Europe (1954, 1956, 1958, 1960 and to some extent in 1962). It has also meant a southward shift of the zone of prevailing easterly and northerly winds in the Atlantic sector, which has been associated with the more frequent snowfalls in the British Isles since 1938. It has been increasingly prominent since 1954 in winter as in summer and has meant that in several recent winters before

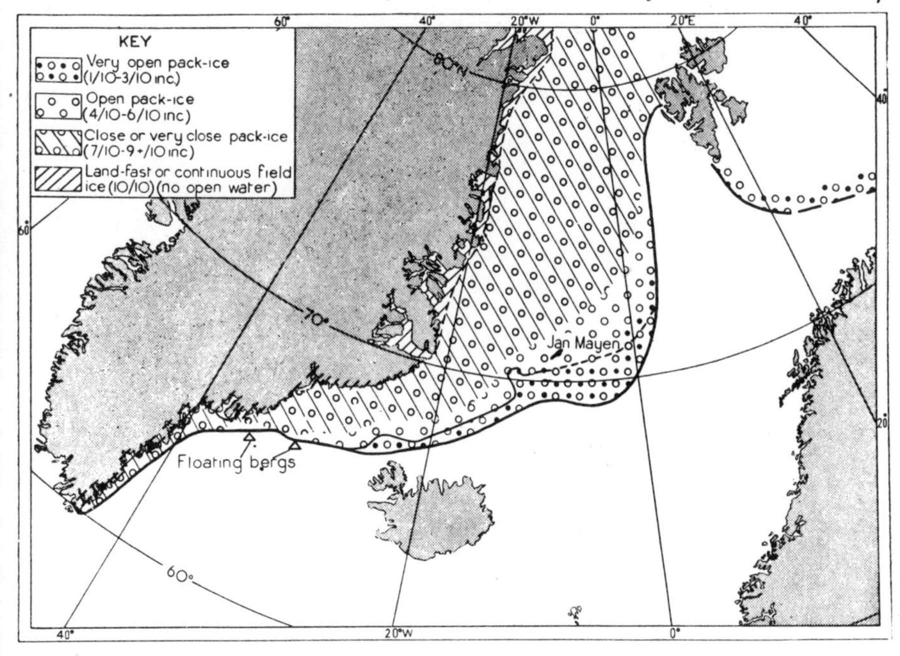

Fig. 3. (*b*) Ice cover surveyed in mid-February 1963. The position of the limit 150–200 miles south-east of the island of Jan Mayen and more generally between 70 and 75°N in the Norwegian and Barents Seas exceeds the extremes of the present century by up to 5 times the previous range of variation and approaches the extreme end-of-winter positions ever known. (Map produced by Mr G. Tunnell and Mr K. Jelly in the Marine Division of the Meteorological Office)

1962 south-east England and Europe south of 55°N escaped severe weather by a rather narrow geographical margin.

The investigation of long-term trends in the general circulation has to be based upon winds and pressure-differences near sea-level, because regular upper-air observations did not begin until the radiosonde network was established after 1940, though useful indications of changes in the usual positions of the upper troughs and ridges over Europe since 1880 have been derived from winds at the Alpine mountain summits. The surface wind and weather patterns are, however, closely related to the dynamics of the great circumpolar vortex in the upper troposphere and the waves (meanderings) in the upper westerlies. It may therefore be possible to deduce changes in the upper circulation from study of the situations at the surface.

Investigation of this point shows that the pattern was displaced east, and the trough-ridge spacing increased, whilst the indices of circulation strength (Fig. 2) were increasing. This is equivalent to an increase of wave-length in the upper westerlies downstream from the semi-permanent disturbance at the Rocky Mountains, an expected accompaniment of increasing strength of the windstream. There are also signs of reversal in the last 40 years. Similarly consistent results are shown over the Southern Ocean. This seems to confirm a world-wide tendency for the vigour of the wind circulation to decrease over the last decades.

The changes in the longitudes most frequently affected by cold troughs in the upper westerlies in the European sector can be held responsible for remarkable changes in the frequency of (surface) northerly outbreaks in the Norwegian Sea. There was a great and persistent drop in the frequency of northerly weather types in this sector from about the 1890s (when the zonal circulation was increasing to its maximum and the trough-ridge pattern moving east). Since about 1950–54 northerly types have been rapidly returning to prominence. The annual mean pressure difference between 40° and 0°W at 70°N, favouring northerly winds, (4·2 mb) in 1951–1960 was 3·0 mb (three and a half times) greater than for 1900–39 (1·2 mb). The increase affected all months.

SURVEY OF CHANGES SINCE THE EARLY MIDDLE AGES

Before the days of meteorological instruments weather diaries were kept in various places, and abundant reports and summaries of the character of the summers and winters appear in the documentary records of European lands. Many collections of these have been compiled (e.g. Britton 1937). The particularly rich historical records of Europe near 50°N probably contain references to all extreme seasons since the early Middle Ages. The effects of a long wet or dry summer, or of a severe or very mild winter, are unambiguous. Counts of the numbers of extreme summer and winter months for each decade since 1100 in different European longitudes have been made from the various compilations of data available. These constitute the longest numerical sequences of weather data available for study. The figures have been related to the temperatures and rainfalls observed since 1700 in order to continue the series to the 1950s. The occurrence of extreme seasons is related to the troughs and ridges in the upper westerlies, and Europe near 50°N is always within the range of influence of these. Hence, it is an ideal region for study, and it may be possible to use the wave-length principle to interpret longitude shifts of the main warm/dry or cold/wet anomalies in terms of displacements of the upper westerlies. The prevailing latitudes followed by the depressions in the European sector are also involved, but this aspect may be treated as related to the wave-length (and preferred longitudes for troughs and ridges) in the upper westerlies—as already described in connection with the recent southward shift of the depression tracks.

Fig. 4 displays the incidence of frequent wet (shaded area) or dry summers, mild (shaded area) or cold winters in different longitudes over Europe over many hundreds of years. The frequencies have been grouped into 50-year averages; this grouping secures greater reliability and complex shorter-term irregularities are smoothed out. It has also been possible to extend the survey very tentatively (broken lines) back to A.D. 800. Arrows help the reader to follow the main direction of movement of the climatic anomalies east and west across Europe, presumably as the prevailing wavelength in the upper westerlies lengthened and shortened. Considering the crude

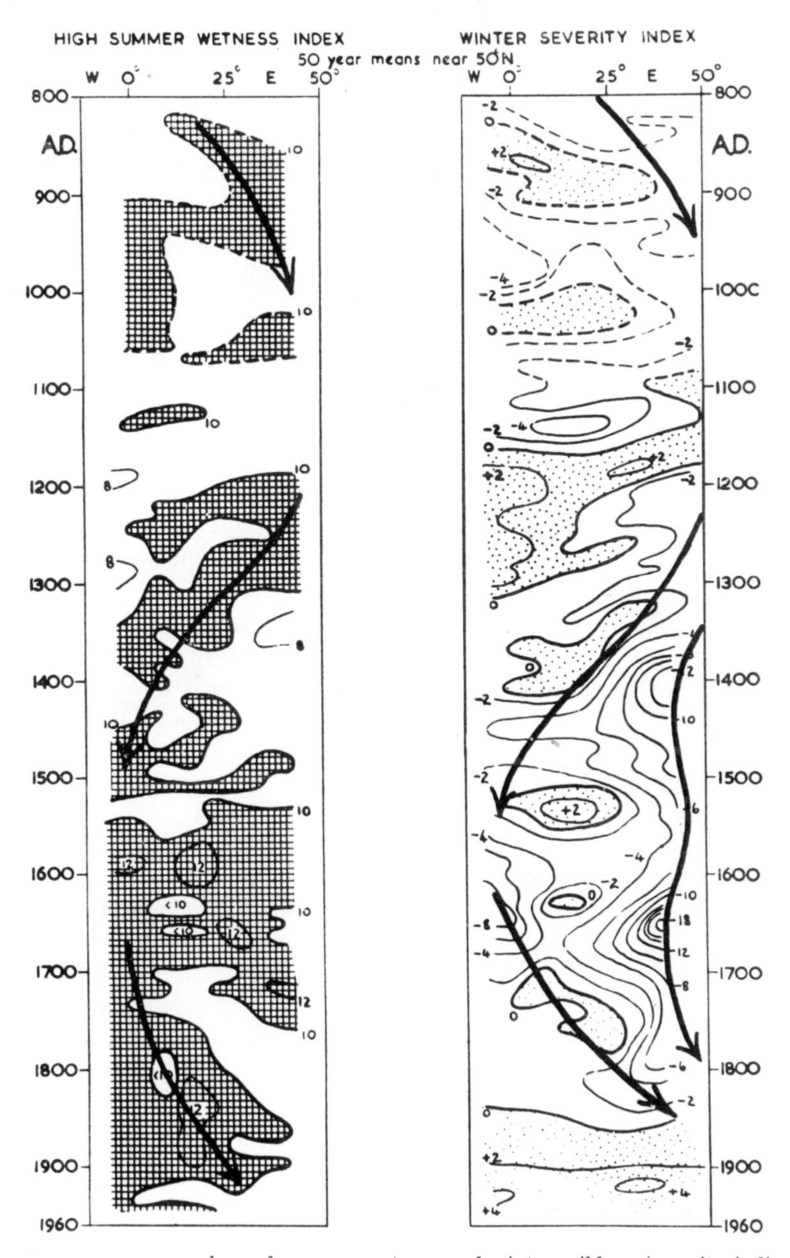

Fig. 4. 50-year mean values of summer wetness and winter mildness/severity indices for different longitudes in Europe near 50°N since A.D. 800. Hatched (dark) areas had excess of wet over dry Julys and Augusts. Stippled (grey) areas had more very mild than very cold winter months (Decembers, Januarys and Februarys). Arrows have been drawn to make it easier for the eye to follow the movement of the maximum incidence of anomalies during times of climatic change. In the periods of climatic standstill (1000–1200 warm, 1550–1700 cold and early 1900s warm epoch) all longitudes tended to fare alike

nature of the source material on which this diagram is founded, it is perhaps surprising that any pattern appears.

The parallel movements in summer and winter make the reality of the pattern more credible. There are unmistakable signs that the maximum incidence of anomalies progressed westwards across Europe during the climatic deterioration from 1300 to 1600 and returned to the east during the recovery from 1700 onwards. These movements could be explained by

(i) shortening wave-length and weakening of the zonal westerlies, with displacement to rather lower latitudes, during the deterioration.

(ii) lengthening wave-length, strengthening and northward displacement of the westerlies during the recovery. These aspects have been substantiated (cf. Fig. 2) during the latter part of the climatic recovery between about 1800 and 1930.

During the climatic optima A.D. 1000–1300 and in the early 1900s, as well as during the ('pessimum') period 1550–1700, all European longitudes had rather similar weather anomalies. The anomalies were such as would accompany high latitude of the main depression tracks in the optima, especially during the greater one of 1000–1300—when sea temperatures higher than in recent times in the northernmost Altantic seem to be implied by what is known of the climate of Greenland. Rather low latitudes (probably near 57–60°N in summer) are likely for the depression tracks in the worst part of the 'Little Ice Age', 1550–1700. Central Europe seems to have had rather smaller anomalies in the Little Ice Age than either Britain or Russia. This probably indicates that northerly winds in preferred channels over the Norwegian Sea and the north Russian plains were important in the climate of that time.

Improvement of climate was fairly continuous from 1700 to the early 1900s, though there were setbacks in the mid-late 1700s and late 1800s. It may be useful to study how far the present deterioration resembles one or other of these earlier ones. In this way it may be possible to judge how much farther the latest downward trend is likely to go.

The writer is compiling charts of winds and weather observed and reported over Europe in each January and July since 1550. Use has been made of the work of Lenke on 17th century weather registers in Germany, as well as compilations of older data and published weather diaries, including Haller's (Schweiz. Met. Zentral Anstalt, 1872, 1873) daily observations in Zürich from 1550 to 1576 and Tycho Brahe's (1876) on the Danish island of Ven from 1583 to 1597. These charts already permit provisional counts of the numbers of Januarys and Julys per decade with net N or S, W or E wind components (estimated direction of the monthly mean isobars) over the region about the southern North Sea from the 1550s to the 1950s.

The provisional figures are given in Tables 4 and 5. The columns headed X and Y indicate cases in which the region appeared to be within the central part of (respectively) anticyclones or depressions for most of the month. The striking features are:

TABLE 4. Provisional numbers of JANUARYS per decade with net N, E, S, W wind components (estimated isobar direction) over the region between London and Copenhagen, centred near Amsterdam.

Decade	N	E	S	W	X	Y
1550s	2	1	1	9	–	–
1560s	1	5	3	3	–	–
1570s	4	4	1	6	–	–
1580s (–81, 82)	5	5	2	3	–	–
1590s (–98)	4	3	5	6	–	–
1600–09 (–04)	1	6	–	3	–	–
1610–19 (–18)	1	1	2	8	–	–
1620s (–20)	3	4	4	3	–	–
1630s	4	4	5	6	–	–
1640s	2	3	4	7	–	–
1650s (–51, 52)	3	4	–	3	–	–
1660s (–65, 66)	2	3	3	4	–	–
1670s	3	2	5	8	–	–
1680s	8	2	2	8	–	–
1690s	6	4	4	6	–	–
1700–09	5	4	5	6	–	–
1710–19	5	4	5	5	–	–
1720s	1	1	9	8	–	–
1730s	3	1	7	9	2	1
1740s	3	3	6	6	6	2
1750s	2	2	5	5	2	–
1760s	1	3	7	3	5	1
1770s	1	1	3	5	1	4
1780s	2	–	5	7	2	–
1790s	–	2	9	7	5	1
1800–09	–	3	9	5	2	1
1810–19	–	2	6	6	2	1
1820s	2	2	3	5	5	1
1830s	1	2	2	7	5	–
1840s	–	3	8	6	–	–
1850s	1	1	8	7	2	1
1860s	–	–	9	8	2	2
1870s	2	1	7	8	1	–
1880s	1	2	4	6	5	–
1890s	–	1	2	7	4	1
1900–09	3	–	3	10	3	–
1910–19	–	2	3	5	3	1
1920s	1	1	4	7	1	–
1930s	–	–	7	8	2	3
1940s	2	3	3	6	1	1
1950s	2	–	2	7	3	–

X means anticyclonic central region
Y means cyclonic central region
1580s (–81, 82) means 1580s omitting 1581 and 1582, for which no estimate was possible

(i) the high frequency of N and E winds in winter in most decades between 1560 and 1720, unmatched since.

(ii) rather high frequency of S winds in winter between about 1700 and 1880 or 1890, and in summer between 1700 and 1810,

(iii) low frequency of anticyclonic influence in summer in most decades between 1580 and 1730.

(i) and (iii) were probably important features of the climatic deterioration and the worst part of the Little Ice Age.

(ii) may have been important for the subsequent climatic warming.

The effects in Britain and continental Europe of the relatively low latitude of the trail of low pressure centres in the summers of the cold climatic epoch of previous centuries seem to have been rather more than offset in the 1700s, but not in the late 1500s and the 1600s, by an enhanced frequency of blocking anticyclones over central and northern Europe. These appear to have produced at times marginally (slightly, but probably not significantly) higher summer temperatures in England and central Europe than in the present century. On the other hand earlier, especially in the 1590s, 1620s, 1640s and 1690s, there were some

TABLE 5. Provisional numbers of JULYS per decade with net N, E, S, W wind components (estimated isobar direction) over the region between London and Copenhagen, centred near Amsterdam.

Decade	N	E	S	W	X	Y
1550s	2	0	6	10	3	3
1560s	6	1	2	9	1	1
1570s	1	0	2	9	2	2
(–79)						
1580s	2	1	6	6	0	1
(–81, 82)						
1590s	3	0	5	9	0	1
(–97)						
1600–9	3	2	3	4	4	1
(–00, 09)						
1610–19	2	0	2	3	2	0
(–10, 11, 13, 14, 17, 18)						
1620s	5	0	2	9	1	3
(–20)						
1630s	3	0	4	10	0	1
1640s	5	0	4	10	1	2
1650s	1	0	3	8	3	0
(–59)						
1660s	0	0	3	6	0	1
(–60, 62, 64, 65)						
1670s	5	0	3	10	0	0
1680s	(4)	0	(4)	10	0	0
Observer poorly exposed for NW'ly winds in the 1680s.						
1690s	7	2	3	7	0	2
1700–09	4	2	4	8	0	0
1710–19	4	2	6	8	1	0

Decade	N	E	S	W	X	Y
1720s	5	1	5	8	0	0
1730s	5	1	3	9	2	0
1740s	2	2	5	8	5	0
1750s	1	0	5	10	3	0
1760s	2	0	3	9	4	0
1770s	1	0	4	8	4	0
1780s	1	0	8	10	7	0
1790s	0	0	9	9	3	0
1800–09	1	2	6	6	6	2
1810–19	4	0	1	9	3	4
1820s	6	1	3	8	2	3
1830s	3	1	1	8	2	4
1840s	4	0	3	10	0	2
1850s	2	0	4	9	4	1
1860s	4	1	2	9	4	3
1870s	4	0	5	10	2	2
1880s	5	1	3	9	3	4
1890s	8	0	1	9	3	1
1900–09	6	1	1	7	5	0
1910–19	6	2	1	8	1	3
1920s	2	0	3	8	2	2
1930s	4	0	5	10	4	5
1940s	5	0	3	10	4	1
1950s	4	1	3	7	4	5

dire years (the effects being aggravated by the less advanced agriculture of those times) with long-continued cyclonic sequences in temperate Europe.

CONCLUSIONS

(1) These studies suggest a long-term climatic fluctuation, the major component of which approximates to a smooth oscillation with maxima around the 1100s and 1900–1940 of (i) temperature, (ii) northern latitude of the depression tracks, (iii) eastern position of features corresponding to the ridge-trough pattern in the upper westerlies over Europe.

(2) Various complications appear to be superimposed upon the smooth trends of the long-term fluctuation and produce irregularities. The following seem to have some importance:

(*a*) the pessimum climate of A.D. 1550–1700 came some time after the mid point between the optima of the 1100s and early 1900s. Also it was probably a good deal colder than any previous cold phase since the major Post-Glacial warm epoch in 5000–3000 B.C. Only the cold epoch around 500 B.C. seems to have approached the severity of A.D. 1550–1700 and produced similar advances of the glaciers.

In both cases there is reason to suppose that abnormal frequency of volcanic dust in the atmosphere may have reduced the incoming radiation.

(*b*) Some shorter-term fluctuations are pronounced. Some of these may be approximately periodic. Periods of about 23, 45–60, 100 and 170 years are those most generally suggested by a periodogram analysis of the decade indices, carried out by Miss M. G. Roy of the Meteorological Office. In no case has the significance of the suggested period yet been established. Since A.D. 1100 the decade values of the winter severity index suggest a tendency for maximum development of the westerlies, with mild winters in Europe, at about half-century intervals, particularly in the first 30 years and in the fifties to seventies of most centuries. Between these (relatively) mildest phases groups of cold winters have been prominent, particularly around the '80s–'90s of most centuries.

Periodicities could be of either solar/astronomical origin or terrestrial—e.g. bound up with a centuries-long cycle of overturning of the ocean water and other more rapid mechanisms. Those who favour solar-terrestrial influences will not fail to notice the near-coincidence of the 23- and 170-year periods with the double sunspot (Hale) cycle and with the time elapsed between the great sunspot peaks of 1778 and 1947–1957. More knowledge of solar processes, and mechanisms by which any effects might be transmitted downwards through the atmosphere, is, however, needed before any connection with weather can be asserted.

The frequency of cold winters since 1938 begins to appear as something more than a temperature minimum associated with shorter-term periodicities only temporarily interrupting the long upward trend of world temperature. The 1950s and '60s might have been expected to be the time for resumed warming. (This could be a reasonable view of the periods 1948–52 and 1957–60, but only in much reduced degree as compared with the period from 1896 to the 1930s.) It seems prudent to assume that the longer-term temperature trend is at present on balance downward and likely to remain so. Nevertheless 1962 is likely to stand out as an exceptionally cold year and 1962–63 as an exceptionally cold winter. We shall not be on firm ground until physical reasons for all the main changes in circulation vigour have been identified.

ACKNOWLEDGMENT

The author is indebted to the Director-General of the Meteorological Office for permission to publish this article.

REFERENCES

ÅNGSTRÖM, A. 1935 Teleconnections of climatic changes in present time. *Geogr. Ann.*, **17**, pp. 242–258, Stockholm

BRAHE, T. 1876 *Tyge Brahes meteorologiske Dagbog holdt paa Uranienborg for Aarene 1582–1597.* Appendix til Collectanea Meteorologica af det K. Danske Videnskabernes Selskab. Copenhagen (Thiele)

BRITTON, C. E. 1937 A meteorological chronology to A.D. 1450. *Geophysical Memoir No. 70*, London (Meteorological Office)

CALLENDAR, G. S. 1961 Temperature fluctuations and trends over the earth. *Quart. J. R. Met. Soc.*, **87**, pp. 1–12

FLOHN, H. 1963 Theories of climatic change from the viewpoint of the global energy budget. *Proceedings of the W.M.O./U.N.E.S.C.O. Rome (October 1961) Symposium on climatic changes* (published) U.N.E.S.C.O., Paris

KRAUS, E. B. 1955 Secular changes in east coast rainfall regimes. *Quart. J. R. Met. Soc.*, **81**, pp. 430–9

1958 Recent climatic changes. *Nature*, **181**, pp. 666–8, London

1960 Synoptic and dynamic aspects of climatic change. *Quart. J. R. Met. Soc.*, **86**, pp. 1–15

LAMB, H. H. 1963 On the nature of certain climatic epochs which differed from the modern (1900–1939) normal. *Proceedings of the W.M.O./U.N.E.S.C.O. Rome (October 1961) Symposium on climatic changes* (published) U.N.E.S.C.O., Paris

LAMB, H. H. and JOHNSON, A. I. 1959 Climatic variation and observed changes in the general circulation. Parts I and II. *Geogr. Ann.*, **41**, pp. 94–134

1961 *Ibid.* Part III. *Geogr. Ann.*, **43**, pp. 363–400, Stockholm

LAMB, H. H., PROBERT JONES, J. R. and SHEARD, J. W. 1962 A new advance of the Jan Mayen glaciers and a remarkable increase of precipitation. *J. Glaciol.*, **4**, pp. 355–365, Cambridge

MANLEY, G. 1959 Temperature trends in England 1698–1957. *Archiv für Met., Geoph. und Biokl., Serie B*, **9**, pp. 413–433, Wien

1961 A preliminary note on early meteorological observations in the London region 1680–1717, with estimates of the monthly mean temperatures 1680–1706. *Met. Mag.*, **90**, pp. 303–310

MITCHELL, J. M. 1961 Recent secular changes of global temperature. *New York Academy of Sciences, Annals*, **95**, *Art. 1*, pp. 235–250, New York

WEXLER, H. 1962 Tiros experiment results. *Space Science Review*, **1**, pp. 7–27, Dordrecht (D. Reidel)

APPENDIX ONE

The production and decay of radioactive carbon C^{14} in the atmosphere

When cosmic ray primary particles, mostly protons, enter the earth's atmosphere, they produce showers of secondary radiation which includes neutrons – in the upper reaches of the atmosphere. Most of the neutrons collide with nitrogen atoms and are captured by the atomic nucleus; few survive to reach ground level. In the collisions the dominant reaction produces radiocarbon, C^{14}, a proton being ejected from the nucleus:

$$_{0}n^{1} + {_{7}N^{14}} \rightarrow {_{6}C^{14}} + {_{1}H^{1}}$$

The radiocarbon is readily oxidized to appear as a minute contribution to the atmospheric carbon dioxide which is taken up by living organisms and by sea-water. Another reaction occurs in the case of about one per cent of the neutrons captured:

$$_{0}n^{1} + {_{7}N^{14}} \rightarrow {_{6}C^{12}} + {_{1}H^{3}}$$

This transmutes the nitrogen atom nucleus into ordinary carbon and releases radioactive hydrogen, tritium.

The rate of decay of any radioactive atoms is always proportional to the number present

$$-\mathrm{d}N/\mathrm{d}t = \lambda N$$

where N is the number of atoms present at any time t. λ, the constant of proportionality, is called the 'decay constant'. If the number of atoms originally present was N_0, the decay follows the exponential curve expressed by

$$N = N_0 \mathrm{e}^{-\lambda t}$$

The half-life $T_{\frac{1}{2}}$ of a radioactive species is given by putting $N = \frac{1}{2}N_0$ in this equation, which leads to

$$T_{\frac{1}{2}} = \frac{1}{\lambda} \log_{e} 2$$

The decay products of a C^{14} atom are nitrogen $_{7}N^{14}$, a β^- particle and a neutrino. The decay of a C^{14} atom is detected by making use of the ionization produced in a gas along the path of the ejected β^- particle.

APPENDIX TWO

Tables of decade values of the indices of summer wetness/dryness and winter mildness/severity from 1100 to the 1950s for different European longitudes near 50° N

TABLE 1. *High Summer Wetness/Dryness Index* (*Europe near* 50° *N*). (*Each July or August with unmistakable evidence of frequent rains counted* 1, *an unremarkable July or August* ½, *a plainly dry month* 0. *Totals per decade.*)

Decade	*Britain ca.* 0° *E*	*Germany ca.* 12° *E*	*Russia ca.* 35° *E*
1100–09	10	10½	9½
1110–19	12½	9½	8½
1120s	10	11½	7½
1130s	6	9½	9½
1140s	11	10½	10½
1150s	11	7½	10½
1160s	7	10½	6½
1170s	7½	11½	10
1180s	7½	5	10½
1190s	10½	12½	9½
1200–09	7	8½	10½
1210–19	9	10½	12½
1220s	12½	10½	10
1230s	7½	10½	9
1240s	8	7½	9½
1250s	12½	12½	10½
1260s	10	9½	10½
1270s	5	6½	11½
1280s	8	7½	12
1290s	7	7½	8½
1300–09	6½	10½	11½
1310–19	15	14	9½
1320s	6½	9½	8½
1330s	7	11½	5½
1340s	10½	13	7½
1350s	12½	11½	8½
1360s	14½	13	8½
1370s	11½	4	7½
1380s	8½	5	9
1390s	11	10½	9½

Decade	Britain ca. 0° E	Germany ca. 12° E	Russia ca. 35° E
1400–09	11	17	7½
1410–19	7½	11½	10
1420s	7	2	9½
1430s	12	10½	8½
1440s	8	8½	8½
1450s	14	16	10
1460s	9	11½	12
1470s	8	9	8½
1480s	12½	11½	9½
1490s	16	10½	12½
1500–09	7	8	9½
1510–19	7½	10½	10
1520s	11	13	9
1530s	8½	6	7½
1540s	8	9½	13
1550s	8½	6½	11
1560s	16	14½	12
1570s	11	15	10
1580s	12½	17	11½
1590s	11	10½	11½
1600–09	11½	12½	13½
1610–19	7	7	8½
1620s	13	14½	10½
1630s	11	6	11½
1640s	11	9½	7½
1650s	11½	11	10
1660s	10½	12½	10½
1670s	10½	8½	10½
1680s	11½	10½	11
1690s	13½	12	13½
1700–09	10½	9½	10½
1710–19	10	8½	10½
1720s	11½	8	13½
1730s	10	10½	13½
1740s	7	6½	10½
1750s	13½	12	10
1760s	11½	12	9
1770s	11½	11	6
1780s	12	10	10
1790s	10½	12½	10

Decade	*Britain ca.* 0° *E*	*Germany ca.* 12° *E*	*Russia ca.* 35° *E*
1800–09	10	12	11
1810–19	10	14½	8
1820s	12	16½	9
1830s	11½	15½	9
1840s	10½	14½	10
1850s	12½	12½	10½
1860s	9	10½	10
1870s	13	17½	12
1880s	10½	13½	10½
1890s	10	12½	7
1900–09	10½	11½	7½
1910–19	11	12	14
1920s	11½	8	7½
1930s	10	10½	10½
1940s	9½	6½	9
1950s	11½		

The index was compared with rainfall records to continue the series to the present century. Best results appeared to be obtained by counting Julys and Augusts as wet or dry if they fell within the highest or lowest quintiles of the present century's records. The figures for Germany are based partly on comparisons with records compiled in connexion with vine harvests as well as on actual weather records. Perhaps because of the abundance of information about central Europe more doubt and difficulty arises over the index figures, which are often a result of compromise, in this series than in those for Britain and Russia.

TABLE 2. *Winter Mildness/Severity Index (Europe near 50° N). (The number of unmistakably mild months (Decembers, Januarys and Februarys only)* minus *the numbers of unmistakably severe months (D, J, F only) per decade.)*

Decade	*Britain ca.* 0° *E*	*Germany ca.* 12° *E*	*Russia ca.* 35° *E*
1100–09	− 1	− 2	0
1110–19	− 4	− 5	0
1120s	− 3	− 3	− 6
1130s	0	− 3	− 6
1140s	− 3	− 9	+ 2
1150s	− 6	− 3	0
1160s	0	− 2	+ 6
1170s	+ 2	+ 2	+ 4
1180s	+ 6	+ 5	− 6
1190s	+ 7	+ 5	+ 6

Decade	*Britain ca.* 0° *E*	*Germany ca.* 12° *E*	*Russia ca.* 35° *E*
1200–09	+ 1	− 3	− 6
1210–19	− 2	− 5	−12
1220s	+ 1	+ 6	+ 2
1230s	+ 6	+ 1	0
1240s	+ 1	+ 3	− 6
1250s	+ 3	− 5	0
1260s	− 3	− 1	0
1270s	+ 7	0	+ 6
1280s	+ 3	+ 3	−18
1290s	+ 2	+ 5	0
1300–09	− 1	+ 1	+ 6
1310–19	− 1	−10	− 6
1320s	0	− 1	0
1330s	− 4	− 1	0
1340s	+ 2	+ 4	0
1350s	− 3	− 4	0
1360s	+ 4	− 2	− 6
1370s	− 3	− 5	−12
1380s	+ 2	+11	− 8
1390s	− 2	+ 2	− 6
1400–09	− 3	− 2	−22
1410–19	+ 2	− 1	−10
1420s	+ 4	+ 7	− 6
1430s	−12	−18	−10
1440s	− 5	− 2	−28
1450s	− 1	− 3	+ 8
1460s	− 9	− 6	− 6
1470s	+ 3	+ 1	− 6
1480s	− 6	+ 1	−10
1490s	− 5	−12	− 8
1500–09	+ 7	− 3	− 6
1510–19	− 2	+ 2	0
1520s	+ 2	+11	− 6
1530s	− 3	+ 6	− 6
1540s	− 2	− 1	+ 6
1550s	− 1	− 3	−12
1560s	− 7	− 3	+ 4
1570s	− 3	− 1	0
1580s	− 7	− 5	+12
1590s	− 5	− 5	0

Decade	*Britain ca.* 0° *E*	*Germany ca.* 12° *E*	*Russia ca.* 35° *E*
1600–09	−10	0	− 6
1610–19	+ 2	− 3	−10
1620s	− 7	− 3	0
1630s	− 5	+ 2	−10
1640s	− 3	+ 5	−36
1650s	− 9	− 7	−24
1660s	− 7	− 3	−14
1670s	0	− 6	−24
1680s	− 2	− 7	0
1690s	− 7	− 5	− 6
1700–09	0	+ 1	− 6
1710–19	− 2	+ 1	0
1720s	− 4	− 1	−12
1730s	+ 9	+ 3	+ 6
1740s	− 4	− 1	− 6
1750s	0	− 5	+10
1760s	− 6	0	−12
1770s	− 1	+ 4	− 6
1780s	− 4	− 4	−20
1790s	− 2	− 2	0
1800–09	− 2	− 1	+ 1
1810–19	− 2	− 3	− 1
1820s	0	0	0
1830s	− 3	− 2	− 1
1840s	− 3	− 2	+ 1
1850s	− 1	− 2	+ 3
1860s	+ 8	+ 6	+ 1
1870s	0	0	− 3
1880s	− 2	0	+ 1
1890s	− 3	− 1	+ 1
1900–09	+ 2	0	+ 2
1910–19	+ 5	+ 6	+ 1
1920s	+ 8	+ 6	+ 2
1930s	+ 4	+ 4	+ 5
1940s	+ 1	− 1	− 1
1950s	0	+ 1	+ 2

APPENDIX THREE

Indices of winter mildness/severity in Europe and Japan compared, decade by decade, since 1440

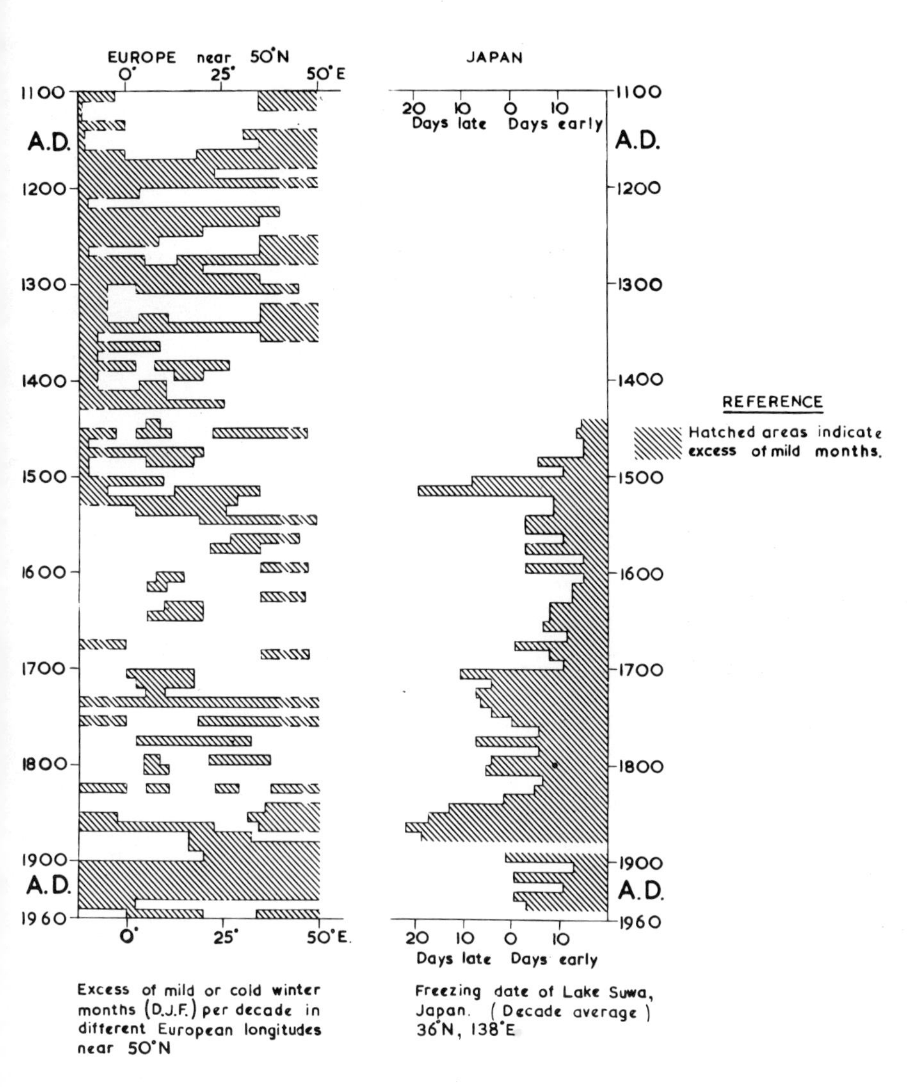

Survey of historical records by decades: European Winter Mildness/Severity Index (see Appendix II) compared with variations in the freezing date of a small lake in Japan, decade by decade, from the over-all mean date (15 January).

Names Index

Subject Index

Bold face type indicates pages on which data are given in maps or tables. Page references to some groups of years of special interest are gathered at the end of the index.